Donald N. Booth
842-0597

Partial Differential Equations

An Introduction

PARTIAL DIFFERENTIAL EQUATIONS

An Introduction

Eutiquio C. Young

The Florida State University

Allyn and Bacon, Inc.

Boston

Library of Congress Catalog Card Number: 70-166551

Printed in the United States of America.

To My Parents and My Family

Contents

Preface ix

Chapter 1 Introduction 1

1. Some Properties of Functions of One Variable **2.** Partial Derivatives **3.** Differentiation of Composite Functions; the Chain Rule **4.** Differentiation of Integrals Depending on a Parameter **5.** Uniform Convergence of Series **6.** Improper Integrals Depending on a Parameter **7.** Directional Derivatives **8.** Green's Theorem and Related Formulas

Chapter 2 Linear Partial Differential Equations 36

1. Basic Concepts and Definitions **2.** General Solutions and Auxiliary Conditions **3.** Linear Operators and Principle of Superposition **4.** Linear First-Order Equations **5.** Solutions of Second-Order Equations with Constant Coefficients **6.** Classification of Second-Order Equations **7.** The Canonical Forms

Chapter 3 The Wave Equation 71

1. The Vibrating String **2.** The Initial Value Problem **3.** Interpretation of the Solution **4.** Domain of Dependence and Characteristic Lines **5.** The Nonhomogeneous Wave Equation **6.** Uniqueness of Solution **7.** Initial-Boundary Value Problems **8.** Nonhomogeneous Problems and Reflection of Waves **9.** Method of Separation of Variables

Chapter 4   Green's Function and Sturm-Liouville Problems   121

1. Homogeneous Boundary Value Problems   **2.** Nonhomogeneous Problems; Green's Function   **3.** Modified Green's Function   **4.** Sturm-Liouville Problems   **5.** Orthogonality of Eigenfunctions   **6.** Eigenfunction Expansions; Mean Convergence   **7.** Nonhomogeneous Sturm-Liouville Problems; Bilinear Expansion

Chapter 5   Fourier Series and Fourier Integral   163

1. Orthogonal Trigonometric Functions   **2.** Fourier Series **3.** Fourier Cosine and Sine Series   **4.** Bessel's Inequality; Riemann-Lebesgue Theorem   **5.** Convergence of Fourier Series   **6.** Uniform Convergence of Fourier Series   **7.** Fourier Integral   **8.** Fourier Transform

Chapter 6   The Heat Equation   212

1. Derivation of the Heat Equation   **2.** Initial and Boundary Conditions   **3.** The Maximum Principle and Uniqueness Theorem   **4.** Initial-Boundary Value Problems   **5.** Nonhomogeneous Initial-Boundary Value Problems   **6.** The Initial Value Problem   **7.** Initial-Boundary Value Problems in Infinite Domain

Chapter 7   Laplace's Equation   250

1. Boundary Value Problems   **2.** Green's Theorem and Uniqueness of Solutions   **3.** Maximum Principle for Harmonic Functions   **4.** Dirichlet Problem in a Rectangle **5.** Dirichlet Problem in a Disk   **6.** Poisson's Integral Formula   **7.** Neumann Problem in a Disk   **8.** Problems in Infinite Domains   **9.** Fundamental Solution and Green's Functions   **10.** Examples of Green's Functions   **11.** Neumann's Function and Examples

References   311

Solutions of the Exercises   313

Index   343

Preface

This book is the outgrowth of an introductory course in partial differential equations which the author has given for a number of years. The students are mostly undergraduates who are majors of mathematics, engineering, or the physical sciences.

The purpose of the book is to acquaint the students with some of the techniques of applied mathematics and to provide them with basic material necessary for further study in partial differential equations. As the needs and interests of the students are varied, the author attempts to strike a balance in emphasis between theory and application.

The book treats principally linear partial differential equations of the first and second order involving two independent variables. Problems involving second-order differential equations are discussed with reference to the three prominent classical equations of mathematical physics, namely, the wave equation, the heat equation, and Laplace's equation. These equations serve as prototypes for the three main types of linear partial differential equations of second order. The kinds of problems that are treated for each of these equations in two variables as well as the properties of the solutions are generally typical of what can be expected with more general differential equations of the same type in three or more independent variables.

Several techniques of applied mathematics—such as the method of eigenfunction expansion, the Fourier transform, and the use of Green's function—are developed and their basic underlying theory are discussed. Along with many examples, a sufficient number of exercises of varying degree of difficulty appear in nearly every section. These exercises form an integral part of the text. They are designed not only to test comprehension of the subject matter presented, but also to introduce other general ideas and procedures. Answers to almost all exercises are given at the back of the book. A list of selected references for further reading on the subject is also given.

As a prerequisite for a course based on this book, the student must have a working knowledge of the topics usually covered in a standard calculus course and must be familiar with the contents of a basic course in ordinary differential equations. Many of the topics in the calculus which are extensively used in later discussion are discussed briefly in the beginning chapter. For those students who have an adequate background, this material can serve as a review.

Although the book is intended for use in a two-quarter course, it can be adopted for a one-quarter or a one-semester course, depending on the background of students and the interest of the instructor. For example, topics selected from Chapters 2, 3, 6, and 7 can be the bases of a one-quarter course for students who are already familiar with the contents of Chapters 4 and 5.

A word about the numbering of equations and theorems: Unless a different chapter is explicitly stated, the first number indicating an equation or a theorem always refers to the section of the particular chapter under study. The exercises are, however, numbered according to the chapters. Thus, the heading Exercises 5.1 refers to the first set of exercises in Chapter 5.

The author wishes to thank Professors Thomas G. Hallam and Howard E. Taylor for testing some of the material in its early version and for making helpful comments, and to Professor C. Y. Chan for reading the manuscript and for making many invaluable suggestions. The author also acknowledges with gratitude the secretarial help extended by the Department of Mathematics. Last but not least, it is a pleasure to thank Mrs. Margaret Parramore for her skillful typing of the manuscript.

Tallahassee, Florida   EUTIQUIO C. YOUNG

Partial Differential Equations

An Introduction

Chapter 1

Introduction

In this chapter we shall review and discuss some topics from the calculus concerning functions of a single variable and of several variables. These topics will be needed in our later work. The consideration of functions of several variables will be limited mostly to functions of two independent variables, as this will be adequate for our purpose.

1. Some Properties of Functions of One Variable

Let f be a function defined on the interval $a \le x \le b$ and let x_0 be a point of this interval. We define the left-hand limit of f at x_0, denoted by $f(x_0^-)$, to be the limit of f as x approaches x_0 from the left of x_0; that is,

$$f(x_0^-) = \lim_{\substack{x \to x_0 \\ x < x_0}} f(x)$$

In a similar manner we define the right-hand limit of f at x_0 to be

$$f(x_0^+) = \lim_{\substack{x \to x_0 \\ x > x_0}} f(x)$$

If both $f(x_0^-)$ and $f(x_0^+)$ exist and are equal to the value of f at x_0, then obviously we have

$$\lim_{x \to x_0} f(x) = f(x_0^-) = f(x_0^+) = f(x_0)$$

In this case the function f is said to be continuous at x_0. On the other hand, if both $f(x_0^-)$ and $f(x_0^+)$ exist but are not equal, then f is said to have a jump discontinuity at x_0. The difference $f(x_0^+) - f(x_0^-)$ is called the jump of the function at the point x_0.

Example 1.1.   The function

$$f(x) = \begin{cases} x - 1 & (x > 0) \\ x + 1 & (x < 0) \end{cases}$$

has a jump discontinuity at $x = 0$, since $f(0^-) = 1$ and $f(0^+) = -1$. The jump of the function at this point is -2.

A function f is said to be continuous on the interval $a \le x \le b$ if f is continuous at all points of the interval. We remark that at the end points $x = a$ and $x = b$, we require only that $f(a^+) = f(a)$ and $f(b^-) = f(b)$. It is well known that if a function is continuous on a closed interval, then it is bounded on that interval. This means that there is a number M such that

$$|f(x)| \le M$$

for all $x, a \le x \le b$. The converse of this statement is, of course, not true. For example, the function considered in Example 1.1 is bounded on the interval $[-1, 1]$ with $M = 1$, but it is not continuous there because it has a jump discontinuity at $x = 0$.

A function f is said to be piecewise continuous on the interval $a \le x \le b$ if it is continuous on that interval, except possibly at a finite number of points where it has jump discontinuities. Thus the function in Example 1.1 is piecewise continuous. It is clear that every piecewise continuous function on a closed interval is also bounded.

Let f be a continuous function on the interval $a \le x \le b$. We say that f has a left-hand derivative at the point x_0 of the interval if the limit

(1.1) $$\lim_{\substack{h \to 0 \\ h < 0}} \frac{f(x_0 + h) - f(x_0)}{h}$$

exists. We denote this one-sided derivative by $f'_-(x_0)$. In the same way, we say that f has a right-hand derivative at x_0, denoted by $f'_+(x_0)$, if

(1.2) $$\lim_{\substack{h \to 0 \\ h > 0}} \frac{f(x_0 + h) - f(x_0)}{h}$$

exists. If both $f'_-(x_0)$ and $f'_+(x_0)$ exist and are equal, then obviously f has a derivative at x_0, and we have

$$f'(x_0) = f'_-(x_0) = f'_+(x_0)$$

It should be noted that $f'_-(x_0)$ and $f'_+(x_0)$ are not the same as $f'(x_0^-)$ and $f'(x_0^+)$, which are the left-hand limit and the right-hand limit of f' at x_0, respectively. The existence of the one-sided derivatives of f at x_0 does not imply the existence of the one-sided limits of f' at x_0. But, if both $f'(x_0^-)$ and $f'(x_0^+)$ exist and are equal to $f'(x_0)$, then we have

$$\lim_{x \to x_0} f'(x) = f'(x_0^-) = f'(x_0^+) = f'(x_0)$$

which means that f' is continuous at the point x_0.

Example 1.2.   Consider the function

$$f(x) = \begin{cases} x^2 \sin \dfrac{1}{x} & (x \neq 0) \\ 0 & (x = 0) \end{cases}$$

This function is continuous at all points, including $x = 0$. Now, for $h < 0$, we have

$$f_-'(0) = \lim_{h \to 0} \frac{h^2 \sin(1/h) - f(0^-)}{h}$$

$$= \lim_{h \to 0} \frac{h^2 \sin(1/h)}{h} = 0$$

Similarly, when $h > 0$, we find $f_+'(0) = 0$, and so $f'(0) = 0$. But when $x \neq 0$, we have

$$f'(x) = 2x \sin \frac{1}{x} - \cos \frac{1}{x}$$

for which neither $f'(0^-)$ nor $f'(0^+)$ exist. In other words, f' is continuous at all points $x \neq 0$, but is discontinuous at $x = 0$, although $f'(0) = 0$.

We say that a function f is smooth on the interval $a \leq x \leq b$ if it has a continuous derivative at every point of the interval. At the points $x = a$ and $x = b$, we require only that $f'(a^+)$ and $f'(b^-)$ exist. Thus, the function considered in Example 1.2 is smooth on any interval $[a, b]$ that does not include the origin. Geometrically, the graph of a smooth function consists of a continuous curve that has a tangent which turns continuously as the tangent moves along the curve; that is, the curve does not have any "corners."

In the case where the function f is piecewise continuous on $a \leq x \leq b$, and x_0 is a point of discontinuity, the definition of left-hand derivative and right-hand derivative given by equations (1.1) and (1.2) remains valid, provided the quantity $f(x_0)$ in those equations is replaced respectively by the left-hand limit and the right-hand limit of f at x_0; that is, by $f(x_0^-)$ and $f(x_0^+)$. In this case, equality between $f_-'(x_0)$ and $f_+'(x_0)$ does not mean existence of f' at x_0, since f is not continuous at x_0. We say that f is piecewise smooth on the interval $a \leq x \leq b$ if it is piecewise continuous and has a piecewise continuous derivative on that interval. It follows that the graph of a piecewise smooth function is either a continuous curve or a discontinuous curve that has a continuously turning tangent between any two consecutive points where f or f' has jump discontinuity.

Example 1.3.   The function

$$f(x) = \begin{cases} e^x & (-1 \le x \le 0) \\ 1 & (0 \le x < 1) \\ \cos \pi x & (1 < x \le 2) \end{cases}$$

whose graph appears in Fig. 1–1, is piecewise smooth, since the function and its derivative are piecewise continuous. The function has a jump discontinuity at $x = 1$, while the derivative f' has jump discontinuities at $x = 0$ and $x = 1$.

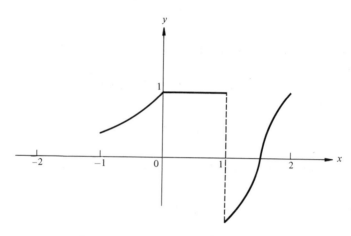

FIG. 1–1   *Piecewise smooth function.*

A function that is defined on the whole x-axis is said to be piecewise continuous or piecewise smooth if it is piecewise continuous or piecewise smooth on every finite interval. This definition applies in particular to a periodic function; that is, to a function f having the property

(1.3) $f(x + T) = f(x)$

for all x and some constant T. The smallest value of T for which equation (1.3) holds is called the period of f.

If f is a function defined only on a finite interval $a \le x \le b$, we can extend it so that it yields a periodic function. In fact, let $T = b - a$ and consider the function ϕ, which satisfies the relation

$$\phi(x + nT) = f(x) \qquad (a \le x \le b)$$

for all integers n. Clearly, ϕ is defined for all x and is periodic with period T. Moreover, it coincides with f on the interval $a \le x \le b$. We call the function ϕ the periodic extension of f with period T.

One important theorem of differential calculus, which we shall have occasion to use later, is stated below.

THEOREM 1.1. (Mean Value Theorem) *If f is continuous on the interval* $a \leq x \leq b$ *and f' exists for each point x inside the interval, then there is a point* x_0 *between a and b such that*

(1.4)
$$\frac{f(b) - f(a)}{b - a} = f'(x_0)$$

The formula (1.4) is frequently written in the form

$$f(a + h) = f(a) + hf'(a + \theta h)$$

where $h = b - a$ and $0 < \theta < 1$. If h is very small, then we can approximate $f(a + h)$ by writing $f(a + h) = f(a) + hf'(a)$.

We next recall some facts from integral calculus. Let f be a piecewise continuous function on the interval $a \leq x \leq b$. Then the integral of f over $[a, b]$ exists and is the sum of the integrals over the subintervals whose end points are the points of discontinuities of f. Moreover, from the geometrical interpretation of definite integrals it is clear that the integral

(1.5)
$$\int_a^b |f(x)| \, dx$$

exists. In this case we say that f is absolutely integrable on the interval $[a, b]$. More generally, we say that a function f is absolutely integrable on the interval $[a, b]$ (where a may be $-\infty$ or b may be ∞) if f is continuous on the interval, except possibly at a finite number of points, and the integral (1.5) exists—possibly as an improper integral. Over a finite interval we see that every piecewise continuous function is absolutely integrable. The converse of this statement is, however, not true. For instance, the function $f(x) = 1/\sqrt{x}$ is absolutely integrable on the interval $0 \leq x \leq 1$, but it is not piecewise continuous there because the right-hand limit $f(0^+)$ does not exist.

It is true, however, that every absolutely integrable function is integrable in the ordinary sense. That is, the existence of the integral (1.5) implies the existence of the integral

$$\int_a^b f(x) \, dx$$

Further, if f is absolutely integrable and g is a bounded function on the interval $a \leq x \leq b$, the product fg is also absolutely integrable on the same interval.

We now state the fundamental theorem of calculus.

THEOREM 1.2. *Let f be a continuous function on the interval* $a \leq x \leq b$ *and let c be a fixed point of the interval. Define the function F by*

(1.6)
$$F(x) = \int_c^x f(t) \, dt$$

for each x, $a \leq x \leq b$. *Then*

(1.7)
$$F'(x) = \frac{d}{dx} \int_c^x f(t) \, dt = f(x)$$

This theorem is also written frequently in the form

(1.8) $$\int_a^b f(x)\,dx = F(b) - F(a)$$

where F is any function such that $F'(x) = f(x)$. It is easy to see that (1.6) and (1.7) together imply (1.8), and vice versa.

Finally, we state a theorem that is the counterpart of Theorem 1.1.

THEOREM 1.3. (Mean Value Theorem for Integrals) *If f is continuous on the interval $a \le x \le b$, then there is a point x_0 between a and b such that*

(1.9) $$\int_a^b f(x)\,dx = f(x_0)(b - a)$$

Geometrically, this formula says that there is a rectangle of height $f(x_0)$ and width $(b - a)$, whose area $f(x_0)(b - a)$ is equal to the area determined by the integral (1.9).

Exercises 1.1

1. Sketch the graph of each of the following functions and determine whether the function is piecewise continuous, continuous, piecewise smooth, and smooth:

   (a) $$f(x) = \begin{cases} -\sqrt{-x} & (-1 < x < 0) \\ x^3 & (0 < x < 1) \end{cases}$$

   (b) $$f(x) = \begin{cases} -x^3 & (x < 1) \\ 0 & (x = 1) \\ \sqrt{x} & (x > 1) \end{cases}$$

2. Let f be a function defined on the interval $-L \le x \le L$. State what properties must be required of f in order for its periodic extension to be piecewise continuous, continuous, piecewise smooth, smooth.

3. Consider the function
   $$f(x) = \begin{cases} x \sin \dfrac{1}{x} & (x \ne 0) \\ 0 & (x = 0) \end{cases}$$

   Show that f is continuous but does not have a derivative at $x = 0$.

4. Consider the function $f(x) = x - [x]$, where $[x]$ denotes the greatest integer that does not exceed x. Show for each integer n that $f'(n^-) = f'(n^+) = f'_+(n) = 1$, but that $f'_-(n)$ does not exist.

5. Let
   $$f(x) = \begin{cases} e^x & (x \le 0) \\ e^{-x} & (x \ge 0) \end{cases}$$

   Graph the function and show that $f'_+(0) = f'(0^+)$ and $f'_-(0) = f'(0^-)$. Does $f'(0)$ exist?

6. Let

$$f(x) = \begin{cases} e^x & (x < 0) \\ -e^{-x} & (x > 0) \end{cases}$$

Show that $f'_-(0) = f'(0^-) = f'_+(0) = f'(0^+)$. Does $f'(0)$ exist? Graph the function.

7. Show that the function

$$f(x) = \begin{cases} x^3 \sin \dfrac{1}{x} & (x \neq 0) \\ 0 & (x = 0) \end{cases}$$

is smooth in any interval $[a, b]$.

8. Give an example to show that the product of two absolutely integrable functions is not necessarily absolutely integrable. *Hint:* Take $f(x) = 1/\sqrt{x}$.

9. Show that the function $f(x) = 1/(1 + x^2)$ is absolutely integrable on the interval $(-\infty, \infty)$.

10. Use the result of Problem 9 to show that the integral

$$\int_0^\infty \frac{\cos x}{1 + x^2} \, dx$$

exists.

11. Give a geometrical interpretation of the mean value theorem (Theorem 1.1).

12. Let $f(x) = Ax^2 + Bx + C, a \leq x \leq b$, where A, B, C are any constants. Show that $x_0 = (a + b)/2$ is the value that satisfies the mean value theorem.

13. Show that there is no continuous function f that satisfies

$$x^n = \int_a^x f(t) \, dt \qquad (n > 0)$$

unless $a = 0$.

14. By using the mean value theorem for integrals, prove that the function defined by (1.6) is continuous on $a \leq x \leq b$. *Hint:* Consider $F(x + h) - F(x) = \int_x^{x+h} f(t) \, dt$ and show that this tends to zero as $h \to 0$.

15. Show that equations (1.6) and (1.7) imply (1.8), and vice versa.

2. Partial Derivatives

We now review some concepts concerning derivatives of functions of several variables. Let u be a function of the two independent variables x, y in a domain D and let (x_0, y_0) be a point of D. If we set $y = y_0$, then u becomes a function of the variable x alone. Its derivative at $x = x_0$ is defined as the limit

$$\lim_{\Delta x \to 0} \frac{u(x_0 + \Delta x, y_0) - u(x_0, y_0)}{\Delta x}$$

whenever the limit exists. This derivative is called the first-order partial derivative of u with respect to x at the point (x_0, y_0), and is denoted by $(\partial u/\partial x)(x_0, y_0)$

or $u_x(x_0, y_0)$. Frequently, we shall also use the simpler notation u_x whenever the point at which the derivative is being evaluated is clear from the context. In the same way, we define the first-order partial derivative of u with respect to y at (x_0, y_0) as the limit

$$\frac{\partial u}{\partial y}(x_0, y_0) = \lim_{\Delta y \to 0} \frac{u(x_0, y_0 + \Delta y) - u(x_0, y_0)}{\Delta y}$$

provided the limit exists. It follows from the foregoing definitions that, given a function u of two variables x, y, the partial derivative of u with respect to either one of the variables, whenever it exists, can be calculated by simply differentiating the function with respect to the variable concerned while treating the other variable as a constant.

Example 2.1. Find the first-order partial derivatives of the function

$$u(x, y) = x \cos xy + y$$

Solution: The first-order partial derivatives of the given function exist. To find u_x, we differentiate with respect to x, treating y as a constant, and obtain

$$u_x(x, y) = \cos xy - xy \sin xy$$

Similarly, we obtain $u_y(x, y) = -x^2 \sin xy + 1$.

The partial derivatives u_x and u_y of a given function u can be given geometrical interpretation if we regard the equation $z = u(x, y)$ as representing a surface in the xyz-space. In fact, when we set $y = y_0$, $z = u(x, y_0)$ represents the curve of intersection of the surface $z = u(x, y)$ and the plane $y = y_0$. Thus, $u_x(x_0, y_0)$ is the slope of the tangent line to the curve $z = u(x, y_0)$ at $x = x_0$. Likewise, $u_y(x_0, y_0)$ represents the slope of the tangent to the curve $z = u(x_0, y)$ at $y = y_0$, where $z = u(x_0, y)$ is the curve of intersection of the surface with the plane $x = x_0$. The tangent plane to the surface at the point (x_0, y_0) can then be shown to have the equation

$$z - z_0 = u_x(x_0, y_0)(x - x_0) + u_y(x_0, y_0)(y - y_0)$$

where $z_0 = u(x_0, y_0)$.

It is clear that the value of u_x and u_y at a point depends on the coordinates (x, y) of that point. This means that the partial derivatives u_x and u_y are also functions of the variables x and y; hence, they, too, may admit partial derivatives with respect to one of or both the variables. These derivatives, if they exist, are called the second-order partial derivatives of u. The four second-order partial derivatives of u, for instance, are

$$u_{xx} = \frac{\partial^2 u}{\partial x^2}, \qquad u_{yx} = \frac{\partial}{\partial x}\left(\frac{\partial u}{\partial y}\right) = \frac{\partial^2 u}{\partial x \, \partial y}$$

$$u_{xy} = \frac{\partial}{\partial y}\left(\frac{\partial u}{\partial x}\right) = \frac{\partial^2 u}{\partial y \, \partial x}, \qquad u_{yy} = \frac{\partial^2 u}{\partial y^2}$$

assuming these exist. Third-order partial derivatives of u are obtained if the preceding derivatives can be further differentiated with respect to x or y. Derivatives of order greater than the first are generally referred to as higher-order derivatives; in particular, the derivatives u_{xy} and u_{yx} together with all higher-order derivatives of u with respect to both x and y are called mixed derivatives.

Example 2.2. Find the second-order partial derivatives of the function $u = x \cos xy + y$ considered in Example 2.1.

Solution: The second-order partial derivatives are

$$u_{xx} = -2y \sin xy - xy^2 \cos xy, \qquad u_{xy} = -2x \sin xy - x^2y \cos xy$$
$$u_{yx} = -2x \sin xy - x^2y \cos xy, \qquad u_{yy} = -x^3 \cos xy$$

We notice in Example 2.2 that the mixed derivatives u_{xy} and u_{yx} are equal. This means that the order in which the differentiations are performed is immaterial. This is by no means true of all functions (see Problem 20, Exercise 1.2); however, whenever the mixed derivatives in question are continuous, it can be shown that the order of differentiation does not matter. Thus, for the function considered above, there also follow $u_{xxy} = u_{xyx} = u_{yxx}$, $u_{xyy} = u_{yxy} = u_{yyx}$, etc., as one easily verifies, since the function has continuous derivatives of all order. Unless otherwise stated, we shall always assume in this work that mixed derivatives are continuous whenever they exist.

Exercises 1.2

In Problems 1 through 5, find the first-order partial derivatives of the given function.

1. $u = x^2y + xy^2$.

2. $u = e^x \cos y + xy$.

3. $u = \ln(x^2 + y^2)$, $(x, y) \neq (0, 0)$.

4. $u = \dfrac{x - y}{x + y}$, $(x, y) \neq (0, 0)$.

5. $u = \tan \dfrac{x}{y}$, $y > 0$.

6. If $u = x^3 + 2x^2y + 3xy^2 + y^3$, verify that $xu_x + yu_y = 3u$.

7. If $u = \arcsin\left(\dfrac{x - y}{x + y}\right)$, $(x, y) \neq (0, 0)$, verify that $xu_x + yu_y = 0$.

8. If $u = (ax + by)^n$, n a real constant, verify that $bu_x - au_y = 0$.

9. If $u = x^2y + y^2z + z^2x$, verify that $u_x + u_y + u_z = (x + y + z)^2$.

10. (Euler's Theorem). A function u of the variables x, y is said to be homogeneous of degree n if $u(tx, ty) = t^n u(x, y)$. If u is homogeneous of degree n with continuous first derivatives, show that $xu_x + yu_y = nu$. *Hint:* Differentiate $u(tx, ty) = t^n u(x, y)$ with respect to t.

In Problems 11 through 14, find the second-order partial derivatives of the given function.

11. $u = (x^2 + y^2)^{1/2}$.

12. $u = e^{ax+by}$.

13. $u = e^x \sin y$.

14. $u = \arctan x/y$.

15. If $u = \ln(x^2 + y^2)^{1/2}$, $(x, y) \neq 0$, show that $u_{xx} + u_{yy} = 0$.

16. If $u = \arctan y/x$, show that $u_{xx} + u_{yy} = 0$.

17. If $u = x^y$, $x > 0$, show that $u_{xy} = u_{yx}$.

18. If $u = \sinh(x + at)$, show that $u_{tt} - a^2 u_{xx} = 0$.

19. If $u = \left(\dfrac{x - y}{x + y}\right)$, $(x, y) \neq (0, 0)$, show that $u_{xy} = u_{yx}$.

20. Consider the function

$$u(x, y) = \begin{cases} xy \dfrac{x^2 - y^2}{x^2 + y^2} & [(x, y) \neq (0, 0)] \\ 0 & [(x, y) = (0, 0)] \end{cases}$$

Using the definition, show that $u_x(0, y) = -y$, and $u_y(x, 0) = x$; hence, deduce that

$$u_{xy}(0, 0) \neq u_{yx}(0, 0)$$

21. Consider the function

$$u(x, y) = x^2 \arctan \frac{y}{x} - y^2 \arctan \frac{x}{y} \qquad [(x, y) \neq (0, 0)]$$

$$u(0, y) = u(x, 0) = 0$$

Show that for $(x, y) \neq (0, 0)$, $u_{xy} = u_{yx}$, but $u_{xy}(0, 0) \neq u_{yx}(0, 0)$.

3.   Differentiation of Composite Functions; the Chain Rule

Suppose that u is a function of the variables x and y in a domain D,

(3.1) $u = U(x, y)$, (x, y) in D

and suppose that x and y are themselves functions of the variable t,

(3.2) $x = f(t)$, $y = g(t)$ $(a \leq t \leq b)$

such that for each t in $[a, b]$, $(f(t), g(t))$ is in D. Then, in effect, u is a function of the single variable t:

(3.3) $u = U(x, y) = U[f(t), g(t)]$ $(a \leq t \leq b)$

The derivative du/dt, if it exists, can then be calculated by simply differentiating the function (3.3) with respect to t. However, it is frequently desirable to obtain the derivative of u with respect to t without an actual substitution for the variables

x and y. One important and useful tool in this connection is called the "chain rule."

THEOREM 3.1. (The Chain Rule) *If the function u in* (3.1) *and its first-order partial derivatives are continuous in D, and if the functions f and g in* (3.2) *are differentiable in a < t < b, then u is a differentiable function of t whose derivative is given by the formula*

$$(3.4) \qquad \frac{du}{dt} = \frac{\partial u}{\partial x}\frac{dx}{dt} + \frac{\partial u}{\partial y}\frac{dy}{dt} = \frac{\partial U}{\partial x}\frac{df}{dt} + \frac{\partial U}{\partial y}\frac{dg}{dt}$$

Several modifications of this formula will be considered in the rest of this section. We first illustrate its use in the following example.

Example 3.1. Let $u(x, y) = e^x \sin y$, where $x = \ln t$ and $y = (1 - t^2)$, $t > 0$. Find du/dt by substitution and direct differentiation and by the use of formula (3.4).

Solution: Substituting for x and y in u, we obtain

$$u = t \sin(1 - t^2), \qquad\qquad (t > 0)$$

whose derivative is easily found to be

$$\frac{du}{dt} = \sin(1 - t^2) - 2t^2 \cos(1 - t^2)$$

On the other hand, we have

$$u_x = e^x \sin y, \qquad u_y = e^x \cos y, \qquad \frac{dx}{dt} = \frac{1}{t}, \qquad \text{and} \qquad \frac{dy}{dt} = -2t$$

so that by (3.4) we find

$$\frac{du}{dt} = (e^x \sin y)\frac{dx}{dt} + (e^x \cos y)\frac{dy}{dt}$$

$$= t[\sin(1 - t^2)]\frac{1}{t} + t[\cos(1 - t^2)](-2t)$$

$$= \sin(1 - t^2) - 2t^2 \cos(1 - t^2)$$

Formula (3.4) extends easily to the case where u is a function of three or more independent variables. For example, if u is a function of the variables x, y, and z,

$$u = U(x, y, z)$$

where

$$x = x(t), \qquad y = y(t), \qquad \text{and} \qquad z = z(t)$$

then

$$(3.5) \qquad \frac{du}{dt} = \frac{\partial U}{\partial x}\frac{dx}{dt} + \frac{\partial U}{\partial y}\frac{dy}{dt} + \frac{\partial U}{\partial z}\frac{dz}{dt}$$

provided U and its first-order partial derivatives are continuous and x, y, z are differentiable. In the special case where $x = t$, so that y and z become functions of the variable x, formula (3.5) reduces to the form

$$(3.6) \qquad \frac{du}{dx} = \frac{\partial U}{\partial x} + \frac{\partial U}{\partial y}\frac{dy}{dx} + \frac{\partial U}{\partial z}\frac{dz}{dx}$$

We shall have special need for this formula in the next section.

Next, suppose that u is a function of the variables x, y where

$$x = x(s, t) \qquad \text{and} \qquad y = y(s, t)$$

that is, x and y are in turn functions of two independent variables s and t. Then u may also be considered as a function of the variables s, t:

$$(3.7) \qquad u = U(x, y) = U[x(s, t), y(s, t)]$$

and we may investigate the partial derivative of u with respect to s or t when the other variable is held constant. Under the condition that U and its first-order partial derivatives are continuous and that the first-order partial derivatives of x and y exist, it can be shown that

$$(3.8) \qquad \frac{\partial u}{\partial s} = \frac{\partial U}{\partial x}\frac{\partial x}{\partial s} + \frac{\partial U}{\partial y}\frac{\partial y}{\partial s}$$

and

$$(3.9) \qquad \frac{\partial u}{\partial t} = \frac{\partial U}{\partial x}\frac{\partial x}{\partial t} + \frac{\partial U}{\partial y}\frac{\partial y}{\partial t}$$

These formulas are modification of the chain rule (3.4).

Finally, we consider a function w of four variables x, y, u, and v, defined by

$$w = W(x, y, u, v)$$

where u and v are, in turn, functions of the independent variables x and y. We are interested in obtaining formulas for the partial derivatives of w with respect to x and y. To determine $\partial w/\partial x$, we hold y fixed and regard w as merely a function of x, u, and v, remembering that both u and v depend also on x. By a modification of formula (3.6) we have

$$(3.10) \qquad \frac{\partial w}{\partial x} = \frac{\partial W}{\partial x} + \frac{\partial W}{\partial u}\frac{\partial u}{\partial x} + \frac{\partial W}{\partial v}\frac{\partial v}{\partial x}$$

In the same way, we have

$$(3.11) \qquad \frac{\partial w}{\partial y} = \frac{\partial W}{\partial y} + \frac{\partial W}{\partial u}\frac{\partial u}{\partial y} + \frac{\partial W}{\partial v}\frac{\partial v}{\partial y}$$

These formulas can, of course, be established under the assumption that all first-order partial derivatives of W are continuous and that all first-order partial derivatives of u and v exist. The student should carefully note the distinction between the terms $\partial w/\partial x$, $\partial w/\partial y$, and the terms $\partial W/\partial x$, $\partial W/\partial y$.

Higher-order partial derivatives of a composite function can be calculated by successive application of the appropriate formulas derived above. For instance, the second-order mixed derivative of the function (3.7) with respect to s and t can be obtained by applying formula (3.9) to the function defined by formula (3.8). This gives

$$\frac{\partial^2 u}{\partial t\, \partial s} = \frac{\partial}{\partial t}\left(\frac{\partial U}{\partial x}\frac{\partial x}{\partial s}\right) + \frac{\partial}{\partial t}\left(\frac{\partial U}{\partial y}\frac{\partial y}{\partial s}\right)$$

$$= \left(\frac{\partial^2 U}{\partial x^2}\frac{\partial x}{\partial t} + \frac{\partial^2 U}{\partial y\, \partial x}\frac{\partial y}{\partial t}\right)\frac{\partial x}{\partial s} + \frac{\partial U}{\partial x}\frac{\partial^2 x}{\partial t\, \partial s}$$

$$+ \left(\frac{\partial^2 U}{\partial x\, \partial y}\frac{\partial x}{\partial t} + \frac{\partial^2 U}{\partial y^2}\frac{\partial y}{\partial t}\right)\frac{\partial y}{\partial s} + \frac{\partial U}{\partial y}\frac{\partial^2 y}{\partial t\, \partial s}$$

$$= \frac{\partial^2 U}{\partial x^2}\frac{\partial x}{\partial s}\frac{\partial x}{\partial t} + \frac{\partial^2 U}{\partial y\, \partial x}\left(\frac{\partial x}{\partial s}\frac{\partial y}{\partial t} + \frac{\partial x}{\partial t}\frac{\partial y}{\partial s}\right)$$

$$+ \frac{\partial^2 U}{\partial y^2}\frac{\partial y}{\partial s}\frac{\partial y}{\partial t} + \frac{\partial U}{\partial x}\frac{\partial^2 x}{\partial t\, \partial s} + \frac{\partial U}{\partial y}\frac{\partial^2 y}{\partial t\, \partial s}$$

where we have assumed that $U_{xy} = U_{yx}$.

Example 3.2. Let $u(x, y) = x^2 + y^2$, where $x = r \cos \theta$ and $y = r \sin \theta$. Find the partial derivatives of u with respect to r and θ up to the second order.

Solution: Using formulas (3.8) and (3.9), with $s = r$ and $t = \theta$, we find

$$u_r = 2x \cos \theta + 2y \sin \theta$$
$$= 2r(\cos^2 \theta + \sin^2 \theta)$$
$$= 2r$$

$$u_\theta = 2x(-r \sin \theta) + 2y(r \cos \theta)$$
$$= -2r^2(\sin \theta \cos \theta - \sin \theta \cos \theta)$$
$$= 0$$

from which there follow

$$u_{rr} = 2, \qquad u_{r\theta} = 0, \qquad u_{\theta\theta} = 0$$

Example 3.3. Show that the function $w = f(x - 2y) + g(x + 3y)$, where f and g are twice differentiable, satisfies the equation

$$6w_{xx} + w_{xy} - w_{yy} = 0$$

Solution: Let $u = x - 2y$ and $v = x + 3y$. Then w becomes a function of the variable u and v:

$$w = f(u) + g(v) = W(u, v)$$

Using formulas (3.10) and (3.11) and noting that W depends only on u and v, we find

$$w_x = W_u u_x + W_v v_x = f'(u) + g'(v)$$
$$w_y = W_u u_y + W_v v_y = f'(u)(-2) + g'(v)(3)$$
$$= -2f'(u) + 3g'(v)$$

Further application of the same formulas gives

$$w_{xx} = f''(u) + g''(v)$$
$$w_{xy} = (-2)f''(u) + (3)g''(v)$$
$$w_{yy} = (-2)^2 f''(u) + (3)^2 g''(v)$$

Thus,

$$6w_{xx} + w_{xy} - w_{yy} = 6(f'' + g'') + (-2f'' + 3g'') - (4f'' + 9g'') = 0$$

Exercises 1.3

In Problems 1 through 4, find du/dt by use of the chain rule and check your result by substitution and direct differentiation.

1. $u = x \ln y$, where $x = t^2$, $y = (1 - t)^{1/2}$.

2. $u = x \cos y + ye^x$, where $x = \ln t$, $y = \sin t$.

3. $u = \arctan y/x$, where $x = \cos t$, $y = \sin t$.

4. $u = \ln(x^2 + y^2)$, where $x = e^t - e^{-t}$, $y = e^t + e^{-t}$.

5. If $u = xyz$, where $y = \ln x$ and $z = (1 + x^2)$, find du/dx by the chain rule and check your result by substitution and direct differentiation.

6. As in Problem 5, if $u = x^2 + y^2 + z^2$, where $y = x \cos x$ and $z = x \sin x$, find du/dx.

In Problems 7 through 10, find the first-order partial derivatives of the given function with respect to r and s.

7. $u = x^2 - 3xy + y^2$, where $x = r + s$, $y = r - s$.

8. $u = e^{x \cos y}$, where $x = (r^2 + s^2)^{1/2}$, $y = \arctan r/s$.

9. $u = x^2 - y^2$, where $x = r \cosh s$, $y = r \sinh s$.

10. $u = x \ln(x - y)$, where $x = r^2 + s^2$, $y = 2rs$.

11. If u is a function of x and y, where $x = s + t$ and $y = s - t$, express $u_{xx} - u_{yy}$ in terms of the new variables s and t.

12. Express $u_{xx} + u_{yy}$ in polar coordinates r and θ, where $r^2 = (x^2 + y^2)$ and $\theta = \arctan y/x$.

13. Let $u = f(x + ct) + g(x - ct)$, where f and g are twice differentiable functions. Show that $u_{tt} - c^2 u_{xx} = 0$.

14. Let u be a function of x and y, where $x = r \cos \theta$ and $y = r \sin \theta$. Show that

$$(u_x)^2 + (u_y)^2 = (u_r)^2 + \frac{1}{r^2} (u_\theta)^2$$

15. If u and v are functions of x and y satisfying the equations $u_x = v_y$, $u_y = -v_x$, show that in polar coordinates

$$\frac{\partial u}{\partial r} = \frac{1}{r} \frac{\partial v}{\partial \theta}, \qquad \frac{1}{r} \frac{\partial u}{\partial \theta} = -\frac{\partial v}{\partial r}$$

and

$$u_{rr} + \frac{1}{r} u_r + \frac{1}{r^2} u_{\theta\theta} = 0$$

4.   Differentiation of Integrals Depending on a Parameter

In our later work we shall have occasion to deal with finding the derivative of a function ϕ defined by a definite integral of the form

(4.1)
$$\phi(x) = \int_{u(x)}^{v(x)} f(x, t)\, dt$$

where the integrand f and the limits of integration u, v depend on the parameter x. If the integration in (4.1) can be effected analytically, then the function ϕ is defined explicitly, and hence its derivative, if it exists, can be obtained by straightforward differentiation. However, it is not always practical, nor possible, to express the integral (4.1) in explicit form. Therefore, in such cases, it is desirable to have an expression for the derivative ϕ' of the function (4.1).

We first state the result in the special case where the limits of integration are constants.

THEOREM 4.1.   *Consider the integral*

(4.2)
$$\phi(x) = \int_{a}^{b} f(x, t)\, dt$$

where a and b are constants. If f and f_x are continuous in the rectangular region $R: \alpha \leq x \leq \beta, a \leq t \leq b$, then the function (4.2) is continuous and possesses a derivative given by

(4.3)
$$\phi'(x) = \int_{a}^{b} f_x(x, t)\, dt \qquad\qquad (\alpha \leq x \leq \beta)$$

The fact that ϕ is continuous on $[\alpha, \beta]$ implies that for each x_0 in $[\alpha, \beta]$

$$\lim_{x \to x_0} \phi(x) = \phi(x_0) = \int_{a}^{b} f(x_0, t)\, dt$$

that is,

$$\lim_{x \to x_0} \int_{a}^{b} f(x, t)\, dt = \int_{a}^{b} \lim_{x \to x_0} f(x, t)\, dt$$

We notice that this involves interchanging the order of the limit operation $x \to x_0$ and integration. Also, formula (4.3) indicates that the derivative of ϕ can be obtained by taking the derivative under the integral sign; that is,

(4.4)
$$\frac{d}{dx} \int_{a}^{b} f(x, t)\, dt = \int_{a}^{b} f_x(x, t)\, dt$$

This also involves interchanging the order of the operations of differentiation and integration. The validity of interchanging the order of two operations, particularly those involving limiting processes, should not be taken lightly. Such problems are of fundamental importance in mathematics and are of frequent occurrence in practice.

We now state the result for the integral (4.1) involving variable limits.

THEOREM 4.2. *Let*

(**4.5**)
$$\phi(x) = \int_{u(x)}^{v(x)} f(x, t)\, dt$$

where u and v are functions of x. If u and v are differentiable in the interval $a \leq x \leq b$, *and f and* f_x *are continuous in the rectangle* $R: a \leq x \leq b$, $u(x) \leq t \leq v(x)$, *then*

$$\frac{d\phi}{dx} = \frac{d}{dx} \int_{u(x)}^{v(x)} f(x, t)\, dt$$

(**4.6**)
$$= \int_{u(x)}^{v(x)} f_x(x, t)\, dt$$

$$+ f(x, v)\frac{dv}{dx} - f(x, u)\frac{du}{dx}$$

Formula (4.6) is commonly known as Leibnitz' rule. It is interesting to note that this formula can be established by regarding the function ϕ as a composite function. We observe that the integral (4.5) depends on the limits u and v as well as on x. Hence, we may write

(**4.7**)
$$\phi(x, u, v) = \int_{u(x)}^{v(x)} f(x, t)\, dt$$

Since u and v are differentiable functions of x, and f and f_x are continuous, ϕ is a continuous and differentiable function of x alone. Then its derivative with respect to x exists, and by formula (3.6) we obtain

(**4.8**)
$$\frac{d\phi}{dx} = \frac{\partial \phi}{\partial x} + \frac{\partial \phi}{\partial u}\frac{du}{dx} + \frac{\partial \phi}{\partial v}\frac{dv}{dx}$$

Now the term $\partial\phi/\partial x$ in (4.8) is to be calculated with u and v treated as constants; therefore, according to Theorem 4.1,

(**4.9**)
$$\frac{\partial \phi}{\partial x} = \int_{u(x)}^{v(x)} f_x(x, t)\, dt$$

By the fundamental theorem of calculus (Theorem 1.2) applied to (4.7), we have

(**4.10**)
$$\frac{\partial \phi}{\partial u} = -f(x, u) \qquad \text{and} \qquad \frac{\partial \phi}{\partial v} = f(x, v)$$

Thus, substituting the results (4.9) and (4.10) in (4.8), we obtain formula (4.6).

Example 4.1. Let

$$\phi(x) = \int_0^x \sin xt\, dt$$

By direct computation, we find

$$\phi(x) = \frac{1 - \cos x^2}{x}$$

and therefore

$$\phi'(x) = 2 \sin x^2 - \frac{1 - \cos x^2}{x^2}$$

By Leibnitz' rule we have

$$\phi'(x) = \int_0^x t \cos xt \, dt + \sin x^2$$

$$= \left[\frac{t \sin xt}{x} + \frac{\cos xt}{x^2} \right]_0^x + \sin x^2$$

which gives the previous result.

Example 4.2.   Let

$$u(x) = \frac{1}{2} \int_0^x (x - t)^2 f(t) \, dt$$

where f is a continuous function. Show that $u'''(x) = f(x)$.

Solution: By (4.6) we find

$$u'(x) = \int_0^x (x - t) f(t) \, dt + \tfrac{1}{2}(x - t)^2 f(t)]_{t=x}$$

$$= \int_0^x (x - t) f(t) \, dt$$

Differentiating once more, we obtain

$$u''(x) = \int_0^x f(t) \, dt$$

which, upon differentiating the third time, gives $u'''(x) = f(x)$.

More generally, when the integrand f in (4.1) involves the parameters x, y, and the limits u, v are functions of x, y, then the integral (4.1) defines ϕ as a function of x, y; that is,

(4.11) $$\phi(x, y) = \int_{u(x,y)}^{v(x,y)} f(x, y, t) \, dt$$

If u and v have first-order partial derivatives and f, f_x, and f_y are continuous, then ϕ is a function of x and y whose partial derivatives ϕ_x and ϕ_y exist. Regarding ϕ as a composite function $\phi = \phi(x, y, u, v)$. we obtain by means of formulas (3.10), (3.11), and Theorem 1.2

(4.12) $$\frac{\partial \phi}{\partial x} = \int_{u(x,y)}^{v(x,y)} f_x(x, y, t) \, dt$$

$$+ f(x, y, v) \frac{\partial v}{\partial x} - f(x, y, u) \frac{\partial u}{\partial x}$$

and

(4.13)
$$\frac{\partial \phi}{\partial y} = \int_{u(x,y)}^{v(x,y)} f_y(x, y, t) \, dt$$

$$+ f(x, y, v) \frac{\partial v}{\partial y} - f(x, y, u) \frac{\partial u}{\partial y}$$

These are extensions of Leibnitz' formula (4.6).

Example 4.3. Let

$$u(x, y) = \int_{x-y}^{x+y} f(t) \, dt$$

where f is a differentiable function. Show that u satisfies the equation

$$u_{xx} - u_{yy} = 0$$

Solution: By (4.12) and (4.13) we have

$$u_x(x, y) = f(x + y) - f(x - y)$$

and

$$u_y(x, y) = f(x + y) + f(x - y)$$

Then, by the chain rule,

$$u_{xx} = f'(x + y) - f'(x - y)$$
$$u_{yy} = f'(x + y) - f'(x - y)$$

Thus $u_{xx} - u_{yy} = 0$.

Exercises 1.4

1. Let $\phi(x) = \int_0^{\pi/2} \cos xt \, dt$. Find $d\phi/dx$ by formula (4.6) and check your result by direct calculation.

2. Let $\phi(x) = \int_0^{x^2} \arctan(t/x^2) \, dt$. Find $d\phi/dx$ in two ways.

3. Let $\phi(x) = \int_{-x}^{\sin x} \frac{dt}{x + t + 1}$. Find $d\phi/dx$ in two ways.

4. Given that $\int_0^{\pi} \frac{dt}{(x - \cos t)} = \frac{\pi}{(x^2 - 1)}$, $x^2 > 1$. Evaluate $\int_0^{\pi} \frac{dt}{(x - \cos t)^2}$.

5. Let $\phi(x) = \int_x^{x^2} \frac{\sin xt}{t} \, dt$. Find $d\phi/dx$.

6. Let $\phi(x) = 1/k \int_0^x f(t) \sin k(x - t) \, dt$, where f is a continuous function and k a constant. Show that $\phi'' + k^2\phi = f$.

7. Let $J_0(x) = 1/\pi \int_0^{\pi} \cos(x \cos \theta) \, d\theta$. Show that J_0 satisfies the Bessel's equation of zero order: $y'' + (1/x)y' + y = 0$. *Hint:* Find J_0' and integrate by parts.

8. Evaluate $\phi(x) = \int_0^1 \frac{t^x - 1}{\ln t} \, dt$, $x > 0$.

Hint: Find $\phi'(x)$ and note that $\phi(x) \to 0$ as $x \to 0$.

9. Let $u(x, t) = 1/2c \int_{x-ct}^{x+ct} f(s)\, ds$, where f is differentiable.
   (a) Find u_t and show that $u_t(x, 0) = f(x)$.
   (b) Show that u satisfies the differential equation $u_{tt} - c^2 u_{xx} = 0$.

5. Uniform Convergence of Series

Let u_n, $n \geq 1$, be a sequence of functions defined on the interval $a \leq x \leq b$. For each point x of this interval, let

$$S_m(x) = \sum_{n=1}^{m} u_n(x)$$

be the partial sum consisting of the first m-terms of the series

(5.1) $$\sum_{n=1}^{\infty} u_n(x)$$

If the limit

(5.2) $$\lim_{m \to \infty} S_m(x) = \lim_{m \to \infty} \sum_{n=1}^{m} u_n(x) = S(x)$$

exists, then we say that the series (5.1) converges to $S(x)$ at x, $a \leq x \leq b$. Recall that equation (5.2) means that for any given number $\varepsilon > 0$, there is an integer $N > 0$ corresponding to the point x, $a \leq x \leq b$, such that

(5.3) $$|S(x) - S_m(x)| = \left| \sum_{n=m+1}^{\infty} u_n(x) \right| < \varepsilon$$

whenever $m > N$. In general, the integer N depends on the point x under investigation as well as on the given number ε. However, if corresponding to a given ε, there exists an integer N that is independent of x such that the inequality (5.3) holds for all x in the interval $a \leq x \leq b$, then we say that the series (5.1) converges uniformly to $S(x)$ on that interval. It is clear that a uniformly convergent series is convergent in the ordinary sense.

A convenient and practical method for determining uniform convergence of a series is given by the following theorem.

THEOREM 5.1. (Weierstrass M-Test) *Let $\sum_{n=1}^{\infty} u_n(x)$ be a series of functions defined on the interval $a \leq x \leq b$. If $\sum_{n=1}^{\infty} M_n$ is a convergent series of positive constants such that $|u_n(x)| \leq M_n$ for each $n \geq 1$ and for all x in the interval $a \leq x \leq b$, then the series $\sum_{n=1}^{\infty} u_n(x)$ converges uniformly on that interval.*

Example 5.1. Show that the series $\sum_{n=0}^{\infty} x^n$ converges uniformly to the function $1/(1 - x)$ on the interval $-a \leq x \leq a$, where $0 < a < 1$.

Solution: For each x in the given interval we note that

$$|x^n| \leq a^n < 1$$

Since the series $\sum_{n=0}^{\infty} a^n$ is convergent when $|a| < 1$, it follows by the Weierstrass M-test that the series $\sum_{n=0}^{\infty} x^n$ converges uniformly for $|x| \leq a < 1$. To show that the series converges to the function $S(x) = 1/(1 - x)$, we note that for $m \geq 1$, we have

$$S_m(x) = \sum_{n=0}^{m-1} x^n = \frac{1 - x^m}{1 - x}$$

Since for $|x| < 1$, $\lim_{m \to \infty} x^m = 0$, it follows that $\lim_{m \to \infty} S_m(x) = 1/(1 - x)$.

There are several important properties of a uniformly convergent series which we shall have occasion to use later in our work. We shall state them here as theorems to facilitate reference.

THEOREM 5.2. (Continuity of Limit Function) *Let the functions $u_n(x)$ ($n \geq 1$) be continuous on the interval $a \leq x \leq b$ and let the series $\sum_{n=1}^{\infty} u_n(x)$ converge uniformly to $S(x)$ on that interval. Then S is a continuous function on the same interval.*

This theorem implies that for each x_0, $a \leq x_0 \leq b$,

$$\lim_{x \to x_0} S(x) = S(x_0)$$

which means that

$$\lim_{\substack{x \to x_0 \\ m \to \infty}} S_m(x) = \lim_{\substack{m \to \infty \\ x \to x_0}} S_m(x)$$

Thus, under the conditions stated in the theorem, the order of taking the limits with respect to x and m can be interchanged.

Example 5.2.   For the series of Example 5.1, it follows that

$$\lim_{x \to \frac{1}{2}} \frac{1}{1 - x} = \sum_{n=0}^{\infty} \left(\frac{1}{2}\right)^n$$

or

$$2 = 1 + \tfrac{1}{2} + \tfrac{1}{4} + \tfrac{1}{8} + \cdots$$

THEOREM 5.3.   (Integration of Series) *Let the functions $u_n(x)$ ($n \geq 1$) be continuous on the interval $a \leq x \leq b$ and let the series $\sum_{n=1}^{\infty} u_n(x)$ converge uniformly to $S(x)$ on that interval. If x_1 and x_2 are any two points such that $a \leq x_1 < x_2 \leq b$, then*

$$\int_{x_1}^{x_2} S(x)\, dx = \sum_{n=1}^{\infty} \int_{x_1}^{x_2} u_n(x)\, dx$$

This theorem gives sufficient conditions under which a convergent series may be integrated term by term to obtain the integral of the limit function. It essentially involves interchanging the order of the integration and summation.

Example 5.3.　Obtain the result

$$- \ln(1 - x) = \sum_{n=0}^{\infty} \frac{x^{n+1}}{n + 1} \qquad (|x| < 1)$$

from the series of Example 5.1.

Solution: Since the series $\sum_{n=0}^{\infty} x^n$ converges uniformly to the limit function $1/(1 - x)$, we can integrate term by term from 0 to any point x, where $|x| < 1$, and obtain

$$\int_0^x \frac{dt}{1 - t} = \sum_{n=0}^{\infty} \int_0^x t^n \, dt$$

$$= \sum_{n=0}^{\infty} \frac{x^{n+1}}{n + 1} \qquad (|x| < 1)$$

The integral on the left-hand side gives $- \ln(1 - x)$.

THEOREM 5.4.　(Differentiation of Series) *If the functions u_n $(n \geq 1)$ of the convergent series*

$$S(x) = \sum_{n=1}^{\infty} u_n(x)$$

have continuous derivatives u_n' on the interval $a \leq x \leq b$, and if the series $\sum_{n=1}^{\infty} u_n'(x)$ converges uniformly on this interval, then

$$S'(x) = \frac{d}{dx} \left(\sum_{n=1}^{\infty} u_n(x) \right) = \sum_{n=1}^{\infty} u_n'(x)$$

for $a \leq x \leq b$.

The theorem gives sufficient conditions under which a convergent series may be differentiated term by term to yield the derivative of the limit function. The process involves interchanging the order of differentiation and summation.

Example 5.4.　From the series of Example 5.1, show that

$$\frac{1}{(1 - x)^2} = 1 + 2x + 3x^2 + \cdots = \sum_{n=1}^{\infty} nx^{n-1}$$

for $|x| < 1$.

Solution: Consider the series $\sum_{n=1}^{\infty} nx^{n-1}$ obtained by formally differentiating the series of Example 5.1. For each x such that $|x| \leq a < 1$ we note that

$$|nx^{n-1}| \leq |na^{n-1}|$$

Using the ratio test, we see that the series $\sum_{n=1}^{\infty} na^{n-1}$ is convergent when $|a| < 1$. Thus, by Weierstrass M-test, series $\sum_{n=1}^{\infty} nx^{n-1}$ converges uniformly for $|x| \leq a < 1$. By Theorem 5.4, it follows that

$$\frac{d}{dx} \left(\frac{1}{1 - x} \right) = \frac{1}{(1 - x)^2} = \sum_{n=1}^{\infty} nx^{n-1} \qquad (|x| < 1)$$

Exercises 1.5

In Problems 1 through 6, show that the series converge uniformly on the given interval.

1. (a) $\displaystyle\sum_{n=1}^{\infty} \frac{\sin nx}{n^2}$, for all x; (b) $\displaystyle\sum_{n=1}^{\infty} \frac{\cos nx}{n^2}$, for all x.

2. $\displaystyle\sum_{n=1}^{\infty} \frac{x^n}{n!}$, $|x| \le a < \infty$

3. $\displaystyle\sum_{n=1}^{\infty} \frac{(-1)^n}{x^2 + n^2}$, for all x.

4. $\displaystyle\sum_{n=1}^{\infty} \frac{e^{-nx}}{n^2}$, for all $x \ge 0$.

5. $\displaystyle\sum_{n=1}^{\infty} e^{-nx}$, for $0 < a \le x$.

6. $\displaystyle\sum_{n=1}^{\infty} \left(\frac{x^n}{1 + x^n} \right) \frac{1}{n^2}$, for $-1 < a \le x < \infty$.

7. From the series of Example 5.1, obtain the series

$$\ln \frac{1 + x}{1 - x} = 2 \left(x + \frac{x^3}{3} + \frac{x^5}{5} + \cdots \right) \qquad (|x| < 1)$$

8. Let $\displaystyle\sum_{n=0}^{\infty} (-1)^n x^{2n} = \frac{1}{1 + x^2}$, $|x| < 1$.

Show that the series converges uniformly and obtain the result

$$\arctan x = x - \frac{x^3}{3} + \frac{x^5}{5} - \frac{x^7}{7} + \cdots \qquad (|x| < 1)$$

9. If $\displaystyle S(x) = \sum_{n=1}^{\infty} \frac{\sin nx}{n^2}$, show that

$$\int_0^{\pi} S(x)\, dx = 2 \sum_{n=0}^{\infty} \frac{1}{(2n + 1)^3}$$

10. If $\displaystyle S(x) = \sum_{n=1}^{\infty} \frac{\cos nx}{n^2}$, find a series for $\displaystyle\int_0^{\pi/2} S(x)\, dx$.

11. If $\displaystyle \frac{1}{1 + x} = \sum_{n=0}^{\infty} (-1)^n x^n$ for $|x| \le a < 1$, show that

$$\frac{1}{(1 + x)^2} = \sum_{n=1}^{\infty} (-1)^{n-1} n x^{n-1} \qquad (|x| < 1)$$

Justify your reasoning.

12. If $\displaystyle S(x) = \sum_{n=1}^{\infty} \frac{\sin nx}{n^{5/2}}$, verify that $\displaystyle S'(x) = \sum_{n=1}^{\infty} \frac{\cos nx}{n^{3/2}}$.

13. If $S(x) = \sum\limits_{n=0}^{\infty} \dfrac{x^n}{n!}$, show that $S'(x) = S(x)$ and $\int_0^x S(t)\, dt = S(x) - 1$.

14. Let $u(x, t) = \sum\limits_{n=1}^{\infty} e^{-n^2 t} \dfrac{\sin nx}{n^3}$, for $0 \le x \le \pi, 0 < t_0 \le t$.

    (a) Show that u_t, u_x, u_{xx} can be calculated by differentiating the series term by term.

    (b) Thus verify that u satisfies the equation $u_t - u_{xx} = 0$ and the boundary conditions $u(0, t) = u(\pi, t) = 0, t \ge t_0 > 0$.

6.   Improper Integrals Depending on a Parameter

A discussion parallel to that of the previous section can be given for an improper integral of the form

$$(6.1) \qquad \int_c^{\infty} f(x, t)\, dt$$

where the integrand f involves the parameter x. We assume that $f(x, t)$ is continuous in the region $D: a \le x \le b, c \le t < \infty$. Then, for each x in the interval $a \le x \le b$ and for each $d, c \le d < \infty$, the integral

$$(6.2) \qquad \int_c^{d} f(x, t)\, dt$$

certainly exists and thus defines a function of x. If the limit

$$(6.3) \qquad \lim_{d \to \infty} \int_c^{d} f(x, t)\, dt = \int_c^{\infty} f(x, t)\, dt = F(x)$$

exists for each x in the interval $a \le x \le b$, then we say that the improper integral (6.1) converges to $F(x)$ on that interval. This means that, for any given $\varepsilon > 0$, there is a number T corresponding to each x such that

$$(6.4) \qquad \left| F(x) - \int_c^{d} f(x, t)\, dt \right| = \left| \int_d^{\infty} f(x, t)\, dt \right| < \varepsilon$$

whenever $d > T$. Presumably, the number T depends on x as well as on the given ε. If a number T exists which is independent of x such that inequality (6.4) holds for all x in the interval $a \le x \le b$, then the integral (6.1) is said to converge uniformly to F on that interval.

We notice the similarity between the definition of uniform convergence of an improper integral and that of uniform convergence of a series. As a consequence of this similarity, we expect to obtain results for a uniformly convergent improper integral which parallel those obtained for a uniformly convergent series. We first state the analogue of Weierstrass M-test for integrals.

THEOREM 6.1. (Weierstrass M-test of Integrals) *Let $g(t) \geq 0$ be a function defined for $c \leq t < \infty$ such that the integral*

$$\int_c^\infty g(t) \, dt$$

exists. If $|f(x, t)| \leq g(t)$ for all x in the interval $a \leq x \leq b$, then the integral

$$\int_c^\infty f(x, t) \, dt$$

converges uniformly (and absolutely) on the interval $a \leq x \leq b$.

Example 6.1. Show that the integral

$$\int_0^\infty \frac{\sin xt}{1 + t^2} \, dt$$

converges uniformly for all values of x.

Solution: For any value of x, we have

$$\left| \frac{\sin xt}{1 + t^2} \right| \leq \frac{1}{1 + t^2}$$

Since $\int_0^\infty [1/(1 + t^2)] \, dt$ converges (to $\pi/2$), it follows from Theorem 6.1 that the given improper integral converges uniformly for all values of x.

The following three theorems correspond in order to Theorems 5.2, 5.3, and 5.4 of the preceding section.

THEOREM 6.2. *Let f be a continuous function in the region $D: a \leq x \leq b$, $c \leq t < \infty$, and let*

$$\int_c^\infty f(x, t) \, dt$$

converge uniformly to F on the interval $a \leq x \leq b$. Then F is continuous on the interval $[a, b]$.

The continuity of F permits us to interchange the order of taking limit and integration. That is, for each x_0 where $a \leq x_0 \leq b$, we have

(6.5) $$\lim_{x \to x_0} \int_c^\infty f(x, t) \, dt = \int_c^\infty \lim_{x \to x_0} f(x, t) \, dt$$

This conclusion generalizes the first part of the result of Theorem 4.1 which concerns a definite integral involving a parameter.

THEOREM 6.3. *Let the same conditions as in Theorem 6.2 hold. If x_1 and x_2 are any two points such that $a \leq x_1 \leq x_2 \leq b$, then*

(6.6) $$\int_{x_1}^{x_2} F(x) \, dx = \int_c^\infty \int_{x_1}^{x_2} f(x, t) \, dx \, dt$$

That is, we may interchange the order of the two integrations, one with respect to x and the other with respect to t. Let us illustrate the use of this property in evaluating certain integrals that otherwise cannot be effected by the usual elementary method of integration.

Example 6.2. Obtain the result

$$\int_0^\infty \frac{e^{-at} - e^{-bt}}{t}\, dt = \ln \frac{b}{a} \qquad (0 < a < b)$$

by integrating the function defined by the improper integral $\int_0^\infty e^{-xt}\, dt$.

Solution: For $0 < a \le x$, we note that

$$e^{-xt} \le e^{-at} \qquad (t \ge 0)$$

Since the integral

$$\int_0^\infty e^{-at}\, dt$$

exists, it follows from Theorem 6.1 that the integral $\int_0^\infty e^{-xt}\, dt$ is uniformly convergent for $a \le x \le b$. By direct integration we find

$$\frac{1}{x} = \int_0^\infty e^{-xt}\, dt \qquad (x > 0)$$

Integrating this with respect to x from $x = a$ to $x = b$ and using (6.6), we obtain

$$\int_a^b \frac{1}{x}\, dx = \int_0^\infty \int_a^b e^{-xt}\, dx\, dt = \int_0^\infty \frac{e^{-at} - e^{-bt}}{t}\, dt$$

The integral on the left gives $\ln(b/a)$.

THEOREM 6.4. *Let the functions f and f_x be continuous in the region $D: a \le x \le b, c \le t < \infty$, and let the integral*

$$\int_c^\infty f(x, t)\, dt$$

converge to F on the interval $a \le x \le b$. If the integral

$$\int_c^\infty f_x(x, t)\, dt$$

converges uniformly on $a \le x \le b$, then F is differentiable and

(6.7) $$F'(x) = \frac{d}{dx} \int_c^\infty f(x, t)\, dt = \int_c^\infty f_x(x, t)\, dt$$

This generalizes the last part of the result of Theorem 4.1.

Example 6.3. Show that for $x \geq 0$,

(6.8)
$$\int_c^\infty e^{-xt} \frac{\sin t}{t} \, dt = -\arctan x + \frac{\pi}{2}$$

Solution: We denote the given integral by $F(x)$ and show that the integral converges uniformly to $F(x)$ for $x \geq 0$. Theorem 6.1 cannot be applied here, so we shall resort to the definition. Let $\varepsilon > 0$ be given. We want to show that there is a number T independent of x such that

(6.9)
$$\left| \int_d^\infty e^{-xt} \frac{\sin t}{t} \, dt \right| < \varepsilon$$

for $x \geq 0$ whenever $d > T$. When $x > 0$, we have, by integration by parts with $u = e^{-xt}/t$ and $dv = \sin t \, dt$,

$$\int_d^\infty e^{-xt} \frac{\sin t}{t} \, dt = \frac{e^{-xd} \cos d}{d} - \int_d^\infty \frac{(1 + xt)e^{-xt}}{t^2} \cos t \, dt$$

Since $|(1 + xt)e^{-xt} \cos t| \leq |e^{xt} \cdot e^{-xt} \cos t| \leq 1$, it follows that

$$\left| \int_d^\infty e^{-xt} \frac{\sin t}{t} \, dt \right| \leq \frac{1}{d} + \int_d^\infty \frac{1}{t^2} \, dt = \frac{2}{d}$$

But the foregoing discussion also holds when $x = 0$. Thus, taking $T = 2/\varepsilon$, it follows that (6.9) holds for $x \geq 0$ whenever $d > 2/\varepsilon$. Therefore, the given improper integral converges uniformly to $F(x)$ for $x \geq 0$. Now, by Theorem 6.1, the integral

$$\int_0^\infty e^{-xt} \sin t \, dt$$

converges uniformly in the interval $0 < c \leq x$ for arbitrary number c, taking $g(t) = e^{-ct}$. Thus, when $x > 0$, we have by Theorem 6.4

$$F'(x) = - \int_0^\infty e^{-xt} \sin t \, dt$$

$$= - \frac{1}{1 + x^2}$$

and hence

$$F(x) = -\arctan x + C$$

where C is a constant. To determine the constant C, we observe that

$$|F(x)| \leq \int_0^\infty e^{-xt} \, dt = \frac{1}{x} \qquad (x > 0)$$

since $|\sin t/t| \leq 1$ for all t. This implies $\lim_{x \to \infty +} F(x) = 0$; therefore, $C = \pi/2$. This establishes (6.8). By Theorem 6.2, $F(x)$ is continuous for $x \geq 0$ and so, letting $x \to 0$, we obtain the important result

(6.10)
$$\int_0^\infty \frac{\sin t}{t} \, dt = \frac{\pi}{2}$$

Exercises 1.6

In Problems 1 through 6, show that the improper integrals converge uniformly on the given interval.

1. $\displaystyle\int_0^\infty \frac{dt}{x^2 + t^2}$, $0 < a \le x$.

2. $\displaystyle\int_0^\infty \frac{\sin t}{x^2 + t^2}\, dt$,   for $0 < a \le x$.

3. $\displaystyle\int_0^\infty \frac{\cos xt}{a^2 + t^2}\, dt$,   for all x, $a \ne 0$.

4. $\displaystyle\int_0^\infty e^{-xt} \cos t\, dt$,   for $0 < a \le x$.

5. $\displaystyle\int_0^\infty e^{-t} \sin xt\, dt$,   for all x.

6. $\displaystyle\int_1^\infty e^{-t} t^{x-1}\, dt$,   for $0 < a \le x \le b$.

7. (a) Show that the integral $\int_0^\infty e^{-t} \cos xt\, dt$ converges uniformly for all x to $F(x) = 1/(1 + x^2)$ and thus prove that

$$\int_0^\infty e^{-t} \frac{\sin xt}{t}\, dt = \arctan x \qquad\qquad (x \ge 0)$$

(b) By changing the variables show that

$$\int_0^\infty e^{-xt} \frac{\sin t}{t}\, dt = \arctan \frac{1}{x} \qquad\qquad (x > 0)$$

(c) Letting $x \to +\infty$, deduce from the result of (b) that

$$\int_0^\infty \frac{\sin t}{t}\, dt = \frac{\pi}{2}$$

8. Assuming that $\int_0^\infty e^{-t} \sin xt\, dt = x/(1 + x^2)$ for all x, show that

$$\int_0^\infty e^{-t} \frac{(\cos at - \cos bt)}{t}\, dt = \frac{1}{2} \ln \frac{1 + b^2}{1 + a^2} \qquad\qquad (a < b)$$

In particular, deduce the result

$$\int_0^\infty e^{-t} \frac{1 - \cos bt}{t}\, dt = \frac{1}{2} \ln(1 + b^2)$$

9. Consider the integral

$$\frac{1}{x} = \int_0^\infty e^{-xt}\, dt \qquad\qquad (x > 0)$$

Verify that differentiation within the integral is permissible any number of times, and thus show that

$$\int_0^\infty t^n e^{-xt}\, dt = \frac{n!}{x^{n+1}}$$

10. Let $F(x) = \int_0^\infty e^{-t^2} \cos xt\, dt$.
   (a) Show that the integral converges uniformly for all x.
   (b) Show that differentiation within the integral is permissible and show by integration by parts that $F'(x) = -(x/2)F(x)$.
   (c) Solve the first-order differential equation in (b) and use the fact $\int_0^\infty e^{-t^2}\, dt = \sqrt{\pi}/2$ to obtain the result

$$F(x) = \frac{\sqrt{\pi}}{2} e^{-x^2/4}$$

11. Let $u(x, y) = \int_0^\infty e^{-t^2 y} \cos xt\, dt$, $y > 0$.
   (a) Show that the integral converges uniformly.
   (b) Show that the derivatives u_y and u_{xx} can be obtained by differentiating within the integral sign, and verify that $u_y - u_{xx} = 0$.
   (c) Show that

$$u(x, y) = \frac{1}{2} \left(\frac{\pi}{y}\right)^{1/2} \exp\left(-\frac{x^2}{4y}\right)$$

Hint: Make the change of variable $z^2 = t^2 y$ and use results of Problem 10.

7. Directional Derivatives

In this section we review a generalization of the concept of derivatives of functions of several variables. Suppose that u is a continuous function of the variables x, y with continuous first-order partial derivatives in some domain containing a point (x_0, y_0). Let L be a directed line through the point (x_0, y_0), which makes an angle θ with the positive x-axis, and consider the function u on this line. If L has the parametric representation

(7.1) $$x = x_0 + s \cos \theta, \qquad y = y_0 + s \sin \theta$$

where s denotes the distance of the point (x, y) from (x_0, y_0), then clearly on the line L the function u becomes a function of s. By the chain rule and from (7.1) we have

(7.2)
$$\frac{du}{ds} = \frac{\partial u}{\partial x}\frac{dx}{ds} + \frac{\partial u}{\partial y}\frac{dy}{ds}$$

$$= \frac{\partial u}{\partial x} \cos \theta + \frac{\partial u}{\partial y} \sin \theta$$

When the derivatives $\partial u/\partial x$ and $\partial u/\partial y$ are evaluated at the point (x_0, y_0), then equation (7.2) is called the directional derivative of u at (x_0, y_0) in the direction of the line L. Geometrically, equation (7.2) represents the rate of change of u with respect to s at (x_0, y_0) in the direction of L.

From the formula (7.2) we observe that the directional derivative of a function u at a point depends only on the value of the angle of inclination θ, inasmuch as the values of the derivatives of u, at a given point, are fixed. As a matter of fact, when $\theta = 0$ so that L is the positive x-axis, we find $du/ds = \partial u/\partial x$; and when $\theta = \pi/2$ so that L is the positive y-axis, $du/ds = \partial u/\partial y$. Thus, the partial derivatives $\partial u/\partial x$ and $\partial u/\partial y$ of u are really directional derivatives in the direction of positive x- and y-axes, respectively.

More generally, let C be a curve with parametric representation

(7.3) $$x = x(s), \qquad y = y(s)$$

where s denotes arc length of C, $0 \leq s \leq L$, L being the length of the curve. We assume that $x(s)$ and $y(s)$ have continuous derivatives on the interval $0 \leq s \leq L$, which do not vanish simultaneously. The curve C is said to be smooth. Let u be a continuous function with continuous first-order partial derivatives on the curve C. The derivative

(7.4) $$\frac{du}{ds} = \frac{\partial u}{\partial x}\frac{dx}{ds} + \frac{\partial u}{\partial y}\frac{dy}{ds}$$

evaluated on the curve C is called the tangential derivative of u on C. The terms dx/ds and dy/ds are the direction cosines of the tangent line to C so that (7.4) is a directional derivative along the tangent of C (Fig. 1.2). Here we adopt the convention that the tangent is pointed in the direction where s is increasing.

Example 7.1. Let $u(x, y) = x^2 + y^2$. (a) Find the directional derivative of u at $(1, 2)$ in the direction $\theta = 45°$; (b) find the direction in which the directional derivative of u at $(1, 2)$ is maximum.

Solution: (a) By (7.2) we have

$$\frac{du}{ds} = 2x|_{(1,2)} \cos 45° + 2y|_{(1,2)} \sin 45°$$

$$= 2(1/\sqrt{2}) + 4(1/\sqrt{2}) = 3\sqrt{2}$$

(b) The derivative of u at $(1, 2)$ in any direction θ is given by

$$\frac{du}{ds} = 2 \cos \theta + 4 \sin \theta$$

which is a function of θ. To find the value of θ for which du/ds is maximum (or minimum), we differentiate du/ds with respect to θ and set the result to zero. We have

$$2(-\sin \theta) + 4 \cos \theta = 0 \qquad \text{or} \qquad \tan \theta = 2$$

If θ_0 is such that $0 \leq \theta_0 \leq \pi/2$ and $\tan \theta_0 = 2$, then $\theta = \theta_0$ and $\theta = \theta_0 + \pi$ are the two values of θ less than 2π, which satisfy the above equation. Clearly, the direction $\theta = \theta_0$ yields maximum value for du/ds, which is $2(1/\sqrt{5}) + 4(2/\sqrt{5}) = 2\sqrt{5}$, and the direction $\theta = \theta_0 + \pi$ gives minimum value for du/ds, which is $-2\sqrt{5}$.

Of great importance in practice is the directional derivative of u on the curve C, which is in the direction of the normal to the curve. This derivative is called normal derivative and is usually denoted by $\partial u/\partial n$. Referring to Figure 1.2 and and using the definition (7.2), it is easy to obtain an expression for the normal derivative of u on the curve (7.3).

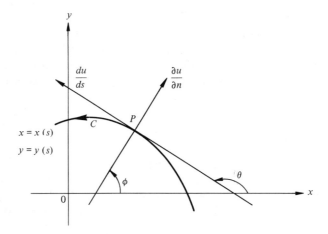

FIG. 1–2   *Normal derivative.*

We note that

$$\frac{dx}{ds} = \cos\theta, \qquad \frac{dy}{ds} = \sin\theta, \qquad \phi = \theta - \frac{\pi}{2}$$

so that

$$\cos\phi = \sin\theta = \frac{dy}{ds}, \qquad \sin\phi = -\cos\theta = -\frac{dx}{ds}$$

Hence, according to (7.2),

(7.5)
$$\frac{\partial u}{\partial n} = \frac{\partial u}{\partial x}\cos\phi + \frac{\partial u}{\partial y}\sin\phi$$

$$= \frac{\partial u}{\partial x}\frac{dy}{ds} - \frac{\partial u}{\partial y}\frac{dx}{ds}$$

In the case where C is a closed curve (not crossing itself), the derivative (7.5) is called the outward normal derivative, since the normal direction in such a case is then pointing away from the domain enclosed by the curve. Of course, here we observe the convention that as the parameter s increases, the curve is traced in the counterclockwise manner.

Example 7.2. Find the outward normal derivative of $u(x, y) = xy$ on the circle $x^2 + y^2 = a^2$.

Solution: An outward normal direction on the circle has direction cosines given by

$$\cos \phi = \frac{x}{a} \quad \text{and} \quad \sin \phi = \frac{y}{a}$$

Thus, according to (7.5),

$$\frac{\partial u}{\partial n} = y \left(\frac{x}{a}\right) + x \left(\frac{y}{a}\right) = \frac{2xy}{a}$$

where x and y satisfy the equation $x^2 + y^2 = a^2$. If we introduce polar coordinates $x = r \cos \phi$, $y = r \sin \phi$, then $\partial u/\partial n = 2a \sin \phi \cos \phi = a \sin 2\phi$. In fact, in polar coordinates we have $u = r^2 \sin \phi \cos \phi$. Since the outward normal direction coincides with the radial direction, it follows that

$$\frac{\partial u}{\partial n} = \frac{\partial u}{\partial r} = 2r \sin \phi \cos \phi = r \sin 2\phi$$

which gives the previous result when $r = a$.

Exercises 1.7

1. Compute the directional derivative of the following functions in the direction indicated:
   (a) $x^2 + 2xy + y^2$, at $(1, 2)$, $\theta = 45°$.
   (b) $x^2 + ye^x$, at $(1, -2)$, $\theta = 30°$.

2. Compute the directional derivative of the function $u = x^2y + y \sin x$ at $(2, 4)$ in the direction of the tangent to the curve $y = x^2$.

3. Find the directional derivative of $u = x^3 + xy^2 - y^3$ at $(-1, -3)$ in the direction of the tangent to the curve $x = 1 + t$, $y = 1 - t^2$.

4. Determine the direction and the maximum value of the directional derivative of $u = xy^2 + x^2y$ at $(1, 1)$.

5. Do as in Problem 4 for the function $u = 9x^2 + 4y^2$ at the point $(1, 1)$.

6. Compute the normal derivative of $u = x^2 + y^2$ at $(2, 0)$ on the curve $9x^2 + 4y^2 = 36$.

7. (a) Find the normal derivative of $u = \ln(x^2 + y^2)$ on the circle $x^2 + y^2 = a^2$.
   (b) Using polar coordinates, show that $du/dn = du/dr$.

8.   Green's Theorem and Related Formulas

We conclude this review chapter with a discussion of one of the important and useful formulas for performing double integration in the plane, known as Green's theorem.   This theorem and its related formulas will be needed in Chapters 3, 6, and 7.

THEOREM 8.1.   (Green's Theorem) *Let C be a piecewise smooth simple closed curve—a piecewise smooth closed curve which does not cross itself—in the xy plane bounding a domain D (Fig. 1.3).   Let P and Q be two functions of x and y, which are continuous together with their first-order partial derivatives in D.   Then*

(8.1) $$\int_C (P\,dx + Q\,dy) = \int\int_D \left(\frac{\partial Q}{\partial x} - \frac{\partial P}{\partial y}\right) dx\,dy$$

where the integration on the left is taken along the curve C in the counterclockwise direction.

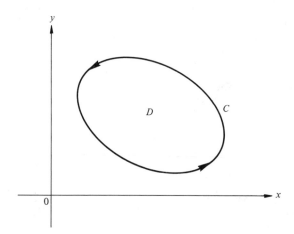

FIG. 1–3   *Green's theorem.*

Let us explain the meaning of the integral on the left of equation (8.1). Suppose that the curve C is given parametrically by the equations

(8.2) $$x = x(t), \qquad y = y(t) \qquad\qquad (t_1 \le t \le t_2)$$

where $x(t)$ and $y(t)$ have continuous derivatives on the interval $t_1 \le t \le t_2$, which do not vanish simultaneously.   Note that $x(t_1) = x(t_2)$ and $y(t_1) = y(t_2)$, since the curve is closed.   Further, observe that as t increases from t_1 to t_2, the curve is traced in the counterclockwise manner.   Then, by the integral

(8.3) $$\int_C (P\,dx + Q\,dy)$$

we mean the ordinary integral

$$\int_{t_1}^{t_2} \left\{ P[x(t), y(t)] \frac{dx}{dt} - Q[x(t), y(t)] \frac{dy}{dt} \right\} dt$$

of the single variable t obtained when the functions (8.2) are substituted for x and y in (8.3). The integral (8.3) is called a line integral on the curve C.

Example 8.1. Compute the line integral $\int_C [x^2 y \, dx + (x^2 - y^2) \, dy]$ from $(0, 0)$ to $(1, 2)$ along the curve $C: y = 2x^2$.

Solution: We convert the line integral into an ordinary integral with x as the variable of integration. We note that on C, $y = 2x^2$ so that $dy = 4x \, dx$. Substituting these for y and dy in the integral, we find

$$\int_C [x^2 y \, dx + (x^2 - y^2) \, dy] = \int_0^1 [2x^4 + (x^2 - 4x^4)4x] \, dx$$

$$= \int_0^1 (2x^4 + 4x^3 - 16x^5) \, dx$$

$$= -\frac{19}{15}$$

Example 8.2. Verify Green's theorem for the functions $P(x, y) = 2xy^2$ and $Q(x, y) = 2x^2 y$, where $C: x^2 + y^2 = 4$.

Solution: Let us introduce polar coordinates, $x = r \cos t$, $y = r \sin t$, $0 \le r \le 2$, $0 \le t \le 2\pi$. Then

$$P = 2xy^2 = 2r^3 \cos t \sin^2 t, \qquad Q = 2x^2 y = 2r^3 \cos^2 t \sin t$$
$$P_y = 4xy = 4r^2 \sin t \cos t, \qquad Q_x = 4xy = 4r^2 \sin t \cos t$$

Hence, in the domain D bounded by the circle $x^2 + y^2 = 4$,

$$\iint_D (Q_x - P_y) \, dx \, dy = 0$$

On the other hand, evaluating the line integral on the circle $r = 2$, we find

$$\int_C (2xy^2 \, dx + 2x^2 y \, dy) = \int_0^{2\pi} [16(\cos t \sin^2 t)(-2 \sin t)$$

$$+ 16(\cos^2 t \sin t (2 \cos t)] \, dt$$

$$= 0$$

Now suppose that u and v are functions of x and y with continuous partial derivatives up to the second order in the domain D. If we replace the functions P and Q in equation (8.1) by the functions $-uv_y$ and uv_x, respectively, we then obtain

(8.4) $\displaystyle\int_C u(v_x \, dy - v_y \, dx) = \iint_D [u(v_{xx} + v_{yy}) + u_x v_x + u_y v_y] \, dx \, dy$

Let the equations (8.2) describing the curve C be given with the arc length s as the parameter; that is, $x = x(s)$, $y = y(s)$, $0 \le s \le L$, L being the length of the curve. Then the line integral in equation (8.4) can be expressed as

$$(8.5) \qquad \int_C u(v_x \, dy - v_y \, dx) = \int_C u \left(v_x \frac{dy}{ds} - v_y \frac{dx}{ds} \right) ds$$

$$= \int_C u \frac{\partial v}{\partial n} \, ds$$

where $\partial v/\partial n$ is the outward normal derivative of v on C as defined in equation (7.5). Thus, equation (8.4) can be written in the form

$$(8.6) \qquad \int_C u \frac{\partial v}{\partial n} \, ds = \iint_D (u \, \Delta v + u_x v_x + u_y v_y) \, dx \, dy$$

Here we have introduced the symbol Δ which stands for the Laplace operator $(\partial/\partial x)^2 + (\partial/\partial y)^2$. The formula (8.6) is often called Green's first identity.

If we interchange the role of u and v in equation (8.6) and subtract the result from (8.6), we further obtain the formula

$$(8.7) \qquad \int_C \left(u \frac{\partial v}{\partial n} - v \frac{\partial u}{\partial n} \right) ds = \iint_D (u \, \Delta v - v \, \Delta u) \, dx \, dy$$

This formula is often known as Green's second identity.

Exercises 1.8

Using Green's theorem, evaluate the following integrals and check your answers by evaluating the line integrals directly.

1. $\int_C (x^2 \, dx + y^2 \, dy)$ along the square with vertices $(0, 0)$, $(1, 0)$, $(1, 1)$, $(0, 1)$.
2. $\int_C [-x^2 y \, dx + (y^2 - 1) \, dy]$ along the triangle with vertices $(0, 0)$, $(1, 0)$, $(1, 1)$.
3. $\int_C [(x^2 + y) \, dx + (y^2 + x) \, dy]$ along the unit circle $x^2 + y^2 = 1$.
4. $\int_C [(x + 1) \, dx + xy^2 \, dy]$ along the closed curve formed by $y = x$ and $y = x^2$ from $(0, 0)$ to $(1, 1)$.
5. Evaluate directly the integral $\int_C (-y \, dx + x \, dy)/(x^2 + y^2)$ along:
   (a) The circle $x^2 + y^2 = 1$ (use polar coordinates).
   (b) The square with sides $x = \pm 1$, $y = \pm 1$.
   (c) Why is Green's theorem not applicable here?
6. (a) Verify formula (8.6) for $u = 1$, $v = x^2 + y^2$, and D the domain bounded by the circle $x^2 + y^2 = 4$.
   (b) Deduce the formula
   $$\int_C \left(\frac{\partial v}{\partial n} \right) ds = \iint_D \Delta v \, dx \, dy$$
   from (8.6) or (8.7).

7. (a) Suppose that $\Delta v = 0$ in D. Deduce the formula

$$\int_C v \left(\frac{\partial v}{\partial n} \right) ds = \iint_D [(v_x)^2 + (v_y)^2] \, dx \, dy$$

from (8.6).

(b) Suppose further that $v = 0$ on C; show that $v = 0$ identically in D.

(c) If $\partial v/\partial n = 0$ on C, instead of $v = 0$, show that $v = $ constant in D.

Chapter 2

Linear Partial
Differential Equations

We now begin our study of partial differential equations. In this chapter we first introduce certain basic concepts and definitions and then proceed to a brief study of linear first-order equations. The rest of the chapter will be devoted to the consideration of linear second-order differential equations with constant coefficients. In particular, the classification of these equations into three principal types and the corresponding canonical forms will be discussed. Then, in the next and the last two chapters, specific problems that are drawn from mathematical physics will be treated for each of the three types of second-order equations.

1. Basic Concepts and Definitions

A partial differential equation is an equation that involves an unknown function of two or more independent variables and certain partial derivatives of the unknown function. More precisely, let u denote a function of the n independent variables $x_1, \ldots, x_n$, $n \geq 2$. Then a relation of the form

$$F(x_1, \ldots, x_n, u, u_{x_1}, \ldots, u_{x_n}, u_{x_1 x_1}, u_{x_1 x_2}, \ldots) = 0,$$

where F is a function of its arguments, is a partial differential equation in u. The following equations are some examples of partial differential equations in two independent variables x and y.

$$
\begin{array}{lll}
\text{(a)} & & xu_x + yu_y - 2u = 0 \\
\text{(b)} & & yu_x - xu_y = x \\
\textbf{(1.1)} \quad \text{(c)} & & u_{xx} - u_y - u = 0 \\
\text{(d)} & & uu_x + yu_y - u = xy^2 \\
\text{(e)} & & u_{xx} + xu_y^2 + yu = y
\end{array}
$$

As in ordinary differential equations, the highest-order derivative appearing in a partial differential equation is called the order of the equation. Thus, in (1.1) equations (a), (b), and (d) are all first-order partial differential equations and the remaining two equations are both second order.

A partial differential equation is usually considered in a certain domain of the independent variables. If there exists a function u in the domain under consideration, such that u and its derivatives identically satisfy the differential equation, then u is called a solution of the equation. It follows from this definition that a solution of a partial differential equation must have partial derivatives of orders equal to those appearing in the differential equation. In practice, however, this condition is often too restrictive. Later, we shall introduce the notion of a generalized solution that will admit other kinds of functions as solutions.

Example 1.1.   Verify that the function $u(x, y) = x^2 + y^2$ is a solution of equation (a) in (1.1).

Solution: The given function can be differentiated and we find

$$u_x = 2x, \qquad u_y = 2y$$

and so

$$xu_x + yu_y - 2u = 2x^2 + 2y^2 - 2(x^2 + y^2) = 0$$

for all x and y.

Example 1.2.   Verify that the function $u(x, y) = e^{-2y} \cos x$ is a solution of equation (c) in (1.1).

Solution: Here we have

$$u_x = -e^{-2y} \sin x, \qquad u_{xx} = -e^{-2y} \cos x, \qquad u_y = -2e^{-2y} \cos x$$

Thus,

$$u_{xx} - u_y - u = 0$$

for all x and y.

A partial differential equation in the function u is said to be linear if it is at most of first degree in u and the derivatives of u. This means that the equation should not contain any term that involves powers or products of u and derivatives of u. Thus, in (1.1) equations (a), (b), and (c) are all linear differential equations. On the other hand, both equations (d) and (e) are not linear because the former involves product of u and u_x, whereas the latter involves second power of u_y. Another way of defining linearity is given in Section 3 of the present chapter. A partial differential equation that is not linear is called a nonlinear differential equation.

Throughout this book we shall be concerned only with linear partial differential equations of the first and second order involving two independent variables. In particular, we shall limit our discussion of second-order equations to the three prominent classical equations of mathematical physics, namely,

$$\text{(i)} \qquad \frac{\partial^2 u}{\partial t^2} - \frac{\partial^2 u}{\partial x^2} = f(x, t)$$

$$\textbf{(1.2)} \qquad \text{(ii)} \qquad \frac{\partial u}{\partial t} - \frac{\partial^2 u}{\partial x^2} = g(x, t)$$

$$\text{(iii)} \qquad \frac{\partial^2 u}{\partial x^2} + \frac{\partial^2 u}{\partial y^2} = h(x, y)$$

and their related forms. These equations are the basic partial differential equations of wave propagation, heat conduction, and potential theory. Not only are these equations of fundamental importance in many branches of physics, but they also serve as prototypes for the three principal types of second-order partial differential equations. The kinds of problems that can be solved for each of these equations and the properties of the corresponding solutions are generally typical of what can be expected in the general case where more than two independent variables are involved.

Exercises 2.1

1. Determine the order of each of the following equations and find which are linear.
   (a) $u_{xx} + xu_y = 0$.
   (b) $uu_y + u_{xx} - u_x = 0$.
   (c) $u_{xx} - u_{yy} + (u_x)^2 = x^2$.
   (d) $yu_x + xu_y + u = 0$.
   (e) $xu_{xx} + yu_{yy} + 2u^2 = 1$.
   (f) $u_{xx} + xu_{yy} - u = xy$.

2. Show that the given function satisfies the accompanying equation:
   (a) $u(x, y) = ax + by$; $xu_x + yu_y = u$.
   (b) $u(x, y) = ax^2 + by^2$; $xu_x + yu_y = 2u$.
   (c) $u(x, y) = (x - a)^2 + (y - b)^2$; $(u_x)^2 + (u_y)^2 = 4u$.
   (d) $u(x, y) = x^2 + y^2$; $yu_x - u_y x = 0$.

3. Show that the given function satisfies the accompanying partial differential equation:
   (a) $u(x, y) = e^x + \sin y + xy$; $u_{xy} = 1$.
   (b) $u(x, y) = \cos(3x + 2y)$; $6u_{xx} - 13u_{xy} + 6u_{yy} = 0$.
   (c) $u(x, y) = x^2 + e^{xy} \sinh x$; $u_{yy} - xu_y = 0$.
   (d) $u(x, y) = (\cosh y) \ln x$; $uu_{xy} = (u_x)(u_y)$.

4. Verify that the following functions are solutions of the wave equation $u_{tt} - c^2 u_{xx} = 0$ for some value of c.
   (a) $u(x, t) = x^2 + t^2$.
   (b) $u(x, t) = \cos x \sin 2t$.
   (c) $u(x, t) = \ln(x + t) + (x - t)^2$.
   (d) $u(x, t) = \sin^2(x + bt) + e^{x - bt}$.

5. Verify that the following functions are solutions of the Laplace equation $u_{xx} + u_{yy} = 0$.
   (a) $u(x, y) = e^x \cos y$.
   (b) $u(x, y) = 3x^2 y - y^3$.
   (c) $u(x, y) = \sin x \cosh y$.
   (d) $u(x, y) = \ln(x^2 + y^2)$.

6. Verify that the following functions are solutions of the heat equation $u_t - c^2 u_{xx} = 0$ for some value of c.
   (a) $u(x, t) = e^{-4t} \cos x$.   (b) $u(x, t) = e^{-a^2 t} \sin bx$.
   (c) $u(x, t) = e^{4 s^2 t} \cosh sx$.   (d) $u(x, t) = e^{s^2 t} \sinh sx$.

2. General Solutions and Auxiliary Conditions

A solution of a partial differential equation that includes every other solution of the equation is called the general solution. We recall that in the theory of ordinary differential equations, the general solution of an nth order differential equation involves n independent arbitrary constants. These constants are determined when the solution is required to satisfy certain conditions. For instance, the first-order differential equation

(2.1)
$$\frac{du}{dx} + u = f(x)$$

has the general solution

(2.2)
$$u(x) = \int_0^x e^{-(x-t)} f(t)\, dt + Ce^{-x}$$

involving an arbitrary constant C. If u is required to satisfy the initial condition $u(0) = 1$, then we find $C = 1$.

In the case of a partial differential equation, the general solution is found to involve arbitrary functions rather than arbitrary constants. The number of these arbitrary functions is generally equal to the order of the differential equation. Moreover, if the differential equation involves m independent variables, the arbitrary functions will depend on $(m - 1)$ variables. Thus, if the function u in equation (2.1) also depends on the variable y, then the constant C could be chosen as an arbitrary function of y. In other words, if u is a function of the independent variables x, y, then the first-order partial differential equation

(2.3)
$$\frac{\partial u}{\partial x} + u = f(x)$$

has for its general solution

(2.4)
$$u(x, y) = \int_0^x e^{-(x-t)} f(t)\, dt + g(y)e^{-x}$$

where g is an arbitrary function of y. It is easy to see that for any choice of the function g, u satisfies equation (2.3).

Example 2.1. Find the general solution of the second-order equation

$$u_{xy} = \sin x + y$$

Solution: The general solution can be obtained by partial integration. That is, we integrate both sides of the equation with respect to y, treating x as a constant, to obtain

$$u_x(x, y) = y \sin x + \frac{y^2}{2} + h(x)$$

h being an arbitrary function of x. Next, integrating with respect to x, treating y as a constant, we obtain

$$u(x, y) = -y \cos x + \frac{xy^2}{2} + \int h(x)\, dx + g(y)$$

If we write

$$f(x) = \int h(x)\, dx$$

then the general solution is given by

$$u(x, y) = -y \cos x + \frac{xy^2}{2} + f(x) + g(y)$$

involving two arbitrary functions f and g.

Example 2.2. Show that $u(x, y) = f(x - 2y) + g(x + y)$, where f and g are twice differentiable functions, is the general solution of the differential equation

$$2u_{xx} - u_{xy} - u_{yy} = 0$$

Solution: We first verify that the given function satisfies the differential equation. Differentiating by the chain rule, we find

$$u_x = f' + g', \qquad u_y = -2f' + g', \qquad u_{xx} = f'' + g''$$
$$u_{xy} = -2f'' + g'', \qquad u_{yy} = 4f'' + g''$$

and so

$$2u_{xx} - u_{xy} - u_{yy} = 0$$

To show that u is the general solution, let us introduce the new variables

$$s = x - 2y, \qquad t = x + y$$

and write $w(s, t) = u(x, y)$. Then

$$u_x = w_s + w_t, \qquad u_y = -2w_s + w_t$$
$$u_{xx} = w_{ss} + 2w_{st} + w_{tt}, \qquad u_{xy} = -2w_{ss} - w_{st} + w_{tt}$$
$$u_{yy} = 4w_{ss} - 4w_{st} + w_{tt}$$

Substitution of these in the equation yields

$$9w_{st} = 0$$

whose general solution is $w(s, t) = f(s) + g(t)$. Thus, the general solution of the equation

$$2u_{xx} - u_{xy} - u_{yy} = 0$$

is

$$u(x, t) = f(x - 2y) + g(x + y)$$

where f and g are arbitrary functions.

In certain special cases the general solution of a partial differential equation may be obtained by one of the methods used to solve ordinary differential equations, as in equation (2.3). We consider two examples to further illustrate the procedure.

Example 2.3. Find the general solution of the equation

$$x^2 u_{xy} + x u_y = y \qquad\qquad (x > 0)$$

Solution: Writing $v(x, y) = u_y(x, y)$ and dividing the equation by x^2, the equation can be put in the form

$$v_x + \frac{1}{x} v = \frac{1}{x^2} y$$

which can be regarded as an ordinary differential equation in the unknown function v, with y appearing as a parameter. The general solution of this equation is

$$v(x, y) = \frac{y \ln x}{x} + \frac{g(y)}{x}$$

where g is an arbitrary function of y. Since $u_y = v$, we find the solution u by integrating v with respect to y, obtaining

$$u(x, y) = \frac{y^2 \ln x}{2x} + \frac{1}{x} h(y) + f(x)$$

where $h(y) = \int g(y)\, dy$ and $f(x)$ are two arbitrary functions.

Example 2.4. Find the general solution of the equation

$$u_{yy} - x^2 u = x \sin y$$

Solution: Treating x as a constant, this equation may be regarded as a second-order differential equation in u, with y as the independent variable. We know that the general solution of the homogeneous equation

$$u_{yy} - x^2 u = 0$$

is

$$u(x, y) = f(x)e^{-xy} + g(x)e^{xy}$$

where f and g are arbitrary functions of x. To find a particular solution u_p of the nonhomogeneous equation, we use the method of undetermined coefficients and assume $u_p(x, y) = A(x) \sin y + B(x) \cos y$. Substituting this in the equation, we have

$$-(1 + x^2)A \sin y - B(1 + x^2) \cos y = x \sin y$$

so that

$$A(x) = -\frac{x}{1 + x^2}, \quad B(x) = 0$$

Hence the general solution is

$$u(x, y) = f(x)e^{-xy} + g(x)e^{xy} - \frac{x \sin y}{1 + x^2}$$

A typical mathematical problem involving a partial differential equation consists in finding in some domain of the independent variables a solution of the differential equation that satisfies certain given conditions, called the auxiliary conditions. For problems arising from physical applications, these auxiliary conditions are usually suggested by the physical problems associated with the differential equations. In a type of problem that involves time as one of the independent variables of the differential equation, the solution is usually sought in some domain of space and time, which assumes prescribed values at an initial instant of time. Such a problem is often called an initial value problem and the corresponding auxiliary conditions are called initial conditions. In contrast is a problem where the solution desired is in a domain in space that is bounded and in which the values of the solution are prescribed on the boundary of the domain; this is called a boundary value problem. The auxiliary conditions in such a case are called boundary conditions. A problem that involves both initial conditions and boundary conditions is termed an initial-boundary value problem or, briefly, a mixed problem.

We recall that in ordinary differential equations an initial-value problem can be solved by first finding the general solution of the differential equation and then determining the arbitrary constants so that the initial conditions are satisfied. This procedure also applies in the case of boundary value problems, as we shall see in Chapter 4. In both cases the determination of the constants in order to satisfy initial or boundary conditions is a simple algebraic problem.

The situation is not so simple with initial value or boundary value problems in partial differential equations. For one thing, it is not always possible to find the general solution of a given partial differential equation. And when the general solution is known, it involves arbitrary functions, and therefore it is often too difficult, if not impossible, to determine those functions directly from the auxiliary conditions. For this reason, the general solutions in partial differential equations are not so useful as they are in ordinary differential equations; hence, their determination is often not the main concern in a given problem. This is a basic difference between ordinary differential equations and partial differential equations.

In many initial value or boundary value problems involving partial differential equations, we usually seek, as many as possible, particular solutions of the differential equation that satisfy some of the auxiliary conditions. Then, by suitably combining these particular solutions, we attempt to find a solution of the equation that satisfies as well all the remaining auxiliary conditions. A very useful and convenient method that accomplishes this is the so-called separation of variables method, which will be introduced in the next chapter.

Exercises 2.2

1. Find the general solution of each of the following partial differential equations:
   (a) $u_y = 3x + y$.
   (b) $u_x = 1/x + e^y$.
   (c) $u_x = y \sin x$.
   (d) $u_y = xy + \tan x$.
   (e) $u_y = f(x)$, where f is an arbitrary function of x.
   (f) $u_x = g(x)$, where g is an arbitrary function of x.

2. Find the general solution of each of the following equations:
   (a) $u_{xy} = e^{x-y}$.
   (b) $u_{xy} = x + 2y$.
   (c) $u_{xx} = ye^x$.
   (d) $u_{yy} = 3y^2 \sin x$.
   (e) $u_{xy} = f(x)g(y)$, where f and g are arbitrary functions.

3. In each of the following equations, introduce the new variables indicated to reduce the equation to one of the forms in Problem 2 above; then find the general solution of the equation.
   (a) $4u_{xx} - u_{yy} = 0$; $s = x + 2y$, $t = x - 2y$.
   (b) $u_{xx} - 6u_{xy} + 5u_{yy} = 0$; $s = 5x + y$, $t = x + y$.
   (c) $u_{xx} + 4u_{xy} + 4u_{yy} = 0$; $s = -2x + y$, $t = y$.
   (d) $u_{xx} - 2u_{xy} + u_{yy} = 0$; $s = x$, $t = x + y$.
   (e) $u_{xx} + 4u_{yy} = 0$; $s = 2x + iy$, $t = 2x - iy$ where $i = \sqrt{-1}$.
   (f) $u_{xx} - 4u_{xy} + 13u_{yy} = 0$; $s = (2 + 3i)x + y$, $t = (2 - 3i)x + y$.

4. Obtain the general solution of each of the following by regarding the equation as an ordinary differential equation.
   (a) $u_x + yu = 2xy$.
   (b) $u_y - (2/y)u = (3 \cos x)/y^2$.
   (c) $u_{xx} - 4y^2u = 3x$.
   (d) $u_{xx} + 2yu_x - 3y^2u = 0$.
   (e) $u_{yy} - 2xu_y + x^2u = 0$.

5. Find the general solution of the partial differential equation

$$xu_{xy} + u_y = 2xe^y$$

6. The general solution of the differential equation $u_{xy} = 0$ is given by $u(x, y) = f(x) + g(y)$, where f and g are arbitrary functions. Determine f and g so that the solution $u(x, y)$ satisfies the auxiliary conditions $u(x, 0) = x(x - 1)$ and $u(0, y) = \sin y$.

7. Find the solution of the equation $u_{xy} = 0$ satisfying the conditions $u(x, 0) = \sinh x$ and $u(0, y) = \cos y - 1$.

8. Solve the problem $u_{xy} = xy$, $u(0, y) = y^2$, $u_x(x, 0) = \sin x$.

9. Solve the problem $u_{xy} = x^2 \cos y$, $u(x, 0) = x$, $u_y(0, y) = e^y - 1$.

3. Linear Operators and the Principle of Superposition

The definition of a linear partial differential equation given in Section 1 can be made more precise if we introduce the notion of an operator. This facilitates at the same time the statement of an important property concerning combination of particular solutions of a linear differential equation.

We say that L is an operator on functions if it transforms each function u of one given class into a function denoted by Lu of another class. For example, the "wave operator"

$$(3.1) \qquad L = \left(\frac{\partial}{\partial t}\right)^2 - c^2 \left(\frac{\partial}{\partial x}\right)^2$$

transforms each function u that has second-order partial derivatives with respect to x and t into the new function

$$Lu = u_{tt} - c^2 u_{xx}$$

The particular operator (3.1) is called a partial differential operator because it involves basically the operation of partial differentiation.

An operator L is said to be linear if, for any constants c_1 and c_2 and any functions u_1 and u_2 for which both Lu_1 and Lu_2 are defined, it is true that

$$(3.2) \qquad L(c_1 u_1 + c_2 u_2) = c_1 L u_1 + c_2 L u_2$$

It follows readily from the rules of partial differentiation that the wave operator (3.1) is a linear partial differential operator. Property (3.2) can be extended immediately to any finite number of functions by induction. That is, if $u_1, \ldots, u_n$ are n-functions and $c_1, \ldots, c_n$ are n-constants, then

$$(3.3) \qquad L\left(\sum_{i=1}^{n} c_i u_i\right) = \sum_{i=1}^{n} c_i L u_i$$

We call the function $\sum_{i=1}^{n} c_i u_i$ a linear combination of $u_1, \ldots, u_n$.

Let L and M denote two linear operators. We define their sum $L + M$ as the operator defined by the equation

$$(3.4) \qquad (L + M)u = Lu + Mu$$

for all functions u for which both Lu and Mu are defined. Thus, if L is the operator (3.1) and M is the linear operator

$$M = y\left(\frac{\partial}{\partial x}\right) + x\left(\frac{\partial}{\partial y}\right) + xy$$

then the operator $L + M$ is defined by

$$(L + M)u = u_{tt} - c^2 u_{xx} + yu_x + xu_y + xyu$$

If we replace u in (3.4) by $c_1 u_1 + c_2 u_2$, we readily see that

$$
\begin{aligned}
(L + M)(c_1 u_1 + c_2 u_2) &= L(c_1 u_1 + c_2 u_2) + M(c_1 u_1 + c_2 u_2) \\
&= (c_1 L u_1 + c_2 L u_2) + (c_1 M u_1 + c_2 M u_2) \\
&= c_1(L u_1 + M u_1) + c_2(L u_2 + M u_2) \\
&= c_1(L + M)u_1 + c_2(L + M)u_2
\end{aligned}
$$

which shows that the operator $L + M$ is also linear. Thus, we conclude that the sum of any finite number of linear operators is a linear operator.

In similar manner we define the product LM of the linear operators L and M by the equation

(3.5) $$(LM)u = L(Mu)$$

for all functions u for which both Mu and $L(Mu)$ are defined. From (3.2) it follows that

(3.6)
$$
\begin{aligned}
(LM)(c_1 u_1 + c_2 u_2) &= L(c_1 M u_1 + c_2 M u_2) \\
&= c_1(LM)u_1 + c_2(LM)u_2
\end{aligned}
$$

which establishes the fact that the product of linear operators is also linear.

Now let L denote a linear partial differential operator. An equation of the form

(3.7) $$Lu = f$$

where f is a given function, is called a linear partial differential equation. If $f = 0$, the equation (3.7) is said to be homogeneous; otherwise, it is called nonhomogeneous.

Let $u_1, \ldots, u_n$ be n-functions that satisfy the homogeneous equation

(3.8) $$Lu = 0$$

Then, by (3.2), it follows that any linear combination of these functions also satisfies equation (3.8). This important fact is known as the principle of superposition. This principle is used extensively in the solution of linear differential equations. Correspondingly, if the functions $v_1, \ldots, v_n$ are such that $Lv_i = f_i$ $(i = 1, \ldots, n)$, then the function $v = v_1 + \cdots + v_n$ satisfies the equation

$$Lv = f_1 + \cdots + f_n$$

In particular, if u is a solution of the homogeneous equation (3.8) and v is a particular solution of the nonhomogeneous equation (3.7), then the function $w = u + v$ satisfies equation (3.7).

Under certain conditions on convergence, the principle of superposition can also be applied in the case where there are infinitely many solutions of a linear homogeneous equation. Suppose that $u_1, \ldots, u_n, \ldots$ is a sequence of functions such that each u_i satisfies equation (3.8). Consider the "infinite linear combination"

$$\text{(3.9)} \qquad \sum_{i=1}^{\infty} c_i u_i$$

This is actually an infinite series. If the constants c_i and the functions u_i are such that the series (3.9) converges to a function u, and such that the series can be differentiated term by term so that the resulting series converges to the corresponding derivative of u, for all derivatives appearing in the operator L, then it is true that

$$\text{(3.10)} \qquad Lu = L\left(\sum_{i=1}^{\infty} c_i u_i\right) = \sum_{i=1}^{\infty} c_i Lu_i$$

Hence, $Lu = 0$, since $Lu_i = 0$ for all $i \geq 1$.

Example 3.1. Consider the wave equation

$$u_{xx} - u_{yy} = 0$$

It is easily seen that the functions $u_n(x, y) = (x - y)^n$, $n = 1, 2, \ldots$ satisfy the equation for each n. Hence, by the principle of superposition,

$$u_N(x, y) = \sum_{n=1}^{N} c_n(x - y)^n$$

is a solution of the wave equation for any integer $N \geq 1$ and for arbitrary constants c_n, $1 \leq n \leq N$. In particular, if the constants c_n are chosen such that $c_{2k} = 0$ and $c_{2k-1} = (-1)^{k-1}/(2k - 1)!$, for $k = 1, 2, \ldots$, then by the Weierstrass M-test the series

$$\sum_{k=1}^{\infty} (-1)^{k-1} \frac{(x - y)^{2k-1}}{(2k - 1)!}$$

and its derivatives of any order converge uniformly in any bounded domain of the xy-plane containing the origin. Hence, by the extended principle of superposition, the preceding series is also a solution of the wave equation. As a matter of fact, we notice that the series converges to the function $u(x, y) = \sin(x - y)$, which is easily seen to satisfy the wave equation.

There is a variation of the principle of superposition concerning solution of a homogeneous differential equation that depends on a parameter. Superposition in such a case is achieved by integration with respect to the parameter rather than by summation. Suppose that v is a solution of the linear homogeneous equation (3.8), which depends on the parameter t. Let h be an arbitrary function of t and consider the function u defined by the definite integral

$$\text{(3.11)} \qquad u(x, y) = \int_a^b h(t)v(x, y; t)\, dt$$

where a and b are constants. If we can legitimately differentiate under the integral sign for all the derivatives involved in the operator L, then clearly the function (3.11) is again a solution of equation (3.8). More generally, if the improper integral

$$\textbf{(3.12)} \qquad \int_{-\infty}^{\infty} h(t)v(x, y; t) \, dt$$

converges suitably with respect to x, y, and if the operator L can be applied inside the integral sign, then the function defined by the integral (3.12) is also a solution of the homogeneous equation (3.8).

Example 3.2. Consider the heat equation

$$u_y - u_{xx} = 0$$

It is clear that for any value of t, the function $v(x, y; t) = e^{-yt^2} \sin xt$ satisfies the heat equation. Let h be an absolutely integrable function on the interval $0 \leq t < \infty$. We shall show that the function u defined by the integral

$$\textbf{(i)} \qquad u(x, y) = \int_0^{\infty} h(t)e^{-yt^2} \sin xt \, dt$$

is a solution of the heat equation in the upper half-plane $-\infty < x < \infty, y > 0$.

First, we note that by Weierstrass M-test the integral **(i)** converges absolutely and uniformly with respect to x and y, since

$$\left| h(t)e^{-yt^2} \sin xt \right| \leq |h(t)| \qquad\qquad (y \geq 0)$$

and h is absolutely integrable on the interval $0 \leq t < \infty$. Thus, u is a continuous function of x, y in the upper half-plane. Next, let $|h(t)| \leq M$ and $y \geq y_0 > 0$ and consider the integral

$$\textbf{(ii)} \qquad -\int_0^{\infty} t^2 h(t)e^{-yt^2} \sin xt \, dt$$

which is the formal derivative of **(i)** with respect to y. Since

$$\left| t^2 h(t)e^{-yt^2} \sin xt \right| \leq M t^2 e^{-y_0 t^2}$$

and the function on the right is integrable from zero to infinity with respect to t, it follows by the M-test that the integral **(ii)** is uniformly convergent. Thus, integral **(i)** is differentiable with respect to y and

$$\frac{\partial u}{\partial y} = \frac{\partial}{\partial y} \int_0^{\infty} h(t)e^{-yt^2} \sin xt \, dt = -\int_0^{\infty} t^2 h(t)e^{-yt^2} \sin xt \, dt$$

In the same way, integral **(i)** can be differentiated twice with respect to x under the integral sign. Therefore, for $-\infty < x < \infty, y > 0$,

$$u_y - u_{xx} = \int_0^{\infty} h(t)[-t^2 e^{-yt^2} \sin xt + t^2 e^{-yt^2} \sin xt] \, dt$$

$$= 0$$

Exercises 2.3

1. Let $L = a(\partial/\partial x) + b(\partial/\partial y) + c$ and $M = \alpha(\partial/\partial x) + \beta(\partial/\partial y) + \gamma$, where a, b, c and α, β, γ are constants. Show that $LM = ML$.

2. Give examples of linear operators L and M to show that LM and ML are not always equal.

3. Verify that each of the functions $u_n(x, t) = \exp[-(n - \frac{1}{2})^2 t] \sin (n - \frac{1}{2}) x$, $n = 1, 2, \ldots$ satisfies the heat equation $u_t - u_{xx} = 0$ and the auxiliary conditions $u(0, t) = 0$, $u_x(\pi, t) = 0$. Then find a linear combination of these functions that satisfies as well the condition $u(x, 0) = 2 \sin \frac{3}{2}x - 4 \sin \frac{5}{2}x$.

4. Verify that each of the functions

$$u_n(x, t) = \exp[-(k + n^2)t] \cos nx \qquad (n = 1, 2, \ldots)$$

satisfies the differential equation

$$u_t - u_{xx} + ku = 0 \qquad (k = \text{const})$$

and the auxiliary conditions $u_x(0, t) = 0$ and $u_x(\pi, t) = 0$. Then find a solution of the given differential equation that also satisfies the condition $u(x, 0) = \cos^3 x$.

5. Verify that each of the functions

$$u_n(x, t) = \cos \sqrt{c^2 + n^2}\, t \sin nx \qquad (n = 1, 2, \ldots)$$

satisfies the differential equation

$$u_{tt} - u_{xx} + c^2 u = 0 \qquad (c = \text{const})$$

and the auxiliary conditions $u(0, t) = 0$, $u(\pi, t) = 0$, $u_t(x, 0) = 0$. Then find a solution of the given differential equation that also satisfies the condition $u(x, 0) = \sin^3 x$.

6. Verify that each of the functions

$$u_n(x, y) = \sin \frac{n\pi x}{2} \sinh \frac{n\pi}{2} (y - 1) \qquad (n = 1, 2, \ldots)$$

satisfies Laplace equation $u_{xx} + u_{yy} = 0$ and the auxiliary conditions $u(0, y) = 0$, $u(2, y) = 0$, $u(x, 1) = 0$. Find a linear combination of these functions that satisfies the condition $u(x, 0) = \sin \pi x - 3 \sin 2\pi x$.

7. Let $y_0 > 0$. Show that the series $\sum_{n=1}^{\infty} c_n e^{-ny} \sin nx$, where the coefficients c_n are all bounded, is twice differentiable with respect to x and y and satisfies Laplace's equation $u_{xx} + u_{yy} = 0$ in the domain $y > y_0$.

8. Show that the series

$$\sum_{n=1}^{\infty} \frac{e^x \cos[(1 + n^2)^{1/2} t] \sin nx}{(1 + n^2)^2}$$

is twice differentiable with respect to x and t, and satisfies the differential equation $u_{tt} - u_{xx} + 2u_x = 0$ for all values of x and t.

9. Consider the Helmholtz equation $u_{xx} + u_{yy} + k^2 u = 0$, ($k$ = const).
   (a) Show that an exponential solution of the type $u = e^{\alpha x + \beta y}$ (where α and β are constants) exists, provided α and β satisfy the equation $\alpha^2 + \beta^2 + k^2 = 0$.
   (b) Let $\alpha = ik \cos \theta$ and $\beta = ik \sin \theta$, where θ is an arbitrary real constant. Verify that

$$\cos[k(x \cos \theta + y \sin \theta)], \qquad \sin[k(x \cos \theta + y \sin \theta)]$$

   are particular solutions of the Helmholtz equation.
   (c) Verify that the integral

$$\int_{\theta_1}^{\theta_2} h(\theta) \exp[ik(x \cos \theta + y \sin \theta)] \, d\theta$$

   also satisfies the Helmholtz equation if h is a function for which differentiation under the integral is valid.

10. Obtain exponential solutions $u = e^{\alpha x + \beta t}$ of the wave equation $u_{tt} - u_{xx} = 0$ and show that the integral

$$\int_{-\infty}^{\infty} h(w) e^{iw(x \pm t)} \, dw$$

   is a solution if h is a function for which the integral converges and can be differentiated under the integral sign.

4. Linear First-Order Equations

In this section we shall study linear first-order differential equations in two independent variables x and y. The general form of such an equation is

(4.1) $$a(x, y)u_x + b(x, y)u_y + c(x, y)u = d(x, y)$$

where the coefficients a, b, c, and d are functions in some domain D of the xy-plane. We assume that the functions a, b, c, and d are continuous and have continuous partial derivatives of the first order in D, and that a and b are not both zero. We shall describe here a method for finding the general solution of equation (4.1). The method is based on the possibility of transforming equation (4.1) into an equation of the form

(4.2) $$w_\xi + s(\xi, \eta)w = t(\xi, \eta)$$

where ξ and η are new independent variables. Equation (4.2) can now be regarded as an ordinary differential equation with ξ as the independent variable and η as a parameter. Hence, its general solution can be found by the use of the standard formula pertaining to such an equation. The integration constant in the solution must, however, be replaced by an arbitrary function of η. The general solution of the original equation is then obtained by returning to the variables x, y.

Indeed, if either one of the coefficients a, b is identically zero, then equation (4.1) is readily reducible to the form (4.2). Let us assume that $a \neq 0$ and $b \neq 0$.

In order to transform equation (4.1) into the form (4.2) we introduce new variables ξ and η by the equations

(4.3) $$\xi = \phi(x, y), \qquad \eta = \psi(x, y)$$

The functions ϕ and ψ, which will be subsequently determined, are assumed to be continuous and have continuous first-order partial derivatives in D such that the Jacobian

(4.4) $$\frac{\partial(\xi, \eta)}{\partial(x, y)} = \phi_x \psi_y - \phi_y \psi_x \neq 0$$

in the neighborhood of some point in D. Writing $u(x, y) = w(\xi, \eta)$, we then have by the chain rule,

$$u_x = w_\xi \phi_x + w_\eta \psi_x$$
$$u_y = w_\xi \phi_y + w_\eta \psi_y$$

and hence equation (4.1) is transformed into the equation

(4.5) $$(a\phi_x + b\phi_y)w_\xi + (a\psi_x + b\psi_y)w_\eta + cw = d$$

The coefficients a, b, c, and d are now to be considered as functions of ξ and η. If we choose the function $\psi(x, y)$ in (4.3) such that

(4.6) $$a\psi_x + b\psi_y = 0 \qquad \text{or} \qquad \frac{\psi_x}{\psi_y} = -\frac{b}{a}$$

then the term involving w_η in (4.5) drops out, and for any choice of ϕ satisfying the condition (4.4), equation (4.5) reduces to the form (4.2). Thus, it remains for us to determine a function ψ that satisfies (4.6).

Suppose for the moment that such a function ψ exists with $\psi_y \neq 0$; set $\psi(x, y) = c$, where c is any constant. Then, on taking the total differential of $\psi = c$, we find

$$\psi_x \, dx + \psi_y \, dy = 0$$

which implies that

$$\frac{dy}{dx} = -\frac{\psi_x}{\psi_y}$$

Hence, if ψ satisfies equation (4.6), then $\psi = c$ must be an integral of the first-order ordinary differential equation

(4.7) $$\frac{dy}{dx} = \frac{b}{a}$$

Conversely, if $\psi = c$ with $\psi_y \neq 0$ is an integral of equation (4.7), then by reversing the foregoing argument it follows that $\eta = \psi(x, y)$ satisfies equation (4.6).

Equation (4.7) is often called the characteristic equation of the partial differential equation (4.1). It defines a one-parameter family of curves called the characteristic curves of equation (4.1). These curves play an important role in the consideration of initial value problems for equation (4.1), as we shall soon see.

Thus, in order to reduce equation (4.5) to the form (4.2), we choose ψ such that $\psi = c$ is a characteristic curve of equation (4.1). The function ϕ may be chosen arbitrarily, subject to the condition (4.4). We choose $\phi(x, y) = x$. Then condition (4.4) is fulfilled and equation (4.5) takes the form

(4.8) $$w_\xi + \left(\frac{c}{a}\right) w = \left(\frac{d}{a}\right)$$

which is of the desired form (4.2).

To obtain the general solution of equation (4.8), we multiply both sides of the equation by the integrating factor

$$v(\xi, \eta) = \exp\left(\int \frac{c}{a} d\xi\right)$$

and observe that

$$\frac{\partial}{\partial \xi}\left(w \exp\left[\int \frac{c}{a} d\xi\right]\right) = \left(w_\xi + \frac{c}{a} w\right) v(\xi, \eta) = \frac{d}{a} v(\xi, \eta)$$

Integrating with respect to ξ, treating η as a parameter, we then find

$$w(\xi, \eta) = \frac{1}{v(\xi, \eta)}\left[\int \frac{d}{a} v(\xi, \eta) d\xi + f(\eta)\right]$$

where f is an arbitrary function of η. Hence, returning to the original variables x, y, we obtain as the general solution of equation (4.1)

(4.9) $$u(x, y) = \frac{1}{v[x, \psi(x, y)]}\{W[x, \psi(x, y)] + f[\psi(x, y)]\}$$

where we have set

$$W(\xi, \eta) = \int \frac{d}{a} v(\xi, \eta) d\xi$$

We note that the first term, $W(x, \psi)/v(x, \psi)$, in formula (4.9) is actually a particular solution of equation (4.1), and the second term, $f(x, \psi)/v(x, \psi)$, is the general solution of the corresponding homogeneous equation

(4.10) $$a(x, y)u_x + b(x, y)u_y + c(x, y)u = 0$$

In many special cases, it may be easier to find a particular solution of (4.1) by some other technique. For instance, the method of undetermined coefficients used to determine particular solutions in ordinary differential equations may be employed under similar conditions

Example 4.1. Find the general solution of equation

$$au_x + bu_y + cu = 0$$

where a, b, c are constants and $a \neq 0$.

Solution: We see that the characteristic equation

$$\frac{dy}{dx} = \frac{b}{a}$$

defines a one-parameter family of characteristic curves

$$bx - ay = \text{const}$$

which are straight lines. Introducing the new variables $\xi = x$, $\eta = bx - ay$, the given equation becomes

$$w_\xi + \frac{c}{a} w = 0$$

The general solution of this equation is

$$w(\xi, \eta) = e^{-c\xi/a} f(\eta)$$

where f is an arbitrary differentiable function. Thus, the general solution of the given differential equation is

$$u(x, y) = e^{-cx/a} f(bx - ay)$$

If $a = 0$, then the differential equation reduces to $u_y + (c/b)u = 0$, whose general solution is readily obtained as

$$u(x, y) = e^{-cy/b} f(x)$$

Example 4.2. Obtain the general solution of the equation

$$xu_x - yu_y + u = x$$

Solution: We consider the characteristic equation

$$\frac{dy}{dx} = -\frac{y}{x}$$

By separation of variables we find that the characteristic curves are given by $xy = c$. We therefore introduce $\xi = x$ and $\eta = xy$. The transformed equation is

$$w_\xi + \frac{1}{\xi} w = 1$$

whose general solution is

$$w(\xi, \eta) = \frac{\xi}{2} + \frac{1}{\xi} f(\eta)$$

Hence, the general solution of the original equation is

$$u(x, y) = \frac{x}{2} + \frac{1}{x} f(xy)$$

where f is an arbitrary differentiable function.

In the study of the first-order ordinary differential equation $dy/dx = f(x, y)$, it is usually required to find a solution of the equation that assumes prescribed value at a specified point on the x-axis. Geometrically, this means finding an integral curve that passes through a specified point in the xy-plane. Under rather general conditions on f, such a problem possesses one and only one solution. A similar problem for the first-order partial differential equation (4.1) consists in determining a solution of the equation that takes on prescribed values at points on a specified curve in the xy-plane. This corresponds to finding an integral surface that contains a specified curve in xyu-space. If the parametric equations of the curve in the xy-plane are

(4.11) $C: x = x(s), \qquad y = y(s)$

and if $u = \phi(s)$ on this curve, then the problem of finding a solution $u = u(x, y)$ of the equation (4.1), such that $u = \phi(s)$ on the curve C, amounts to the determination of the function f in the general solution (4.9). In general, the function f can be uniquely determined in terms of the initial value ϕ and the other specific functions in (4.9) when the equations (4.11) of the curve C are substituted for x, y in (4.9) and u is set equal to ϕ.

Example 4.3.   Find the solution of the equation

$$2u_x - 3u_y + 2u = 2x$$

which assumes the value $u = x^2$ on the line $y = -x/2$.

Solution: By formula (4.9) the general solution of the differential equation is

$$u(x, y) = (x - 1) + e^{-x}f(3x + 2y)$$

Substituting $y = -x/2$ in the solution and setting $u = x^2$, we have

$$x^2 = x - 1 + e^{-x}f(2x)$$

or

$$f(2x) = (x^2 - x + 1)e^x$$

Let $t = 2x$ so that $x = t/2$. Then

$$f(t) = \left(\frac{t^2}{4} - \frac{t}{2} + 1\right)e^{t/2}$$

Thus, the solution of the problem is

$$u(x, y) = x - 1 + e^{-x}\left[\frac{(3x + 2y)^2}{4} - \frac{(3x + 2y)}{2} + 1\right]e^{(3x+2y)/2}$$

$$= x - 1 + \left[\frac{(3x + 2y)^2}{4} - \frac{(3x + 2y)}{2} + 1\right]e^{(x+2y)/2}$$

It should be pointed out that the curve C on which the values of u are prescribed cannot be taken arbitrarily. Specifically, it cannot be a characteristic curve of the differential equation. The reason for this restriction is apparent when we look at the form of the general solution (4.9) of equation (4.1). On a characteristic curve, say, $\psi(x, y) = c_1$, the solution (4.9) assumes the form

$$u = \frac{W(x, c_1)}{v(x, c_1)} + \frac{f(c_1)}{v(x, c_1)}$$

Consequently, unless the prescribed function ϕ is of the special form

(4.12) $$\phi(x) = \frac{W(x, c_1)}{v(x, c_1)} + \frac{k}{v(x, c_1)}$$

where k is a constant, the problem has no solution. On the other hand, if ϕ has the form (4.12), then there exists infinitely many solutions given by (4.9), where f is any differentiable function such that $f(c_1) = k$.

Example 4.4. Show that the problem

$$2u_x - 3u_y + 2u = 2x, \quad u = \phi(x), \text{ on } y = -3x/2$$

has no solution unless ϕ has the form

$$\phi(x) = x - 1 + ke^{-x}$$

where k is a constant. If ϕ has the indicated form, give a solution of the problem.

Solution: The general solution of the differential equation is

$$u(x, y) = (x - 1) + e^{-x}f(3x + 2y)$$

Substituting the prescribed conditions, we have

$$\phi(x) = x - 1 + e^{-x}f(0)$$

But for any function f, $f(0)$ is a constant. Hence, the problem has a solution only if ϕ is of the form so indicated. In such a case,

$$u(x, y) = x - 1 + e^{-x}f(3x + 2y)$$

is a solution for any differentiable function f such that $f(0) = k$.

Exercises 2.4

In Problems 1 through 5, find the general solution of each of the equations.

1. $u_x + u_y - u = 0$.
2. $2u_x - 3u_y = x$.
3. $u_x - 2u_y + u = \sin x + y$.
4. $3u_x - 4u_y + 2u = x^2y + 2e^x + 1$.
5. $u_x - u_y - 2u = e^{2x} \cos 3y$.
6. Let $Lu = au_x + bu_y + cu = 0$, where a, b, c are constants. Show that by introducing the new variables $\xi = \alpha x + \beta y$, $\eta = \gamma x + \delta y$, $(\alpha\delta - \beta\gamma \neq 0)$, the equation is transformed into

$$u_\xi + cu = 0$$

when the coefficients α, β, γ, δ are chosen so that

$$a\alpha + b\beta = 1, \qquad a\gamma + b\delta = 0$$

Hence, rederive the solution obtained in Example 4.1.

In Problems 7 through 13, find the general solution of the given equation.

7. $xu_x + yu_y = 1$.

8. $xu_x - yu_y - xu = 2e^x + x^2y$.

9. $yu_x + xu_y = y$.

10. $x^2u_x - xyu_y + 2yu = 0$.

11. $y^2u_x - xyu_y - 2xu = x^2 + y^2$.

12. $(x + y)(u_x - u_y) + u = e^{-x/(x+y)}$.

13. $xyu_x - x^2u_y - yu = xy$.

14. Let $Lu = Au_x + Bu_y + Cu_z + Du = 0$ be a linear equation in three variables x, y, z, where A, B, C, D are constants. Introduce the new variables

$$\xi = a_1x + b_1y + c_1z$$
$$\eta = a_2x + b_2y + c_2z$$
$$\zeta = a_3x + b_3y + c_3z$$

where the determinant of the coefficients a_i, b_i, c_i, $i = 1, 2, 3$ is not zero.
(a) Show that the coefficients a_i, b_i, c_i, $1 \le i \le 3$, can be chosen such that the equation is reduced to the form

$$u_\xi + Du = 0$$

(b) Hence, obtain the general solution in the form

$$u(x, y, z) = e^{-Dx/A}f(Bx - Ay, Cy - Bz)$$

assuming that none of the coefficients A, B, C are zero.
(c) Obtain the general solution when one of the coefficients A, B, C is zero.

15. Apply the result of Problem 14 to find the general solution of the following equations:
(i) $u_x + 2u_y - 3u_z + u = 0$.
(ii) $2u_x - u_y + 2u_z + 3u = x + y + z$.

In Problems 16 through 22, find the solution of the differential equation satisfying the prescribed condition.

16. $u_x + u_y = 1$, $u = e^x$ when $y = 0$.

17. $u_x + u_y - u = 0$, $u = 1 + \cos x$, when $y = 2x$.

18. $2u_x - 5u_y + 4u = x^2$, $u = \sin y + e^y + \frac{1}{8}$, when $x = 0$.

19. $u_x + (\cos x)u_y = \sin x$, $u = y - 1 + \cos y$, when $x = 0$.

20. $xu_x - yu_y + u = x$, $u = x^2$, when $y = x$.

21. $yu_x - xu_y + xu = 0$, $u = y$, when $x^2 + 2y^2 = 4$.

22. $yu_x - xu_y + 2xyu = 0$, $u = e^x \sin(x + 1)$, when $y^2 = 2x + 1$.

23. Show that no solution exists for the differential equation of Problem 22, which assumes the prescribed value $\phi(x)$ on the circle $x^2 + y^2 = a^2$, unless ϕ is of the form $\phi(x) = ke^{-x^2}$, where k is a constant. If ϕ has the indicated form, show that the problem has infinitely many solutions.

24. Obtain the general solution of the equation $yu_x + xu_y - yu = xe^x$ in the form $u(x, y) = e^x y + e^x f(y^2 - x^2)$. If u is prescribed as ϕ on the upper portion of the hyperbola $y^2 - x^2 = 1$ $(y \geq 1)$, show that no solution exists unless ϕ is of special form. Find this form and show that in such a case there are infinitely many solutions.

5. Solutions of Second-Order Equations with Constant Coefficients

The general linear second-order partial differential equation in two independent variables x, y has the form

$$(5.1) \qquad Au_{xx} + Bu_{xy} + Cu_{yy} + Du_x + Eu_y + Fu = G$$

where the coefficients A, B, C, D, E, F, and G are functions of x and y in some domain of the xy-plane. Unlike the first-order equation (4.1), it is impossible to obtain the general solution of (5.1) except in some special cases. We shall consider here the special case

$$(5.2) \qquad au_{xx} + bu_{xy} + cu_{yy} + du_x + eu_y + fu = 0$$

where a, b, c, d, e, and f are constants such that a, b, and c are not zero simultaneously. It is convenient to write equation (5.2) in the form

$$(5.3) \qquad Lu = 0$$

where L denotes the second-order differential operator

$$L = aD_x^2 + bD_xD_y + cD_y^2 + dD_x + eD_y + f$$

with $D_x = \partial/\partial x$ and $D_y = \partial/\partial y$.

Consider the polynomial $P(x, y)$ obtained by formally replacing D_x and D_y in (5.3) by x and y, respectively. Suppose that $P(x, y)$ can be factored as a product of two linear factors; that is,

$$P(x, y) = (a_1x + b_1y + c_1)(a_2x + b_2y + c_2)$$

Then, accordingly, the operator L can be written in the factored form

$$L = L_1L_2$$

where L_1 and L_2 are linear first-order operators given by

$$(5.4) \qquad L_1 = a_1D_x + b_1D_y + c_1, \qquad L_2 = a_2D_x + b_2D_y + c_2$$

Since the coefficients of L_1 and L_2 are all constants, we know (Problem 1, Exercises 2.3) that $L_1L_2 = L_2L_1$, and so we have

$$(5.5) \qquad L = L_1L_2 = L_2L_1$$

When this is the case, we say that L is factorable or reducible.

In case the operator L is factorable, a solution of equation (5.3) that involves two arbitrary functions can be obtained by means of the result of the preceding section. Such a solution constitutes the general solution of the equation. Indeed, suppose (5.5) holds, where L_1 and L_2 are given by (5.4) and $L_1 \neq L_2$. Let u_1 be the general solution of $Lu_1 = 0$ and let u_2 be the general solution of $Lu_2 = 0$. Set $u = u_1 + u_2$. Then it follows from (5.5) and the linearity of L that

$$L_1$$

(5.6)
$$\begin{aligned}
Lu &= L(u_1 + u_2) \\
&= Lu_1 + Lu_2 \\
&= L_2(L_1 u_1) + L_1(L_2 u_2) = 0
\end{aligned}$$

showing that $u = u_1 + u_2$ satisfies equation (5.3). Now, according to Example 4.1, if $a_1 \neq 0$ and $a_2 \neq 0$, then

$$u_1(x, y) = e^{-c_1 x/a_1} f_1(b_1 x - a_1 y) \quad or \qquad e^{-\frac{c_1}{b_1} y} F(b_1 x - a_1 y)$$

and

$$u_2(x, y) = e^{-c_2 x/a_2} f_2(b_2 x - a_2 y)$$

Hence, if $a = a_1 a_2 \neq 0$, the general solution of equation (5.3) is

(5.7) $$u(x, y) = e^{-c_1 x/a_1} f_1(b_1 x - a_1 y) + e^{-c_2 x/a_2} f_2(b_2 x - a_2 y)$$

where the functions f_1 and f_2 are arbitrary and twice differentiable. $\quad Lu = bu + cu = 0$
If either $a_1 = 0$ or $a_2 = 0$, the corresponding term in (5.7) must be replaced by $e^{-c_1 x/b_1} f_1(x)$ or $e^{-c_2 x/b_2} f_2(x)$. $\quad e^{-c_1 y/b_1} f_1(x) \ or \ e^{-c_2 y/b_2} f_2(x)$
The general solution of the nonhomogeneous equation $Lu = G$ is obtained by adding to the solution (5.7) any particular solution of the nonhomogeneous equation.

Example 5.1. Find the general solution of the equation

$$u_{xx} - u_{yy} - u_x + u_y = 2\cos(3x + 2y)$$

Solution: The differential operator $L = D_x^2 - D_y^2 - D_x + D_y$ can be factored with $L_1 = (D_x + D_y - 1)$ and $L_2 = (D_x - D_y)$. The general solution of the equation $L_1 u_1 = 0$ is

$$u_1(x, y) = e^x f(x - y)$$

and the general solution of the equation $L_2 u_2 = 0$ is

$$u_2(x, y) = g(x + y)$$

Thus, the general solution of the corresponding homogeneous equation $Lu = 0$ is

$$u(x, y) = e^x f(x - y) + g(x + y)$$

where f and g are arbitrary functions that are twice differentiable.

We now look for a particular solution of the nonhomogeneous equation $Lu = 2\cos(3x + 2y)$. We use the method of undetermined coefficients and assume a particular solution in the form

$$v(x, y) = A\cos(3x + 2y) + B\sin(3x + 2y)$$

$$-9A\cos(\ ) - 9B\sin(\ ) \qquad (-5A-B)\cos$$
$$+4A\cos(\ ) + 4B\sin(\ ) \qquad -5B+A$$
$$+3A\sin(\ ) - 3B\cos$$
$$-2A\sin + 2B\cos$$

Substituting this in the equation and collecting similar terms, we have

$$-(5A + B)\cos(3x + 2y) + (A - 5B)\sin(3x + 2y) = 2\cos(3x + 2y)$$

Hence,

$$-(5A + B) = 2$$
$$A - 5B = 0$$

which gives $A = -\frac{5}{13}$ and $B = -\frac{1}{13}$. Therefore, the general solution of the given equation is

$$u(x, y) = e^x f(x - y) + g(x + y) - \tfrac{5}{13}\cos(3x + 2y) - \tfrac{1}{13}\sin(3x + 2y)$$

Next we consider the case when $L_1 = L_2$; that is, when L has repeated factors. We wish to determine the general solution of the equation

$$(5.8) \qquad\qquad L_1^2 u = (a_1 D_x + b_1 D_y + c_1)^2 u = 0$$

If we set $L_1 u = v$, then in order that u be a solution of equation (5.8), v must satisfy the equation

$$(5.9) \qquad\qquad L_1 v = a_1 v_x + b_1 v_y + c_1 v = 0$$

When $a_1 \neq 0$, we know that

$$v(x, y) = e^{-c_1 x/a_1} g_1(b_1 x - a_1 y)$$

Thus, to determine the function u, we have to solve the equation

$$(5.10) \qquad a_1 u_x + b_1 u_y + c_1 u = e^{-c_1 x/a_1} g_1(b_1 x - a_1 y)$$

By the method of Section 4, we introduce new variables $\xi = x, \eta = b_1 x - a_1 y$. Then equation (5.10) is transformed into the equation

$$a_1 w_\xi + c_1 w = e^{-c_1 \xi/a_1} g_1(\eta)$$

where $w(\xi, \eta) = u(x, y)$. The general solution of this equation is

$$w(\xi, \eta) = e^{-c_1 \xi/a_1} \left[\frac{1}{a_1} \int g_1(\eta)\, d\xi + f_2(\eta) \right]$$

$$= \frac{1}{a_1} e^{-c_1 \xi/a_1} \xi g_1(\eta) + e^{-c_1 \xi/a_1} f_2(\eta)$$

Therefore, the general solution of equation (5.8) has the form

$$(5.11) \qquad u(x, y) = e^{-c_1 x/a_1} \{ x f_1(b_1 x - a_1 y) + f_2(b_1 x - a_1 y) \}$$

where f_1 and f_2 are arbitrary functions that are twice differentiable.

The procedure described above can also be used to find a particular solution of the nonhomogeneous equation $Lu = G$, whenever L is factorable. Suppose $L = L_1 L_2$. Let v be a particular solution of $L_1 v = G$ and let u be a particular solution of $L_2 u = v$. Then

$$Lu = (L_1 L_2)u = L_1(L_2 u) = L_1 v = G$$

showing that u is a particular solution of the equation $Lu = G$. Here L_1 and L_2 need not be distinct.

Example 5.2.   Find the general solution of the equation

$$u_{xx} - 2u_{xy} + u_{yy} = xy$$

Solution: The operator $L = D_x^2 - 2D_xD_y + D_y^2$ has repeated factors $L_1 = L_2 = (D_x - D_y)$. Hence, by formula (5.11), the general solution of the corresponding homogeneous equation is

$$u(x, y) = xf(x + y) + g(x + y)$$

To find a particular solution w of the nonhomogeneous equation, we let v be a particular solution of the equation

(i) $v_x - v_y = xy$

and determine w from the equation

(ii) $w_x - w_y = v$

Making the change of variables $\xi = x$, $\eta = x + y$, equation (i) becomes

$$v_\xi = \xi(\eta - \xi)$$

with a particular solution

(iii) $v = -\dfrac{\xi^3}{3} + \dfrac{\xi^2\eta}{2}$

Introducing the same new variables in (ii) and using (iii), we obtain

$$w_\xi = -\frac{\xi^3}{3} + \frac{\xi^2\eta}{2}$$

whose particular solution is

$$w = -\frac{\xi^4}{12} + \frac{\xi^3\eta}{6}$$

Thus, a particular solution of $Lu = xy$ is

$$w(x, y) = -\frac{x^4}{12} + \frac{x^3(x + y)}{6} = \frac{x^4}{12} + \frac{x^3y}{6}$$

Combining this with the function u, we obtain the general solution of the given equation.

Exercises 2.5

In Problems 1 through 8, find the general solution of the differential equations.

1. $u_{xy} + u_x + u_y + u = 0$.

2. $u_{xx} - u_{yy} - u_x + u_y = 0$.

3. $u_{xx} + u_{yy} = 0$.

4. $u_{xx} + 2u_{xy} + 2u_{yy} = 0.$

5. $u_{xy} - 2u_{yy} + 3u_y = 0.$

6. $\dfrac{1}{c^2} \dfrac{\partial^2 u}{\partial t^2} - \dfrac{1}{r^2} \dfrac{\partial^2}{\partial r^2} (r^2 u) = 0.$ (Let $v = r^2 u$.)

7. $\dfrac{\partial^4 u}{\partial x^4} - \dfrac{\partial^4 u}{\partial y^4} = 0.$

8. $\dfrac{\partial^4 u}{\partial x^4} - 2 \dfrac{\partial^4 u}{\partial x^2 \partial y^2} + \dfrac{\partial^4 u}{\partial y^4} - 0.$

9. Consider the homogeneous operator with constant coefficients

$$L = A \frac{\partial^2}{\partial x^2} + 2B \frac{\partial^2}{\partial x \, \partial y} + C \frac{\partial^2}{\partial y^2}$$

(a) Show that this operator is always factorable with real coefficients if and only if $B^2 - AC \geq 0$.

(b) Show that if f is an arbitrary twice-differentiable function, then $u = f(mx + y)$ is a solution of the equation $Lu = 0$ if and only if m satisfies the equation $Am^2 + 2Bm + C = 0$.

(c) If $B^2 - AC = 0$, verify that a second solution of $Lu = 0$ is given by $u = xf(mx + y)$.

In Problems 10 through 13, find a particular solution of each of the given non-homogeneous equations.

10. $u_{xx} - 4u_{yy} = x + y.$

11. $u_{xx} - 6u_{xy} + 9u_{yy} = xy^2.$

12. $u_{xy} + u_x + u_y + u = e^{x-y}.$

13. $u_{xx} - 2u_{xy} + u_{yy} + u_x - u_y = \sin(2x + y).$

14. Show that the equation with variable coefficients $ax^2 u_{xx} + bxy u_{xy} + cy^2 u_{yy} + dx u_x + ey u_y + fu = 0$, where $a, \ldots, f$ are constants, is reduced to an equation with constant coefficients by the change of variables $\xi = \ln x$, $\eta = \ln y$.

15. Use the method of Problem 14 to obtain the general solution of each of the following equations:

(a) $x^2 u_{xx} - y^2 u_{yy} + xu_x - yu_y = \ln x.$

(b) $xy u_{xy} + xu_x + yu_y + u = xy.$

(c) $x^2 u_{xx} + 2xy u_{xy} + y^2 u_{yy} - nxu_x - nyu_y + nu = x + y, \ n = \text{const} \neq 0.$

16. Find the general solution of each of the following equations:

(a) $(D_x - D_y)(D_x + D_z)u \equiv u_{xx} - u_{xy} + u_{xz} - u_{yz} = 0.$

(b) $(D_x - D_y + D_z)(D_x + 2D_y + 1)u$
$$\equiv u_{xx} + u_{xy} - 2u_{yy} + u_{xz} + 2u_{yz} + u_x - u_y + u_z = 0.$$

(c) $(D_x + D_y + D_z)^2 u \equiv u_{xx} + u_{yy} + u_{zz} + 2u_{xy} + 2u_{yz} + 2u_{zx} = 0.$

6. Classification of Second-Order Equations

The study of a linear second-order partial differential equation is often facilitated by a recognition of the type of the differential equation in question. For, depending on the type of the equation, it is frequently possible by means of a coordinate transformation to reduce the equation to one of three canonical forms. These canonical forms correspond to different simple forms in which the second-order derivative terms can appear in the equation. Moreover, the type of a partial differential equation plays a decisive role in determining the kind of auxiliary condition that can be considered with the equation so that the resulting problem has a unique solution.

In this section we shall consider the classification of linear second-order partial differential equations in the special case

$$(6.1) \qquad Au_{xx} + 2Bu_{xy} + Cu_{yy} + Du_x + Eu_y + Fu = 0$$

where all the coefficients, $A, \ldots, F$ are constants, with A, B, C not all zero. In an attempt to simplify the form of the second-order terms of this equation, we introduce new variables ξ and η by means of the linear transformation

$$(6.2) \qquad \xi = \alpha x + \beta y, \qquad \eta = \gamma x + \delta y$$

The coefficients α, β, γ, and δ are constants, which will be determined subject to the condition $\alpha\delta - \beta\gamma \neq 0$. This last condition, which is the Jacobian $\partial(\xi, \eta)/\partial(x, y)$ enables us to solve for x and y in terms of ξ and η. Writing $u(x, y) = w(\xi, \eta)$, we have by the chain rule

$$u_x = \alpha w_\xi + \gamma w_\eta$$
$$u_y = \beta w_\xi + \delta w_\eta$$
$$u_{xx} = \alpha^2 w_{\xi\xi} + 2\alpha\gamma w_{\xi\eta} + \gamma^2 w_{\eta\eta}$$
$$u_{xy} = \alpha\beta w_{\xi\xi} + (\alpha\delta + \beta\gamma)w_{\xi\eta} + \gamma\delta w_{\eta\eta}$$
$$u_{yy} = \beta^2 w_{\xi\xi} + 2\beta\delta w_{\xi\eta} + \delta^2 w_{\eta\eta}$$

Substituting these in equation (6.1) and collecting similar terms, we have

$$(6.3) \qquad aw_{\xi\xi} + 2bw_{\xi\eta} + cw_{\eta\eta} + \cdots = 0$$

where

$$(6.4) \qquad \begin{aligned} a &= A\alpha^2 + 2B\alpha\beta + C\beta^2 \\ b &= A\alpha\gamma + B(\alpha\delta + \beta\gamma) + C\beta\delta \\ c &= A\gamma^2 + 2B\gamma\delta + C\delta^2 \end{aligned}$$

The dots in (6.3) represent terms involving w and its first derivatives w_ξ and w_η. It is easy to verify that

$$(6.5) \qquad b^2 - ac = (B^2 - AC)(\alpha\delta - \beta\gamma)^2$$

by simply substituting the expressions (6.4) for a, b, and c.

Now, since the constants α, β, γ, and δ are at our disposal, we shall choose them in such a way that at least one of the second-order terms in (6.3) drops out. As a matter of fact, we shall show that according as (a) $B^2 - AC > 0$, (b) $B^2 - AC = 0$, (c) $B^2 - AC < 0$, the constants α, β, γ, and δ can be chosen such that

(a) $a = 0$, $c = 0$, (b) $b = 0$, $c = 0$, (c) $a = c$, $b = 0$, thus simplifying the equation to one of the three canonical forms:

$$\text{(i)} \qquad w_{\xi\eta} + \cdots = 0$$

(6.6) $\quad$ (ii) $\qquad w_{\xi\xi} + \cdots = 0$

$$\text{(iii)} \qquad w_{\xi\xi} + w_{\eta\eta} + \cdots = 0$$

We say that the partial differential equation (6.1) is of the

$$\text{(i)} \qquad \textit{hyperbolic type, if } B^2 - AC > 0$$

(6.7) $\quad$ (ii) $\qquad$ *parabolic type, if $B^2 - AC = 0$*

$$\text{(iii)} \qquad \textit{elliptic type, if } B^2 - AC < 0$$

We see in the above classification that only the coefficients of the second-order terms matter. The quantity $B^2 - AC$ is called the discriminant of the equation. In view of formula (6.5), we see that the sign of the discriminant remains unaltered under the change of variables (6.2). Thus, the type of equation (6.1) is invariant with respect to the linear transformation (6.2). This invariance property is, of course, to be desired if the definitions (6.7) of hyperbolicity, parabolicity, and ellipticity of partial differential equations are to have any significance.

Example 6.1. The partial differential equation

$$u_{xx} - u_{yy} = 0$$

is hyperbolic, since $A = 1$, $B = 0$, $C = -1$ and $B^2 - AC = 1 > 0$. This equation is called the wave equation.

Example 6.2. The partial differential equation

$$u_x - u_{yy} = 0$$

is parabolic, since $A = B = 0$, $C = -1$, and $B^2 - AC = 0$. This equation is called the heat equation.

Example 6.3. The partial differential equation

$$u_{xx} + u_{yy} = 0$$

is elliptic, since $B^2 - AC = -1 < 0$. This is called Laplace's equation.

We remark that in the general case where the coefficients $A, \ldots, F$ of equation (6.1) are functions of x, y in a domain D, the equation is said to be of the hyperbolic type in D if $B^2 - AC > 0$ at all points in D. Similarly, equation (6.1) is said to be of the parabolic or of the elliptic type in D according to whether $B^2 - AC = 0$ or $B^2 - AC < 0$ at all points in D. The reduction of such an equation to one of the canonical forms (6.6) is accomplished by means of a transformation

$$\xi = \xi(x, y), \qquad \eta = \eta(x, y)$$

The determination of the functions ξ and η, however, involves solving first-order differential equations, which we shall not pursue in this book.

It should be noticed that if equation (6.1) involves variable coefficients, it can very well happen that the equation is of one type in one part of the domain and of a different type in another part. For example, consider the equation

$$u_{xx} - yu_{yy} = 0$$

where $A = 1$, $B = 0$, and $C = -y$ in the whole xy-plane. Since $B^2 - AC = y$, it follows that the equation is of the hyperbolic type in the upper half-plane ($y > 0$), of the parabolic type on the x-axis ($y = 0$), and of the elliptic type in the lower half-plane ($y < 0$).

Exercises 2.6

Classify each of the following partial differential equations.

1. $u_{xx} + u_{xy} - u_{yy} + u_x = 0$.

2. $2u_{xx} - 4u_{xy} + u_{yy} - u_y = u$.

3. $3u_{xx} - 2u_{xy} + u_{yy} = xy$.

4. $4u_{xy} + 7u_{yy} - 2u_x + u_y + 3u = 0$.

5. $2u_{xx} + u_{xy} + u_{yy} - xu = e^{xy}$.

6. $4u_{xx} - 4u_{xy} + u_{yy} + 3u_x = x^2 + y^2$.

7. $4u_{xx} + 12u_{xy} + 9u_{yy} - 2u_x + u = 0$.

8. $u_{xx} - u_{xy} + 5u_{yy} + xu_x + yu_y = 0$.

9. Determine the region in which the equation

$$(x^2 - 1)u_{xx} + 2yu_{xy} - u_{yy} + u_x + u_y = 0$$

is (i) hyperbolic, (ii) elliptic, (iii) parabolic.

10. Determine the region in which the equation

$$u_{xx} + 2xu_{xy} + yu_{yy} - u = 0$$

is (i) hyperbolic, (ii) elliptic, (iii) parabolic.

7. The Canonical Forms

We now consider the problem of choosing the constants α, β, γ, and δ in (6.2) so that equation (6.3) will reduce to one of the canonical forms (6.6).

(i) *Hyperbolic Type*, $B^2 - AC > 0$. In this case we shall show that (6.2) can be chosen such that the coefficients a and c in (6.3) vanish, while $b \neq 0$. We therefore consider the equations

(7.1)
$$a \equiv A\alpha^2 + 2B\alpha\beta + C\beta^2 = 0$$
$$c \equiv A\gamma^2 + 2B\gamma\delta + C\delta^2 = 0$$

If $A = C = 0$, then of necessity $B \neq 0$ and thus equation (6.1) is readily put in the canonical form (6.6i) by dividing out by $2B$. In this case, the transformation (6.2) may be chosen as the identity transformation

$$\xi = x, \quad \eta = y$$

with $\alpha = \delta = 1$ and $\beta = \gamma = 0$.

Suppose that $A \neq 0$. If $\beta = 0$ or $\delta = 0$, then from (7.1) we would have $\alpha = 0$ or $\gamma = 0$. In either case, the condition $\alpha\delta - \beta\gamma \neq 0$ is violated. Therefore, β and δ cannot be zero and hence equations (7.1) can be written as

(7.2)
$$A \left(\frac{\alpha}{\beta} \right)^2 + 2B \left(\frac{\alpha}{\beta} \right) + C = 0$$

$$A \left(\frac{\gamma}{\delta} \right)^2 + 2B \left(\frac{\gamma}{\delta} \right) + C = 0$$

Thus, in order that the coefficients a and c will vanish, we shall choose α, β, γ, and δ such that α/β and γ/δ are roots of the quadratic equation

(7.3)
$$Am^2 + 2Bm + C = 0$$

Since $B^2 - AC > 0$, equation (7.3) has two distinct real roots

$$m_1 = \frac{-B + (B^2 - AC)^{1/2}}{A}, \quad m_2 = \frac{-B - (B^2 - AC)^{1/2}}{A}$$

Let us choose $\alpha = -B + (B^2 - AC)^{1/2}$, $\beta = A$, $\gamma = -B - (B^2 - AC)^{1/2}$, and $\delta = A$. Then $\alpha\delta - \beta\gamma = 2(B^2 - AC)^{1/2} > 0$ and the coefficients a and c in equation (6.3) drop out. From (6.4), we see that

$$b = A\alpha\gamma + B(\alpha\delta + \beta\gamma) + C\beta\delta$$
$$= -2A(B^2 - AC) \neq 0$$

Therefore, when equation (6.1) is of the hyperbolic type, the transformation

(7.4)
$$\xi = [-B + (B^2 - AC)^{1/2}]x + Ay$$
$$\eta = [-B - (B^2 - AC)^{1/2}]x + Ay$$

will reduce the equation to the form

$$2bw_{\xi\eta} + \cdots = 0$$

where $b \neq 0$. We now have only to divide through by the coefficient $2b$ in order to obtain the desired canonical form (6.6i).

The case $A = 0$, $C \neq 0$ can be treated in a very similar way.

If we further introduce the variables ξ' and η' defined by the equations

(7.5)
$$\xi' = \frac{\xi + \eta}{2}, \quad \eta' = \frac{\xi - \eta}{2}$$

$$= \xi + \eta \qquad = \xi - \eta$$

the canonical form (6.6i) becomes

(7.6) $$w_{\xi'\xi'} - w_{\eta'\eta'} + \cdots = 0$$

This is the alternative canonical form for equation (6.1) of the hyperbolic type. This alternative form can, of course, be achieved directly from equation (6.1) by means of the transformations

(7.7)
$$\xi' = -Bx + Ay$$
$$\eta' = (B^2 - AC)^{1/2}x$$

and dividing out the result by the coefficient $-A(B^2 - AC)$, which is different from zero.

Example 7.1. Show that the second-order partial differential equation

$$u_{xx} + 6u_{xy} - 16u_{yy} = 0$$

is hyperbolic and find its canonical form and its general solution.

Solution: Here $A = 1$, $B = 3$, and $C = -16$ so that $B^2 - AC = 25$. Thus, the differential equation is of the hyperbolic type. By (7.4) we introduce the new variables

$$\xi = 2x + y, \qquad \eta = -8x + y$$

Then

$$u_x = 2u_\xi - 8u_\eta$$
$$u_y = u_\xi + u_\eta$$
$$u_{xx} = 4u_{\xi\xi} - 32u_{\xi\eta} + 64u_{\eta\eta}$$
$$u_{xy} = 2u_{\xi\xi} - 6u_{\xi\eta} - 8u_{\eta\eta}$$
$$u_{yy} = u_{\xi\xi} + 2u_{\xi\eta} + u_{\eta\eta}$$

Substituting these in the differential equation we find the canonical form

$$-100u_{\xi\eta} = 0 \qquad \text{or} \qquad u_{\xi\eta} = 0$$

If we have used the variables given in (7.5), we find the alternative canonical form

$$u_{\xi'\xi'} - u_{\eta'\eta'} = 0$$

The first canonical form has the general solution

$$u = f(\xi) + g(\eta)$$

while the second canonical form has the general solution

$$u = f(\xi' + \eta') + g(\xi' - \eta')$$

Either one leads to the general solution

$$u(x, y) = f(2x + y) + g(-8x + y)$$

of the original differential equation.

This agrees with the result obtained when the method of Section 5 is used. In fact, we notice that the differential operator corresponding to the given differential equation has the factorization

$$(D_x^2 + 6D_xD_y - 16D_y^2) = (D_x - 2D_y)(D_x + 8D_y)$$

Let us observe that the curves

$$\xi(x, y) = \text{constant}, \qquad \eta(x, y) = \text{constant}$$

where the functions ξ and η are defined in (7.4), are integral curves of the ordinary differential equations

(7.8)
$$\frac{dy}{dx} = -m_1, \qquad \frac{dy}{dx} = -m_2$$

respectively. They actually define two one-parameter families of straight lines, which are called the characteristics of the second-order equation (6.1). We notice that the equations in (7.8) can be combined into the single equation

$$A \left(\frac{dy}{dx}\right)^2 - 2B \left(\frac{dy}{dx}\right) + C = 0$$

or

(7.9)
$$A \, dy^2 - 2B \, dx \, dy + C \, dx^2 = 0$$

This equation is called the characteristic equation of (6.1). Thus, when equation (6.1) is of the hyperbolic type, its characteristic equation (7.9) has two families of characteristic lines. These characteristics play a fundamental role in the consideration of initial value or boundary value problems for partial differential equations of the hyperbolic type.

(ii) *Parabolic Type, $B^2 - AC = 0$.* In this case, it is clear that the coefficients A and C cannot be both zero. Suppose that $A \neq 0$; the case $C = 0$ can be treated in similar manner. Then the quadratic equation (7.3) has only one distinct root, $m = -B/A$. If we choose $\gamma = B$, $\delta = -A$, and let α and β be any numbers such that $\alpha\delta - \beta\gamma \neq 0$—say, $\alpha = 1$ and $\beta = 0$—then from (6.4) it follows that $a = A$, $b = 0$, and $c = 0$. Here we have used the fact that $B^2 - AC = 0$. Thus, in the parabolic case, the transformation

(7.10)
$$\xi = x, \qquad \eta = Bx - Ay$$

reduces equation (6.1) to the form

$$A \frac{\partial^2 w}{\partial \xi^2} + \cdots = 0$$

which results in the canonical form (6.6ii) when divided out by the coefficient $A \neq 0$.

In terms of the characteristic equation (7.9), we conclude that in the parabolic case, there is only one family of characteristics given by $Bx - Ay = \text{constant}$.

Example 7.2. Reduce the partial differential equation

$$u_{xx} + 2u_{xy} + u_{yy} = 0$$

to its canonical form and obtain its general solution.

Solution: Here $A = 1$, $B = 1$, and $C = 1$, so that $B^2 - AC = 0$. Thus, the given equation is of the parabolic type. By formula (7.10), we make the change of variables: $\xi = x, \eta = x - y$. Then

$$u_x = u_\xi + u_\eta$$
$$u_y = -u_\eta$$
$$u_{xx} = u_{\xi\xi} + 2u_{\xi\eta} + u_{\eta\eta}$$
$$u_{xy} = -u_{\xi\eta} - u_{\eta\eta}$$
$$u_{yy} = u_{\eta\eta}$$

and thus the differential equation reduces to the canonical form

$$u_{\xi\xi} = 0$$

The general solution of this equation is

$$u = \xi f(_\eta) + g(\eta)$$

Hence, the general solution of the given differential equation is

$$u(x, y) = xf(x - y) + g(x - y)$$

Again, this result can also be obtained by the method of Section 5.

(iii) *Elliptic, $B^2 - AC < 0$.* Here it is clear that neither A nor C can be zero. Following the discussion in the hyperbolic case, we see that since $B^2 - AC < 0$, the quadratic equation (7.3) has complex roots

$$m_1 = \frac{-B + i(AC - B^2)^{1/2}}{A}, \qquad m_2 = \frac{-B - i(AC - B^2)^{1/2}}{A}$$

The choice $\alpha = -B + i(AC - B^2)^{1/2}$, $\beta = \delta = A$, and $\gamma = \bar{\alpha}$ would then make the coefficients a and c of equation (6.3) vanish, with $b = 2A(AC - B^2) > 0$. Thus, under the change of variables

$$(7.11) \qquad \xi = [-B + i(AC - B^2)^{1/2}]x + Ay$$
$$\eta = [-B - i(AC - B^2)^{1/2}]x + Ay$$

equation (6.1) would be reduced to the form

$$(7.12) \qquad 2b \frac{\partial^2 w}{\partial \xi \, \partial \eta} + \cdots = 0$$

However, from (7.11) we see that ξ and η are now complex variables such that $\bar{\xi} = \eta$. In order that we may have a canonical form in real variables, we further make the change of variables

$$(7.13) \qquad \xi' = \frac{\xi + \eta}{2}, \qquad \eta' = \frac{\xi - \eta}{2i}$$

Then, as is easily verified,

$$w_{\xi\eta} = \tfrac{1}{4}(w_{\xi'\xi'} + w_{\eta'\eta'})$$

so that (7.12) reduces to the canonical form

(7.14) $$w_{\xi'\xi'} + w_{\eta'\eta'} + \cdots = 0$$

after dividing through by $A(AC - B^2)$.

If we substitute ξ and η from (7.11) in (7.13), we see that

(7.15)
$$\xi' = -Bx + Ay$$
$$\eta' = (AC - B^2)^{1/2}x$$

Writing ξ and η again in place of ξ' and η', the transformations (7.15) correspond to the choice $\alpha = -B$, $\beta = A$, $\gamma = (AC - B^2)^{1/2}$, and $\delta = 0$ in (6.2). With this choice, it is easily verified from (6.4) that $a = c = A(CA - B^2)$ and $b = 0$. Therefore, under the change of variables

(7.16)
$$\xi = -Bx + Ay$$
$$\eta = (AC - B^2)^{1/2}x$$

equation (6.1) can be reduced to the desired canonical form (6.6iii) in the elliptic case.

We notice that since $B^2 - AC < 0$, equation (7.9) has no real integral curves. This means that an equation (6.1) of the elliptic type has no real characteristic.

Example 7.3.   Reduce the elliptic partial differential equation

$$u_{xx} - 2u_{xy} + 5u_{yy} = 0$$

to its canonical form.

Solution: We have $A = 1$, $B = -1$, and $C = 5$ so that $B^2 - AC = -4 < 0$. Making the changes of variables

$$\xi = x + y, \qquad \eta = 2x$$

we see that

$$u_x = u_\xi + 2u_\eta$$
$$u_y = u_\xi$$
$$u_{xx} = u_{\xi\xi} + 4u_{\xi\eta} + 4u_{\eta\eta}$$
$$u_{xy} = u_{\xi\xi} + 2u_{\xi\eta}$$
$$u_{yy} = u_{\xi\xi}$$

Substituting these in the differential equation, we have the desired canonical form

$$u_{\xi\xi} + u_{\eta\eta} = 0$$

The general solution of this last equation is of the form

$$u = f(\zeta) + g(\bar{\zeta})$$

involving arbitrary functions of a complex variable ζ, where $\zeta = \xi + i\eta$. Thus, the given differential equation in the variables x, y has the general solution

$$u = f[(x + y) + 2ix] + g[(x + y) - 2ix]$$ $\bar{\zeta} = \xi - i\eta$

Exercises 2.7

Reduce the following hyperbolic partial differential equations to the canonical forms (6.1i) and (7.6).

1. $3u_{xx} + 2u_{xy} - 5u_{yy} + u_x = 0$.
2. $u_{yy} + 2u_{xy} + u_x + u_y = xy$.
3. $8u_{xx} + 2u_{xy} - 3u_{yy} - xu_y = 0$.
4. $3u_{xx} + u_{xy} - 2u_{yy} - u = x^2$.
5. $2u_{xx} - 3u_{xy} + u_{yy} + u_x - u_y = 1$.

Reduce the following parabolic partial differential equations to canonical forms.

6. $4u_{xx} - 4u_{xy} + u_{yy} - u_x = 0$.
7. $u_{xx} - 6u_{xy} + 9u_{yy} + u_y = xy$.
8. $9u_{xx} + 6u_{xy} + u_{yy} - u = 0$.
9. $u_{xx} + 2u_{xy} + u_{yy} - 4u = 0$.

Reduce the following elliptic partial differential equations to the canonical form (7.14).

10. $u_{xx} + 4u_{yy} + u = 0$.
11. $2u_{xx} - 2u_{xy} + 5u_{yy} - xu_y = 0$.
12. $u_{xx} + 2u_{xy} + 2u_{yy} - yu_x = 0$.
13. $3u_{xx} - 8u_{xy} + 6u_{yy} - u = 0$.
14. $4u_{xx} - 6u_{xy} + 3u_{yy} + u_x + u_y + u = 0$.
15. $u_{xx} + 4u_{xy} + 5u_{yy} - e^x u = \sin y$.

In Problems 16 through 19, find the general solution of the differential equation by first reducing the equation to its canonical form.

16. $3u_{xx} - u_{xy} - 2u_{yy} = 0$.
17. $5u_{xx} + 2u_{xy} + 2u_{yy} = 0$.
18. $u_{xx} + 4u_{xy} + 4u_{yy} = 0$.
19. $u_{xx} - 4u_{xy} + 5u_{yy} = 0$.
20. Consider the equation of the hyperbolic type

$$u_{xx} - u_{yy} + au_x + bu_y + cu = 0$$

where a, b, and c are constants. Show that by introducing the new variable v, defined by $v(x, y) = e^{\alpha x + \beta y} u(x, y)$, the equation can be put in the form

$$v_{xx} - v_{yy} + \gamma u = 0$$

where $\gamma = (b^2 - a^2 + 4c)/4$.

21. Consider the differential equation of the parabolic type

$$u_t - a u_{xx} - b u_x - c u = 0$$

where a, b, and c are constants. Show that by introducing the new variable v, defined by $v(x, t) = e^{\alpha x + \beta t} u(x, t)$, the equation can be put in the canonical form $v_t - k v_{xx} = 0$.

Chapter 3

The Wave Equation

In this chapter we shall study certain types of problems that are generally associated with linear hyperbolic partial differential equations. We shall consider these problems in connection with the equation

$$\frac{\partial^2 u}{\partial t^2} - c^2 \frac{\partial^2 u}{\partial x^2} = F(x, t)$$

where x and t are the two independent variables and c is a constant. This equation, called the wave equation, serves as the prototype for a class of hyperbolic differential equations involving two independent variables. It arises in the study of many important physical problems involving wave propagation phenomena, such as the transverse vibrations of an elastic string, and the longitudinal vibrations or the torsional oscillations of a rod. The wave equation is certainly one of the most important classical equations of mathematical physics.

1. The Vibrating String

We consider a uniform string of length L and constant density ρ, which is stretched between two supports. The string is assumed to rest on the interval $[0, L]$ of the x-axis, with its ends fixed at $x = 0$ and $x = L$. Each point of the string is thus determined initially by its coordinate x. If the string is displaced from its resting position and then released, it will vibrate. Let $u(x, t)$ denote the displacement of a given point x at any subsequent instant of time t. We assume that other conditions of the string are such that only transverse vibration

71

(vertical motion) takes place in the xu-plane. The problem, then, is to determine $u(x, t)$ for $0 < x < L$ and $t > 0$.

We first show that under certain simplifying assumptions the displacement u satisfies the wave equation. We shall assume that the tensile force in the string is very large so that the weight of the string can be ignored. Further, we shall assume that the string is perfectly elastic and offers no resistance to bending; this implies that the tensile force at any point of the string acts in a direction tangential to the profile of the string. Finally, we shall assume that the string has only small transverse vibrations so that the slope u_x at any point of the displaced string is small; in particular, we shall take u_x^2 to be negligible compared with unity.

Now let us consider an arbitrary segment AB of the string with length Δs (see Fig. 3.1). Let x and $x + \Delta x$ be the coordinates of the points A and B, and let T_1 and T_2 be the tensile forces acting at these points, respectively. These forces are tangential to the shape of the string at the points A and B, as we have assumed above. Since we have only vertical motion, the algebraic sum of the horizontal components of the tensile force must be equal to zero. Thus, we have

$$T_2 \cos \alpha_2 - T_1 \cos \alpha_1 = 0$$

where α_1 and α_2 are the acute angles between the tangents at A and B and the x-axis. By the assumption on u_x^2, we have

$$\cos \alpha_1 = \frac{1}{(1 + \tan^2 \alpha_1)^{1/2}} = \frac{1}{(1 + u_x^2)^{1/2}}\bigg|_x \cong 1$$

$$\cos \alpha_2 = \frac{1}{(1 + \tan^2 \alpha_2)^{1/2}} = \frac{1}{(1 + u_x^2)^{1/2}}\bigg|_{x+\Delta x} \cong 1$$

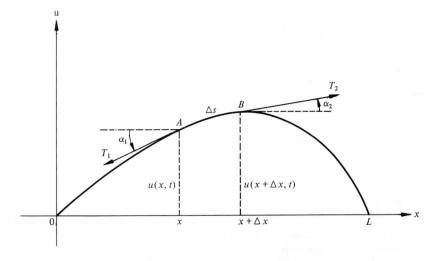

FIG. 3–1 *Vibrating string.*

and therefore

$$T_1 = T_2 = T = \text{const}$$

That is, the tension in the string is constant.

The vertical forces acting on the segment AB consist of $T \sin \alpha_2$, which is directed upward, and $T \sin \alpha_1$, directed downward. Hence, the resultant force is

$$R = T \sin \alpha_2 - T \sin \alpha_1$$

Since the vibrations of the string are assumed to be small, we may replace $\sin \alpha_i$ by $\tan \alpha_i$, $i = 1, 2$, so that we have

$$R = T(\tan \alpha_2 - \tan \alpha_1) = T\left[\frac{\partial u}{\partial x}(x + \Delta x, t) - \frac{\partial u}{\partial x}(x, t)\right]$$

From the fact that

$$\Delta s = (1 + u_x^2)^{1/2}\, \Delta x \cong \Delta x$$

the mass of the segment AB is approximately $(\Delta x)\rho$. Therefore, in accordance with Newton's second law of motion (mass times acceleration equals force), we have

(1.1) $$\rho(\Delta x)\frac{\partial^2 u}{\partial t^2}(\xi, t) = T\left[\frac{\partial u}{\partial x}(x + \Delta x, t) - \frac{\partial u}{\partial x}(x, t)\right]$$

where $x < \xi < x + \Delta x$. Dividing both sides of equation (1.1) by Δx and taking the limit as Δx tends to zero, we obtain

(1.2) $$\frac{\partial^2 u}{\partial t^2}(x, t) - c^2\frac{\partial^2 u}{\partial x^2}(x, t) = 0$$

where $c = (T/\rho)^{1/2}$ is a positive constant. Equation (1.2) is called the one-dimensional wave equation. It is a hyperbolic partial differential equation with constant coefficients. The constant c has the dimension of a velocity, as the reader can easily verify by substituting appropriate units to T and ρ. This constant represents the maximum velocity of propagation of a disturbance in the string, as we shall see later.

If there is an external vertical force—say, $f(x, t)$ per unit length—acting on the string, then the term $f(x, t)\,\Delta x$ must be added to the right-hand side of equation (1.1). In passing to the limit, we obtain the equation

(1.3) $$\frac{\partial^2 u}{\partial t^2}(x, t) - c^2\frac{\partial^2 u}{\partial x^2}(x, t) = \frac{f(x, t)}{\rho} \equiv F(x, t)$$

This is called the nonhomogeneous wave equation.

Now, in order to determine completely the subsequent motion of the string, it is necessary that we know initially the position or shape of the string, the velocity with which the string is set into vibration, and the conditions at the ends of the string. Mathematically, this means that we must specify $u(x, t)$ and $\partial u / \partial t(x, t)$ at the initial time, say, $t = 0$; that is,

(1.4) $u(x, 0) = f(x), \qquad u_t(x, 0) = g(x)$

where f and g are some given functions defined for $0 \leq x \leq L$. Further, since the ends of the string are fixed at $x = 0$ and $x = L$, the displacement function at these points must always be equal to zero; hence,

(1.5) $u(0, t) = 0, \qquad u(L, t) = 0$ $\hspace{3cm}$ $(t \geq 0)$

It should be noted that physical considerations dictate that $f(0) = g(0)$ and $f(L) = g(L) = 0$.

We call the conditions (1.4) the initial conditions, and the conditions (1.5), the boundary conditions. In particular, the functions f and g in (1.4) are called the initial data.

Therefore, to obtain the displacement of a vibrating string with fixed ends, we must find a solution of the wave equation (1.2), or (1.3) if there is a forcing term F, that satisfies the initial conditions (1.4) and the boundary conditions (1.5). This type of problem is called an initial-boundary value problem.

Of course, if the ends of the string are not fixed but are allowed to move subject to some constraints, other boundary conditions arise. For example, if the ends of the string are allowed to move vertically without a restraining force, then the displacement function must always satisfy the conditions

(1.6) $u_x(0, t) = 0, \qquad u_x(L, t) = 0$

which are called free boundary conditions. On the other hand, if the ends are attached to a spring, the boundary conditions assume the forms

(1.7) $u_x(0, t) + hu(0, t) = 0, \qquad u_x(L, t) + hu(L, t) = 0$

where h is a constant. These are called elastic boundary conditions. The boundary conditions (1.5), (1.6), and (1.7) are often referred to as boundary conditions of the first, second, and third kind, respectively.

In contrast to an initial-boundary value problem consisting of the wave equation (1.2) or (1.3), the initial conditions (1.4), and one of the boundary conditions (1.5), (1.6), and (1.7) in which the variable x is restricted to the interval $[0, L]$, we may seek a solution of the wave equation in the infinite domain $-\infty < x < \infty$, $t > 0$, which satisfies only the initial conditions (1.4) given for $-\infty < x < \infty$. Such a problem is simply called an initial value problem. Physically, an initial value problem for the wave equation corresponds to the problem of a vibrating string that is so long that the effect of its boundary conditions can be neglected. As we shall see in the discussions to follow, our solution formula for an initial value problem can be used to find a solution of an initial-boundary value problem with boundary conditions of type (1.5) or (1.6) at either end point.

Exercises 3.1

1. Let u and v be two solutions of the wave equation

$$Lw \equiv w_{tt} - c^2 w_{xx} = 0 \qquad\qquad (|x| < \infty)$$

each satisfying the corresponding initial conditions

$$u(x, 0) = f(x), \quad u_t(x, 0) = 0; \qquad v(x, 0) = 0, \quad v_t(x, 0) = g(x)$$

Set $w = u + v$ and show that w satisfies the wave equation $Lw = 0$ together with the initial conditions

$$w(x, 0) = f(x), \qquad w_t(x, 0) = g(x)$$

2. Consider the initial-boundary value problem

$$u_{tt} - c^2 u_{xx} = 0 \qquad\qquad (0 < x < L, t > 0)$$
$$u(x, 0) = f(x), \qquad u_t(x, 0) = g(x) \qquad (0 \le x \le L)$$
$$u(0, t) = a(t), \qquad u(L, t) = b(t) \qquad (t \ge 0)$$

Let v be a twice-differentiable function satisfying the conditions

$$v(0, t) = a(t), \qquad v(L, t) = b(t)$$

Determine the differential equation and the initial and boundary conditions satisfied by w, where $w = u - v$.

3. Suppose that the initial value problem

$$Lu \equiv u_{tt} - u_{xx} + c^2 u = 0 \qquad\qquad (|x| < \infty)$$
$$u(x, 0) = 0 \qquad\qquad (|x| < \infty)$$
$$u_t(x, 0) = 0 \qquad\qquad (|x| < \infty)$$

is known to have only the trivial solution $u \equiv 0$. Prove that the problem

$$Lu = F, \qquad u(x, 0) = f(x), \qquad u_t(x, 0) = g(x) \qquad (|x| < \infty)$$

has at most one solution.

4. Verify that the function $u(x, t) = \sin 2x \cos 2t$ satisfies the equation $u_{tt} - u_{xx} = 0$ and the initial conditions $u(x, 0) = 2 \sin x \cos x$, and $u_t(x, 0) = 0$.

5. Verify that the function $u(x, t) = \sin 2x \sin 2t$ satisfies the wave equation of Problem 4 and the initial conditions $u(x, 0) = 0$, $u_t(x, 0) = 2 \sin 2x$.

6. Show that $u(x, t) = t \sin \pi x$ is a solution of the initial-boundary value problem

$$u_{tt} - u_{xx} = \pi^2 t \sin \pi x \qquad\qquad (0 < x < 1, t > 0)$$
$$u(x, 0) = 0, \qquad u_t(x, 0) = \sin \pi x \qquad (0 \le x \le 1)$$
$$u(0, t) = 0, \qquad u(1, t) = 0 \qquad (t \ge 0)$$

7. Show that $u(x, t) = xt^2 + \sin(x + t)$ is a solution of the initial value problem

$$u_{tt} - u_{xx} = 2x \qquad\qquad (|x| < \infty)$$
$$u(x, 0) = \sin x \qquad\qquad (|x| < \infty)$$
$$u_t(x, 0) = \cos x \qquad\qquad (|x| < \infty)$$

8. Show that $u(x, t) = (e^{x-t} + e^{x+t})/2$ is a solution of the initial-boundary value problem

$$u_{tt} - u_{xx} = 0 \qquad\qquad (x > 0)$$
$$u(x, 0) = e^x \qquad\qquad (x \geq 0)$$
$$u_t(x, 0) = 0 \qquad\qquad (x \geq 0)$$
$$u(0, t) = \cosh t \qquad\qquad (t \geq 0)$$

9. Show that $u(x, t) = \cos x \sin t$ is a solution of the initial-boundary value problem

$$u_{tt} - u_{xx} = 0 \qquad\qquad (x > 0)$$
$$u(x, 0) = 0 \qquad\qquad (x > 0)$$
$$u_t(x, 0) = \cos x \qquad\qquad (x > 0)$$
$$u_x(0, t) = 0 \qquad\qquad (t \geq 0)$$

10. Let

$$u(x, t) = \begin{cases} h\left(t - \dfrac{x}{c}\right) + \dfrac{f(x + ct) - f(ct - x)}{2} & (0 \leq x < ct) \\[3mm] \dfrac{f(x - ct) + f(x + ct)}{2} & (ct < x) \end{cases}$$

where h and f are twice continuously differentiable for $x > 0$. Show that u satisfies

$$u_{tt} - c^2 u_{xx} = 0 \qquad\qquad (x > 0, t > 0)$$
$$u(x, 0) = f(x), \qquad u_t(x, 0) = 0 \qquad\qquad (x > 0)$$
$$u(0, t) = h(t) \qquad\qquad (t > 0)$$

11. Let

$$u(x, t) = \begin{cases} -c \displaystyle\int_0^{t - x/c} h(s)\, ds & (0 \leq x < ct) \\[3mm] 0 & (ct < x) \end{cases}$$

Show that u satisfies

$$u_{tt} - c^2 u_{xx} = 0 \qquad\qquad (x > 0, t > 0)$$
$$u(x, 0) = 0, \qquad u_t(x, 0) = 0 \qquad\qquad (x > 0)$$
$$u_x(0, t) = h(t) \qquad\qquad (t > 0)$$

2. The Initial Value Problem

We are concerned with determining a solution of the homogeneous wave equation

$$(2.1) \qquad\qquad \frac{\partial^2 u}{\partial t^2} - c^2 \frac{\partial^2 u}{\partial x^2} = 0 \qquad (-\infty < x < \infty, t > 0)$$

satisfying the initial conditions

(**2.2**) $\qquad u(x, 0) = f(x), \qquad u_t(x, 0) = g(x) \qquad (-\infty < x < \infty)$

This problem is one special case where the general solution of the differential equation actually leads to a solution of the problem.

Since the equation is hyperbolic, we introduce the new variables ξ, η defined by

(**2.3**) $\qquad \xi = x + ct, \qquad \eta = x - ct$

and set $u(x, y) = w(\xi, \eta)$. Then equation (2.1) reduces to the canonical form

(**2.4**) $$\frac{\partial^2 w}{\partial \xi \, \partial \eta} = 0$$

which has the general solution

$$w(\xi, \eta) = F(\xi) + G(\eta)$$

Thus, the general solution of (2.1) is of the form

(**2.5**) $\qquad u(x, t) = F(x + ct) + G(x - ct)$

where F and G are arbitrary functions of one variable and are twice differentiable.

Now we determine the functions F and G so that (2.5) may satisfy (2.2). Setting $t = 0$ in (2.5) and using the value of $u(x, 0)$ from (2.2), we have

(**2.6**) $\qquad f(x) = F(x) + G(x)$

Let us differentiate (2.5) with respect to t to obtain

$$u_t(x, t) = cF'(x + ct) - cG'(x - ct)$$

Here the primes indicate differentiation with respect to the argument of the function. If we set $t = 0$ and use the value of $u_t(x, 0)$ from (2.2), we find

(**2.7**) $\qquad g(x) = cF'(x) - cG'(x)$

The system of equations consisting of (2.6) and (2.7) enables us to determine F and G in terms of f and g. Indeed, by integrating (2.7) from 0 to any point x, we obtain

$$F(x) - G(x) = \frac{1}{c} \int_0^x g(s) \, ds + C$$

where C is a constant of integration. Combining this result with (2.6) we obtain

$$F(x) = \frac{1}{2} f(x) + \frac{1}{2c} \int_0^x g(s) \, ds + \frac{C}{2}$$

Therefore, from (2.6), we have

$$G(x) = \frac{1}{2} f(x) - \frac{1}{2c} \int_0^x g(s) \, ds - \frac{C}{2}$$

If we replace the variable x in the expressions for F and G by $x + ct$ and $x - ct$, respectively, and substitute the results in (2.5), we finally arrive at the formula

$$(2.8) \qquad u(x, t) = \frac{f(x - ct) + f(x + ct)}{2} + \frac{1}{2c} \int_{x-ct}^{x+ct} g(s)\, ds$$

This is known as d'Alembert's formula for the solution of the initial value problem (2.1), (2.2).

It can be easily verified by direct differentiation (Exercises 1.4, Problem 9) that when f has a continuous second-order derivative and g has a continuous first-order derivative, the function (2.8) is twice continuously differentiable and satisfies (2.1) and (2.2). As a matter of fact, our derivation of d'Alembert's formula shows that any solution of (2.1), (2.2) that is twice continuously differentiable must have the representation (2.8); hence, the solution is uniquely determined by the initial data f and g. Thus, d'Alembert's formula represents the unique solution of (2.1), (2.2). Formula (2.8) also shows that if small perturbations are made in the initial data in an arbitrary fixed time interval $0 \leq t \leq T < \infty$, then the resulting perturbation in the solution is also small; that is, u depends continuously on the initial data f and g. More precisely, suppose u_1 is the solution of the problem (2.1), (2.2) corresponding to initial data f_1, g_1, and u_2 is the solution corresponding to initial data f_2, g_2. Then, for a given $\varepsilon > 0$, we can find a number $\delta > 0$ such that

$$|u_1(x, t) - u_2(x, t)| < \varepsilon$$

whenever

$$|f_1(x) - f_2(x)| < \delta, \qquad |g_1(x) - g_2(x)| < \delta$$

for all x and $0 \leq t \leq T$. Indeed, using the representation for u_1 and u_2, we see that

$$|u_1(x, t) - u_2(x, t)| \leq \frac{1}{2} |f_1(x - ct) - f_2(x - ct)|$$

$$+ \frac{1}{2} |f_1(x + ct) - f_2(x + ct)|$$

$$+ \frac{1}{2c} \int_{x-ct}^{x+ct} |g_1(s) - g_2(s)|\, ds$$

$$\leq \frac{1}{2}(\delta + \delta) + \frac{1}{2c} 2ct\delta < (1 + T)\delta$$

which can be made less than ε if we take $\delta = \varepsilon/(1 + T)$.

A problem that has a unique solution which depends continuously on the initial data or boundary conditions is said to be well posed or correctly set. Thus, the initial value problem (2.1), (2.2) is well posed. It is clear that well-posed problems are meaningful in applications, since the initial or boundary data are usually known only approximately; thus the corresponding solution represents only an approximation to the exact solution of the problem. It is by no means true, however, that an initial value or boundary value problem involving a second-order partial differential equation is always well posed. In fact, whether or not a mathematical problem is well posed depends on the kind of auxiliary condition (initial or boundary, or both) imposed and the type of the equation and domain considered. For instance, we have just seen that an initial value problem is well posed for the hyperbolic wave equation, but (as we shall see later) it does not lead to a well-posed problem for Laplace's elliptic equation. In the light of this fact, our classification of second-order partial differential equations into hyperbolic, parabolic, and elliptic types is all the more significant and essential.

Returning to the d'Alembert's formula (2.8), we note that if we assume only that f is continuous and f' and g are piecewise smooth, then there will be points (x, t) where the first- or second-order derivatives of u may fail to exist. In such a case, the function (2.8) cannot satisfy the wave equation, and therefore it cannot be a solution of the problem (2.1), (2.2). However, except only those points (x, t), the function u may still satisfy equation (2.1) and initial conditions (2.2). In this case, we shall regard (2.8) as the generalized solution of the problem. By this notion we really mean that u is the limit of a uniformly convergent sequence of solutions $u_n(x, t)$ of (2.1) satisfying the initial conditions

$$u_n(x, 0) = f_n(x), \qquad \frac{\partial u_n(x, 0)}{\partial t} = g_n(x)$$

where the sequence of functions f_n have continuous second-order derivative and the sequence of functions g_n have continuous first-order derivative such that

$$\lim_{n \to \infty} f_n = f, \qquad \lim_{n \to \infty} g_n = g$$

uniformly for $-\infty < x < \infty$. This concept will be further illuminated in Section 9 of the present chapter.

Example 2.1. Find the solution of the wave equation (2.1) satisfying the initial conditions $u(x, 0) = \sin x$, $u_t(x, 0) = 0$, $-\infty < x < \infty$.

Solution: By the d'Alembert's formula (2.8) we have

$$u(x, t) = \frac{\sin(x - ct) + \sin(x + ct)}{2}$$

$$= \sin x \cos ct$$

It is easily seen that this function indeed satisfies the wave equation and the given initial conditions.

Example 2.2. Find the solution of the problem (2.1), (2.2) when

$$u(x, 0) = 0 \qquad \text{and} \qquad u_t(x, 0) = \sin 2x$$

Solution: Again by d'Alembert's formula, the solution is

$$u(x, t) = \frac{1}{2c} \int_{x-ct}^{x+ct} \sin 2s \, ds$$

$$= \frac{\sin 2x \sin 2ct}{2c}$$

as can be easily verified.

As examples in which the initial conditions are not differentiable, let us consider the next two problems.

Example 2.3. Find the generalized solution of the problem

$$u_{tt} - 4u_{xx} = 0 \qquad (-\infty < x < \infty, t > 0)$$

$$u(x, 0) = \begin{cases} \frac{1}{2}x & (0 \le x \le \frac{1}{2}) \\ \frac{1}{2}(1 - x) & (\frac{1}{2} \le x \le 1) \\ 0 & \text{(otherwise)} \end{cases}$$

$$u_t(x, 0) = 0 \qquad (-\infty < x < \infty)$$

and evaluate $u(1, 1)$ and $u(\frac{1}{2}, \frac{1}{8})$.

Solution: The generalized solution is given by

$$u(x, t) = \frac{f(x - 2t) + f(x + 2t)}{2}$$

where $f(x) = \frac{1}{2}x$ for $0 \le x \le \frac{1}{2}$, $f(x) = \frac{1}{2}(1 - x)$ for $\frac{1}{2} \le x \le 1$, and $f(x) = 0$ for $x \le 0$ and $x \ge 1$. It is clear that except for x and t, such that $x - 2t$ or $x + 2t$ is equal to 0 or $\frac{1}{2}$ or 1, u satisfies the wave equation and the initial conditions. In particular, at $(1, 1)$ we find

$$f(x - 2t)\,|_{(1,1)} = f(-1) = 0, \qquad f(x + 2t)\,|_{(1,1)} = f(3) = 0$$

and thus $u(1, 1) = 0$.

At $(\frac{1}{2}, \frac{1}{8})$ we have

$$f(x - 2t)\,|_{(\frac{1}{2},\frac{1}{8})} = f(\tfrac{1}{4}) = \tfrac{1}{8}, \qquad f(x + 2t)\,|_{(\frac{1}{2},\frac{1}{8})} = f(\tfrac{3}{4}) = \tfrac{1}{8}$$

and therefore $u(\frac{1}{2}, \frac{1}{8}) = \frac{1}{8}$.

Example 2.4. Find the generalized solution of the problem

$$u_{tt} - u_{xx} = 0 \qquad (-\infty < x < \infty, t > 0)$$

$$u(x, 0) = 0 \qquad (-\infty < x < \infty)$$

$$u_t(x, 0) = g(x)$$

where

$$g(x) = \begin{cases} \sin \pi x & (0 \le x \le 1) \\ 0 & \text{(otherwise)} \end{cases}$$

and evaluate $u(\frac{1}{2}, \frac{3}{4})$ and $u(\frac{5}{6}, \frac{1}{2})$.

Solution: The generalized solution is given by

$$u(x, t) = \frac{1}{2} \int_{x-t}^{x+t} g(z)\, dz$$

and this satisfies the differential equation at all points except at those for which $x - t$ or $x + t$ equals 0 or 1, where the second derivatives of u fail to exist. At $(\frac{1}{2}, \frac{3}{4})$ we have

$$u\left(\frac{1}{2}, \frac{3}{4}\right) = \frac{1}{2} \int_{-\frac{1}{4}}^{\frac{5}{4}} g(z)\, dz = \frac{1}{2} \int_{0}^{1} \sin \pi z\, dz = \frac{1}{\pi}$$

At $(\frac{5}{6}, \frac{1}{2})$ we have

$$u\left(\frac{5}{6}, \frac{1}{2}\right) = \frac{1}{2} \int_{\frac{1}{3}}^{\frac{4}{3}} g(z)\, dz = \frac{1}{2} \int_{\frac{1}{3}}^{1} \sin \pi z\, dz = \frac{3}{4\pi}$$

Exercises 3.2

1. The displacement of a string is given by the forward wave

$$u(x, t) = \sin(x - ct)$$

Find the initial displacement and velocity. By substituting your initial conditions in the d'Alembert's formula, verify that $u(x, t) = \sin(x - ct)$.

2. Do as in Problem 1 when the displacement is given by the backward wave

$$u(x, t) = (x + ct)^2$$

3. Find the solution of the initial value problem

$$u_{tt} - 4u_{xx} = 0 \qquad\qquad (|x| < \infty, t > 0)$$
$$u(x, 0) = 2 \sin x \cos x \qquad\qquad (|x| < \infty)$$
$$u_t(x, 0) = \cos x \qquad\qquad (|x| < \infty)$$

4. Find the solution of the initial value problem

$$u_{tt} - 9u_{xx} = 0 \qquad\qquad (|x| < \infty, t > 0)$$
$$u(x, 0) = x \sin x \qquad\qquad (|x| < \infty)$$
$$u_t(x, 0) = \cos 2x \qquad\qquad (|x| < \infty)$$

In Problems 5 to 8, find the solution of the initial value problem (2.1), (2.2) with the given initial conditions. Take $c = 1$.

5. $f(x) = 1/(1 + x^2)$, $g(x) = e^x$; $|x| < \infty$.

6. $f(x) = e^{-x}$, $g(x) = 1/(1 + x^2)$; $|x| < \infty$.

7. $f(x) = \cos(\pi/2)x$, $g(x) = \sinh ax$; $|x| < \infty$.

8. $f(x) = \sin 3x$, $g(x) = \sin 2x - \sin x$; $|x| < \infty$.

In Problems 9 to 12 find the generalized solution of the initial value problem (2.1), (2.2), ($c = 1$) with the given initial conditions, and evaluate the solution at the given points.

9. At $(\frac{1}{8}, \frac{11}{8})$ and $(\frac{1}{4}, 1)$ with

$$f(x) = \begin{cases} 1 & (|x| \le 1) \\ 0 & (|x| > 1) \end{cases}$$

$$g(x) = 0 \qquad (|x| < \infty)$$

10. At $(-\pi/12, 7\pi/12)$ and $(-\pi/2, 5\pi/6)$ with

$$f(x) = \begin{cases} \sin x & (|x| \le \pi) \\ 0 & (|x| > \pi) \end{cases}$$

$$g(x) = 0 \qquad (|x| < \infty)$$

11. At $(0, \frac{3}{4})$, $(-\frac{1}{2}, \frac{3}{4})$, and $u(\frac{9}{8}, \frac{7}{8})$ with

$$f(x) = \begin{cases} x(1 - x) & (0 \le x \le 1) \\ 0 & (\text{otherwise}) \end{cases}$$

$$g(x) = \begin{cases} 1 - x^2 & (|x| \le 1) \\ 0 & (|x| > 1) \end{cases}$$

12. At $(-\pi/6, 5\pi/6)$ and $(3\pi/8, 5\pi/8)$ with

$$f(x) = e^{-|x|/\pi} \qquad (|x| < \infty)$$

$$g(x) = \begin{cases} \cos x & (|x| \le \pi/2) \\ 0 & (|x| > \pi/2) \end{cases}$$

13. Let $u(x, t)$ be thrice continuously differentiable solution of the initial value problem

$$u_{tt} - c^2 u_{xx} = 0 \qquad (|x| < \infty, t > 0)$$
$$u(x, 0) = 0 \qquad u_t(x, 0) = g(x) \qquad (|x| < \infty)$$

where g is twice continuously differentiable. Set $v(x, t) = u_t(x, t)$. Show that $v(x, t)$ satisfies the same differential equation and the initial conditions $v(x, 0) = g(x)$, $v_t(x, 0) = 0$.

14. Suppose that $u(x, t)$ satisfies the "damped wave equation"

$$u_{tt} - u_{xx} + c^2 u = 0 \qquad (|x| < \infty)$$

together with the initial conditions $u(x, 0) = 0$, $u_t(x, 0) = g(v)$. Proceeding as in Problem 13, verify that $v(x, t) = u_t(x, t)$ satisfies the same equation and the conditions $v(x, 0) = g(x)$, $v_t(x, 0) = 0$.

3. Interpretation of the Solution

Let us examine the solution (2.8) in more detail to get a clearer idea of the behavior of the solution of the wave equation. Suppose that the string is released with zero velocity after being given an initial displacement defined by $f(x)$. According to (2.8), the displacement of a point x at any time t is

(3.1) $$u(x, t) = \frac{f(x - ct) + f(x + ct)}{2}$$

Consider the function $f(x - ct)$. We observe that the graph of $f(x - ct)$ is the same as the graph of $f(x)$ translated to the right by a distance equal to ct (Fig. 3.2). This means that as t increases, $f(x - ct)$ represents a wave of the form $f(x)$ traveling to the right with velocity c. We call the wave represented by $f(x - ct)$ a forward wave. Similarly, the function $f(x + ct)$ can be interpreted as representing a wave with shape $f(x)$ traveling to the left with velocity c. This wave is called a backward wave. With this interpretation, we see that the solution (3.1) is a superposition of forward and backward waves traveling with the same velocity c and having the shape of the initial profile $f(x)$ with half the amplitude.

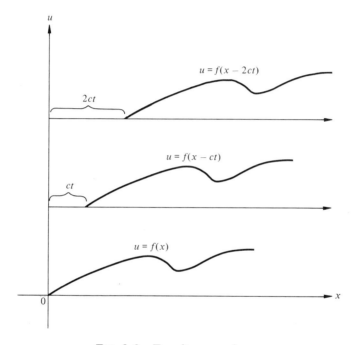

FIG. 3–2　*Traveling wave form.*

To illustrate this, suppose that the string has an initial displacement defined by [Fig. 3.3(a)]

$$f(x) = \begin{cases} x + a & (-a \leq x \leq 0) \\ -x + a & (0 \leq x \leq a) \\ 0 & \text{(otherwise)} \end{cases}$$

The forward and backward waves indicated by the dotted curve in Figure 3.3(a) coincide at $t = 0$. At $t = a/2c$, both waves have moved in opposite direction through a distance $a/2$, resulting in the shape of the string shown in Figure 3.3(b). At $t = a/c$, the forward and backward waves are on the verge of separating from each other. For $t > a/c$, the motion of the string consists of the forward and backward waves traveling toward the ends of the string at the same velocity,

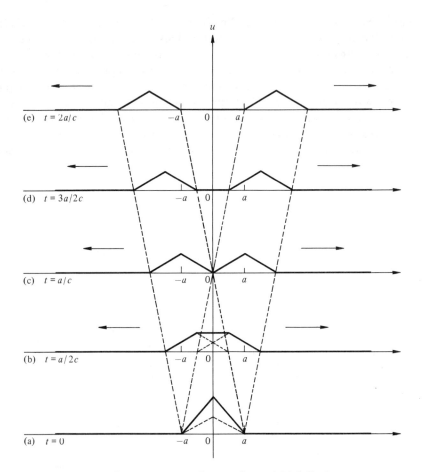

FIG. 3-3   *The propagation of waves due to initial displacement.*

Figure 3.3(d) and (e).   It is seen from the figure that each point of the string returns to its original position of rest after the passage of each wave.

In the case when $u(x, 0) = 0$ and $u_t(x, 0) = g(x)$, the displacement is given by

(3.2)
$$u(x, t) = \frac{1}{2c} \int_{x-ct}^{x+ct} g(s) \, ds$$

Let us define

(3.3)
$$\phi(x) = \frac{1}{2c} \int_0^x g(s) \, ds$$

Then (3.2) can be written as

(3.4)
$$u(x, t) = -\phi(x - ct) + \phi(x + ct)$$

which again shows that the solution is a superposition of a forward wave $-\phi(x - ct)$ and a backward wave $\phi(x + ct)$ traveling with the same velocity c. The forms of these waves are determined by the function ϕ, which is related to the initial velocity function g through the integral (3.3).

In illustration, suppose that

$$g(x) = \begin{cases} 2c & (|x| < 1) \\ 0 & (|x| > 1) \end{cases}$$

Then

$$-\phi(x - ct) = -\frac{1}{2c} \int_0^{x-ct} g(z)\, dz$$

$$= \begin{cases} -(x - ct) & (|x - ct| < 1) \\ -1 & (x - ct > 1) \\ 1 & (x - ct < -1) \end{cases}$$

and

$$\phi(x + ct) = \frac{1}{2c} \int_0^{x+ct} g(z)\, dz$$

$$= \begin{cases} x + ct & (|x + ct| < 1) \\ 1 & (x + ct > 1) \\ -1 & (x + ct < -1) \end{cases}$$

The graphs of $-\phi(x - ct)$ and $\phi(x + ct)$ together with the resulting shape of the string for various values of t are shown in Figure 3.4.

At $t = 0$, the forward wave $-\phi(x)$ and the backward wave $\phi(x)$ nullify each other so that the string has zero displacement; that is, it is at rest. At $t = \frac{1}{2}c$, the forward and the backward waves have moved in opposite direction through a distance $\frac{1}{2}$ unit. The shape of the string at this instant is obtained by adding graphically the two wave forms. At $t = 1/c$, the point $x = 0$ attains its maximum displacement $u = 2$, and from this instant on, more and more points of the string assume this maximum displacement and remain at rest in that position. This is evident from (3.2), since for a given point x of the string,

$$u(x, t) = \frac{1}{2c} \int_{x-ct}^{x+ct} g(z)\, dz$$

$$= \frac{1}{2c} \int_{-1}^{1} 2c\, dz = 2$$

as soon as t reaches a value for which $x - ct < -1$ and $x + ct > 1$.

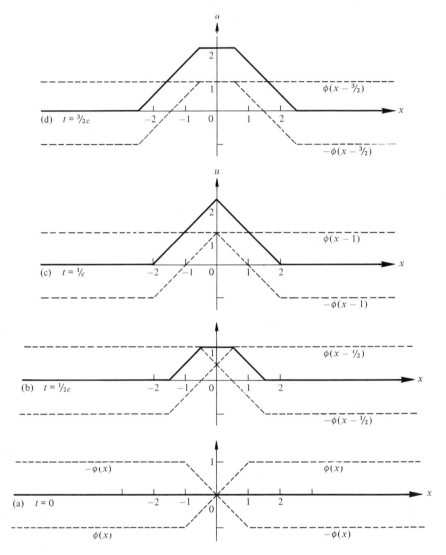

FIG. 3–4 *Propagation of waves due to initial velocity.*

4. Domain of Dependence and Characteristic Lines

We saw in the preceding section that the solution of the wave equation consists of forward and backward waves. The forms of these waves can be illustrated graphically for simple functions *f* and *g* in the *xu*-plane. In order to see how these waves are propagated, we shall now consider the *xt*-plane in which each point can be taken to correspond to a definite position on the string at a particular time.

Let (x, t) be a point in the xt-plane. From formula (2.8) we see that the solution at (x, t) depends only on the value of f at the two points $x - ct$ and $x + ct$, and on the initial velocity g over the interval $[x - ct, x + ct]$. This means that a change in the initial position and velocity of the string at points outside the interval $[x - ct, x + ct]$ will have no effect on the displacement at (x, t). Consequently, if f and g are known to vanish identically on an interval $a \leq x \leq b$, then $u(x, t) = 0$ for all points (x, t) such that $b < x - ct$ or $x + ct < a$.

The interval $[x - ct, x + ct]$ on which the value of $u(x, t)$ depends is called the domain of dependence of the point (x, t).

It is easy to see that the domain of dependence of a given point (ξ, τ) is precisely the interval cut out of the x-axis by the two straight lines passing through the point with slopes $\pm 1/c$ (Fig. 3.5). These lines, with the equations

(4.1) $x - ct = \xi - c\tau, \qquad x + ct = \xi + c\tau$

are the characteristics (lines) of the wave equation (1.2). The triangle formed by the characteristics and the interval of dependence of a given point (x, t) will be called the characteristic triangle determined by (x, t).

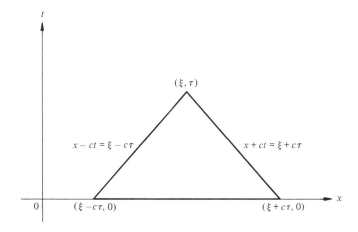

FIG. 3–5   *Characteristic triangle.*

Now let us see the significance of the characteristics. We note that d'Alembert's formula, which gives the displacement of a point (ξ, τ), can be written in the form

(4.2) $u(\xi, \tau) = \phi(\xi - c\tau) + \psi(\xi + c\tau)$

where

(4.3) $\phi(\xi - c\tau) = \dfrac{1}{2} f(\xi - c\tau) - \dfrac{1}{2c} \displaystyle\int_0^{\xi - c\tau} g(z)\, dz$

and

(4.4) $$\psi(\xi + c\tau) = \frac{1}{2} f(\xi + c\tau) + \frac{1}{2c} \int_0^{\xi + c\tau} g(z) \, dz$$

Thus, along the line $x - ct = \xi - c\tau$, $\phi(x - ct)$ has constant value, namely, $\phi(\xi - c\tau)$. This means that points on the characteristic $x - ct = \xi - c\tau$ have the same displacement caused by the forward wave $\phi(x - ct)$. Likewise, $\psi(x + ct)$ is constant along the line $x + ct = \xi + c\tau$ so that points on this line have the same displacement due to the backward wave $\psi(x + ct)$. It is in this sense and for this reason that we say the disturbance on the string is propagated with velocity c along the characteristics.

In Figure 3.6 we illustrate graphically the concept of propagation of waves along the characteristics. We consider a string that is initially at rest, with isolated initial disturbance at the points $\xi - c\tau$ and $\xi + c\tau$. According to our discussion in Section 3, the disturbances at these points will each split into two identical waves, the forward wave and the backward wave, both having the same form as the original disturbance but with half the amplitude. Each of the forward waves will travel along the characteristic

$$x - ct = \text{const}$$

that passes through the point from which the wave originated. Thus, referring to the figure, points on the characteristics

$$x - ct = \xi - c\tau, \qquad x - ct = \xi + c\tau$$

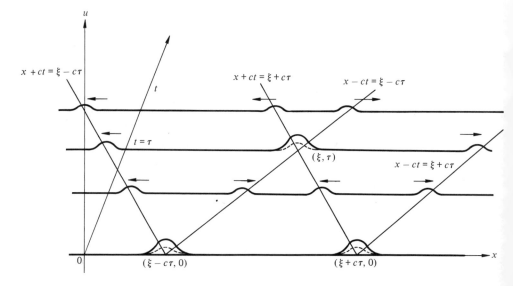

FIG. 3–6 *Propagation of waves along characteristics.*

experience the same displacement due to the forward waves originating from the points $\xi - c\tau$ and $\xi + c\tau$, respectively. The same discussion can be made for the backward waves and the points on the characteristics

$$x + ct = \xi - c\tau, \qquad x + ct = \xi + c\tau$$

through the respective points $\xi - c\tau$ and $\xi + c\tau$. Thus, the displacement at the point (ξ, τ) is the superposition of the forward wave from $\xi - c\tau$ and the backward wave from $\xi + c\tau$.

In Figure 3.7 we show how the other points of the xt-plane are affected by a disturbance confined to an interval $[x_1, x_2]$. We observe that the characteristics through the points x_1 and x_2 divide the xt-plane into six regions, indicated in the figure. For points in regions V and VI, their domains of dependence never overlap the interval $[x_1, x_2]$. This means that the points on the string that correspond to the points in these regions are not affected by the initial disturbance at the corresponding times. In region I the points are affected by both forward and backward waves originating from points in the interval $[x_1, x_2]$. In region II the points are affected only by backward waves, and in III only by forward waves. For points in region IV, the corresponding times are such that the corresponding points on the string have already experienced the passage of the waves and thus remain at rest with a permanent displacement equal to (see also Fig. 3.4)

$$\frac{1}{2c} \int_{x_1}^{x_2} g(s) \, ds$$

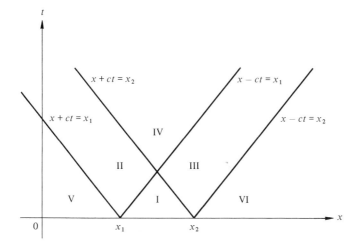

FIG. 3–7   *Region of influence of the interval $[x_1, x_2]$.*

The region bounded by the characteristics $x + ct = x_1$ and $x - ct = x_2$ and the interval $(x_1, x_2]$ is called the region of influence of the interval $[x_1, x_2]$. In particular, the region of influence of a given point consists of all points lying above the two characteristics passing through that point.

5. The Nonhomogeneous Wave Equation

We now consider the initial value problem

$$\textbf{(5.1)} \qquad \frac{\partial^2 u}{\partial t^2} - c^2 \frac{\partial^2 u}{\partial x^2} = F(x, t) \qquad\qquad (t > 0)$$

$$\textbf{(5.2)} \qquad u(x, 0) = f(x), \quad \frac{\partial u}{\partial t}(x, 0) = g(x) \qquad (-\infty < x < \infty)$$

which involves the nonhomogeneous wave equation. As we noted before, this problem corresponds to the problem of an infinite vibrating string with the presence of an external force. Since the difference of any two solutions of (5.1) is a solution of the homogeneous wave equation for which we have uniqueness, it follows that the solution of (5.1) is again uniquely determined by the initial data (5.2).

Let (ξ, τ) be the point at which we wish to find the solution of the problem (5.1), (5.2) and let Δ denote the characteristic triangle determined by this point (see Fig. 3.5). We integrate the expression on both sides of (5.1) over the domain Δ to obtain

$$\textbf{(5.3)} \qquad -\iint_\Delta F(x, t)\, dx\, dt = \iint_\Delta (c^2 u_{xx} - u_{tt})\, dx\, dt$$

By Green's theorem (Section 8, Chapter 1), the right-hand side of (5.3) can be written as an integral around the boundary C of the domain Δ so that we have

$$\textbf{(5.4)} \qquad -\iint_\Delta F(x, t)\, dx\, dt = \int_C (u_t\, dx + c^2 u_x\, dt)$$

The boundary C consists of segments of the characteristics $L_1: x - ct = \xi - c\tau$ and $L_2: x + ct = \xi + c\tau$ passing through the point (ξ, τ), and the interval $I: [\xi - c\tau, \xi + c\tau]$ that is cut off from the initial line $t = 0$ by the characteristics. Now on I, $t = 0$ so that $dt = 0$, while on L_1 and L_2 we have $dx = c\, dt$ and $dx = -c\, dt$, respectively. Hence, it follows that

$$\int_I (u_t \, dx + c^2 u_x \, dt) = \int_{\xi - c\tau}^{\xi + c\tau} u_t(x, 0) \, dx$$

$$\int_{L_1} (u_t \, dx + c^2 u_x \, dt) = c \int_{L_1} (u_t \, dt + u_x \, dx)$$

$$= c \int_{L_1} du$$

(5.5)

$$= c[u(\xi - c\tau, 0) - u(\xi, \tau)]$$

$$\int_{L_2} (u_t \, dx + c^2 u_x \, dt) = -c \int_{L_2} (u_t \, dt + u_x \, dx)$$

$$= -c \int_{L_2} du$$

$$= -c[u(\xi, \tau) - u(\xi + c\tau, 0)]$$

Substituting the initial data (5.2) into the results on the right side of (5.5), we have

$$\int_C (u_t \, dx + c^2 u_x \, dt) = -2cu(\xi, \tau) + cf(\xi - c\tau) + cf(\xi + c\tau)$$

$$+ \int_{\xi - c\tau}^{\xi + c\tau} g(x) \, dx$$

Therefore, on substituting this result in (5.4) and solving for u, we find

(5.6)
$$u(x, t) = \frac{f(x - ct) + f(x + ct)}{2} + \frac{1}{2c} \int_{x - ct}^{x + ct} g(\xi) \, d\xi$$

$$+ \frac{1}{2c} \iint_\Delta F(\xi, \tau) \, d\xi \, d\tau$$

in which we have interchanged the role of (ξ, τ) and (x, t). This represents the unique solution of our problem (5.1), (5.2).

In fact, we observe that the sum of the first two terms on the right of (5.6) is precisely d'Alembert's solution of the homogeneous wave equation with the initial conditions (5.2). Further, by writing the integral

(5.7)
$$v(x, t) = \frac{1}{2c} \iint_\Delta F(\xi, \tau) \, d\xi \, d\tau$$

as an iterated double integral with appropriate limits determined from the characteristic triangle Δ, it can be verified directly that (5.7) satisfies (5.1) and the homogeneous initial conditions

(5.8)
$$v(x, 0) = 0, \qquad \frac{\partial v}{\partial t}(x, 0) = 0$$

(Exercises 3.3, Problem 10.) In view of the linear nature of our problem, it follows from the principle of superposition that (5.6) satisfies (5.1) and (5.2). In this connection we assume that f is twice continuously differentiable, g is continuously differentiable, and F and F_x are continuous for $-\infty < x < \infty$, $t \geq 0$.

Example 5.1. Find the solution of the equation

$$u_{tt} - u_{xx} = x$$

satisfying the homogeneous conditions $u(x, 0) = u_t(x, 0) = 0$.

Solution: By the formula (5.7) we have

$$
\begin{aligned}
u(x, t) &= \frac{1}{2} \int_0^t \int_{x-(t-\tau)}^{x+(t-\tau)} \xi \, d\xi \, d\tau \\
&= \frac{1}{4} \int_0^t \left[(x + t - \tau)^2 - (x - t + \tau)^2 \right] d\tau \\
&= \frac{1}{4} \int_0^t 4x(t - \tau) \, d\tau = \frac{xt^2}{2}
\end{aligned}
$$

It is easily seen that this function satisfies the equation and the homogeneous initial conditions.

Example 5.2. Find the solution of the initial value problem

$$u_{tt} - u_{xx} = t$$

$$u(x, 0) = x, \qquad u_t(x, 0) = 0$$

Solution: The solution can be obtained by the use of (5.6). However, since $F(x, t) = t$ is independent of x, we readily find a particular solution of the differential equation (by integrating $u_{tt} = t$) in the function

$$u(x, t) = \frac{t^2}{6}$$

which satisfies the homogeneous initial conditions: $u = 0$ and $u_t = 0$ at $t = 0$. Hence, by superposition, the solution of the problem is

$$
\begin{aligned}
u(x, t) &= \frac{(x - t) + (x + t)}{2} + \frac{t^3}{6} \\
&= x + \frac{t^3}{6}
\end{aligned}
$$

The reader may check that

$$\frac{1}{2} \int_0^t \int_{x-(t-\tau)}^{x+(t-\tau)} \tau \, d\xi \, d\tau = \frac{t^3}{6}$$

As illustrated by the preceding example, the problem (5.1), (5.2) can sometimes be reduced to one involving a homogeneous differential equation if we can find a particular solution of the nonhomogeneous differential equation by some special method. This will, of course, avoid the use of (5.6), which involves a term requiring double integration. For suppose v is a particular solution of (5.1). Let u denote the solution of (5.1), (5.2) and set $w = u - v$. Then, by the principle of superposition, the function w satisfies the homogeneous wave equation and the initial conditions

$$(5.9) \qquad w(x, 0) = u(x, 0) - v(x, 0) = f(x) - v(x, 0)$$

$$w_t(x, 0) = u_t(x, 0) - v_t(x, 0) = g(x) - v_t(x, 0)$$

Hence, w can be found by the use of d'Alembert's formula corresponding to the initial conditions (5.9). Then the solution of (5.1), (5.2) is given by

$$u(x, t) = v(x, t) + w(x, t)$$

As an illustration, consider again the problem in Example 5.1. A particular solution of the equation is easily found to be $v(x, t) = -x^3/6$. Let

$$w(x, t) = u(x, t) + \frac{x^3}{6}$$

Then

$$w_{tt} - w_{xx} = 0, \qquad w(x, 0) = \frac{x^3}{6}, \qquad w_t(x, 0) = 0$$

Hence, by (2.8),

$$w(x, t) = \frac{(x - t)^3 + (x + t)^3}{12}$$

$$= \frac{x^3}{6} + \frac{xt^2}{2}$$

and therefore

$$u(x, t) = v(x, t) + w(x, t) = \frac{xt^2}{2}$$

which agrees with our earlier result.

Exercises 3.3

In Problems 1 through 6, find the solution of each of the initial value problems on $-\infty < x < \infty$, $t > 0$, by using (5.6).

1. $u_{tt} - u_{xx} = 2x$, $u(x, 0) = x^2$, $u_t(x, 0) = 0$.

2. $u_{tt} - u_{xx} = 2x - t$, $u(x, 0) = \sin x$, $u_t(x, 0) = x$.

3. $u_{tt} - u_{xx} = xt$, $u(x, 0) = 0$, $u_t(x, 0) = e^x$.

4. $u_{tt} - 4u_{xx} = e^x$, $u(x, 0) = \cos x$, $u_t(x, 0) = \sin x$.

5. $u_{tt} - 4u_{xx} = e^x + \sin t$, $u(x, 0) = 0$, $u_t(x, 0) = 1/(1 + x^2)$.

6. $u_{tt} - 9u_{xx} = t \sin x$, $u(x, 0) = x^2(1 - x)$, $u_t(x, 0) = 0$.

In Problems 7 through 9 find the solution of each of the problems on $-\infty < x < \infty$, $t > 0$ by finding a particular solution of the homogeneous differential equation and reducing the problem to one involving a homogeneous equation.

7. $u_{tt} - u_{xx} = \sin x$, $u(x, 0) = x$, $u_t(x, 0) = 0$.

8. $u_{tt} - u_{xx} = x \sin x - 2 \cos x$, $u(x, 0) = u_t(x, 0) = 0$.   *Hint:* $x \sin x$ is a particular solution.

9. $u_{tt} - u_{xx} = x^2/(1 + t)^2 + 2 \ln(1 + t)$, $u(x, 0) = u_t(x, 0) = 0$.   *Hint:* Take $v(x, t) = -x^2 \ln(1 + t)$ as a particular solution.

10. Verify that formula (5.7) satisfies the nonhomogeneous wave equation (5.1) and the homogeneous initial conditions (5.8).

11. (Duhamel's Principle)   Let $u(x, t, \tau)$ be the solution of the initial value problem

$$u_{tt} - c^2 u_{xx} = 0 \qquad\qquad (|x| < \infty)$$

$$u(x, 0, \tau) = 0, \qquad u_t(x, 0, \tau) = F(x, \tau)$$

Set

$$v(x, t) = \int_0^t u(x, t - \tau, \tau) \, d\tau$$

(a) Show that $v(x, t)$ satisfies the nonhomogeneous equation $v_{tt} - c^2 v_{xx} = F(x, t)$ and the initial conditions

$$v(x, 0) = 0, \qquad v_t(x, 0) = 0.$$

(b) Express $u(x, t, \tau)$ by using d'Alembert's formula and verify that $v(x, t)$ agrees with (5.7).

12. Find the solution of the initial value problem

$$u_{tt} - u_{xx} - \alpha u_t - \alpha u_x = 0 \qquad\qquad (|x| < \infty, t > 0)$$

$$u(x, 0) = f(x), \qquad u_t(x, 0) = g(x)$$

Hint: Let $u(x, t) = v(x, t)e^{ax+bt}$ and choose the constants a and b in such a way that the equation reduces to the wave equation.

6. Uniqueness of Solution

In the preceding section we deduced the uniqueness of the solution of the initial value problem

(6.1) $$u_{tt} - c^2 u_{xx} = F(x, t) \qquad (-\infty < x < \infty, t > 0)$$

(6.2) $$u(x, 0) = f(x), \qquad u_t(x, 0) = g(x) \qquad (-\infty < x < \infty)$$

from the fact that the solution of the corresponding problem involving the homogeneous wave equation is uniquely represented by d'Alembert's formula. It is important to note, however, that uniqueness can actually be established, even without knowing that a solution of the problem exists. In this section we shall present a method for proving uniqueness of the solution of an initial value problem for the more general hyperbolic partial differential equation

(6.3) $$u_{tt} - c^2 u_{xx} + hu = F(x, t)$$

where $c > 0$ and $h \geq 0$ are constants. This equation is known as the damped wave equation, which physically describes the motion of a vibrating string under the action of a restoring force $-hu$ and an external force F. We shall show that the initial value problem consisting of the differential equation (6.3) and initial conditions (6.2) has at most one solution.

Suppose that u and v are two solutions of (6.3), (6.2), which are both twice continuously differentiable. Set $w = u - v$; then, clearly, w is a solution of the homogeneous problem

(6.4)
$$w_{tt} - c^2 w_{xx} + hw = 0 \qquad (-\infty < x < \infty, t > 0)$$
$$w(x, 0) = 0, \qquad w_t(x, 0) = 0 \qquad (-\infty < x < \infty)$$

Let (ξ, τ) be any point in the xt-plane, $\tau > 0$, and denote by Δ the characteristic triangle determined by (ξ, τ), Figure 3.8. We shall prove that w vanishes identically throughout the region Δ, and in particular at the vertex (ξ, τ). Since the point (ξ, τ) is chosen arbitrarily, this will mean that $u = v$ at all points; that is, the two solutions u and v are identical.

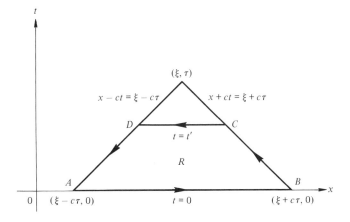

FIG. 3–8 *Proof of uniqueness.*

Let us multiply the differential equation in (6.4) by w_t and observe that

$$w_t w_{tt} = \frac{1}{2} \frac{\partial}{\partial t} (w_t^2)$$

$$w_t w_{xx} = \frac{\partial}{\partial x} (w_x w_t) - w_x w_{xt}$$

$$= \frac{\partial}{\partial x} (w_x w_t) - \frac{1}{2} \frac{\partial}{\partial t} (w_x^2)$$

$$w_t w = \frac{1}{2} \frac{\partial}{\partial t} (w^2)$$

Then

(6.5) $$w_t(w_{tt} - c^2 w_{xx} + hw) = \frac{1}{2} \frac{\partial}{\partial t} (w_t^2 + c^2 w_x^2 + hw^2)$$

$$- c^2 \frac{\partial}{\partial x} (w_x w_t) = 0$$

Let us draw the line $t = t'$, $0 \leq t' < \tau$, intersecting the characteristics at the points C and D (see Fig. 3.8). If we integrate equation (6.5) over the domain R bounded by the line segments AB, BC, CD, and DA, and recall Green's theorem, we obtain

(6.6) $$\iint_R \left[\frac{1}{2} \frac{\partial}{\partial t} (w_t^2 + c^2 w_x^2 + hw^2) - c^2 \frac{\partial}{\partial x} (w_x w_t) \right] dx \, dt$$

$$= -\int_L \left[\frac{1}{2} (w_t^2 + c^2 w_x^2 + hw^2) \, dx + c^2 w_x w_t \, dt \right]$$

$$= 0$$

where L denotes the boundary $AB + BC + CD + DA$ of R. Now, on the line segment AB, $w(x, 0) = 0$, $w_t(x, 0) = 0$, and hence also $w_x(x, 0) = 0$. Thus, the line integral along AB vanishes. On the characteristic segments BC and DA, we have $dx = -c \, dt$ and $dx = c \, dt$, respectively. Hence,

$$\int_{BC+DA} \left[\frac{1}{2} (w_t^2 + c^2 w_x^2 + hw^2) \, dx + c^2 w_x w_t \, dt \right]$$

$$= \int_{BC} \left[\frac{1}{2} (w_t^2 + c^2 w_x^2 + hw^2) \, dx - cw_x w_t \, dx \right]$$

$$+ \int_{DA} \left[\frac{1}{2} (w_t^2 + c^2 w_x^2 + hw^2)(c \, dt) + c^2 w_x w_t \, dt \right]$$

$$= \frac{1}{2} \int_{BC} [(w_t - cw_x)^2 + hw^2] \, dx + \frac{c}{2} \int_{DA} [(w_t + cw_x)^2 + hw^2] \, dt$$

which are nonnegative quantities. Finally, on CD we have $dt = 0$ so that the integral there reduces to

$$\frac{1}{2} \int_{CD} [(w_t^2 + c^2 w_x^2 + hw^2)] \, dx$$

which is also nonnegative. Now, according to (6.6), the sum of these integrals is zero. Since the sum of nonnegative terms can never be zero unless each of the terms is zero, we conclude in particular that

(6.7) $$\int_{CD} [(w_t^2 + c^2 w_x^2 + hw^2)] \, dx = 0$$

Since w and its first- and second-order partial derivatives are continuous, the integrand in (6.7) is continuous. It follows that

(6.8) $$w_t^2 + c^2 w_x^2 + hw^2 = 0$$

identically on CD. Indeed, if (6.8) were positive at a point on CD, it would be positive in some interval containing that point, and thus the integral over the interval would be positive, contradicting (6.7). Now equation (6.8) is true if and only if w vanishes identically on CD, since each of the terms in (6.8) is nonnegative. Therefore, $w(x, t') = 0$ for $\xi - c(\tau - t') \le x \le \xi + c(\tau - t')$, $0 \le t' < \tau$. The continuity of w implies that $w(\xi, \tau) = 0$ also. Hence, $u(\xi, \tau) = v(\xi, \tau)$, and consequently u and v are identical. Thus, we have established the following uniqueness theorem.

THEOREM 6.1. *The solution $u(x, t)$ of the initial value problem (6.3), (6.2) is uniquely determined by the values of f and g on the interval $[x - ct, x + ct]$ and by the values of F in the characteristic triangle determined by (x, t).*

The integral

(6.9) $$E(t) = \frac{1}{2} \int_{\xi - c(\tau - t)}^{\xi + c(\tau - t)} (u_t^2 + c^2 u_x + hu^2) \, dx$$

from (6.7) is often called the energy integral of the function u at time t over the interval $[\xi - c(\tau - t), \xi + c(\tau - t)]$ for the damped wave equation (6.3). It can be interpreted physically as representing the total kinetic and potential energy of the portion $[\xi - c(\tau - t), \xi + c(\tau - t)]$ of the string and the work done by the restoring force on that portion. If $h = 0$, then (6.9) represents the energy integral of u for the wave equation.

As a consequence of the uniqueness of the solution of the problem (6.1), we can deduce the solution of the initial-boundary value problem

(6.10)

$$u_{tt} - c^2 u_{xx} = 0 \qquad\qquad (x > 0, t > 0)$$

$$u(x, 0) = f(x) \qquad\qquad (x \ge 0)$$

$$u_t(x, 0) = g(x) \qquad\qquad (x \ge 0)$$

$$u(0, t) = 0 \qquad\qquad (t \ge 0)$$

for a vibrating semi-infinite string $x \geq 0$ fixed at the end $x = 0$. Indeed, consider the initial value problem

(6.11)

$$u_{tt} - c^2 u_{xx} = 0 \qquad (-\infty < x < \infty, t > 0)$$

$$u(x, 0) = \phi(x) \qquad (-\infty < x < \infty)$$

$$u_t(x, 0) = \psi(x) \qquad (-\infty < x < \infty)$$

where the initial data ϕ and ψ are the odd extensions of f and g, respectively; that is, $\phi(x) = f(x)$, $\psi(x) = g(x)$ for $x \geq 0$, and $\phi(x) = -f(-x)$, $\psi(x) = -g(-x)$ for $x < 0$. Clearly, the solution u of the problem (6.11) satisfies the differential equation and the initial conditions of (6.10). It remains only to show that u also satisfies the boundary condition $u(0, t) = 0$. To this end, let v be defined by $v(x, t) = -u(-x, t)$. By direct differentiation, using the chain rule, it is easily seen that v satisfies the wave equation. Moreover, from the definition of ϕ and ψ it is seen that

$$v(x, 0) = -u(-x, 0) = -\phi(-x) = \phi(x)$$

$$v_t(x, 0) = -u_t(-x, 0) = -\psi(-x) = \psi(x)$$

Hence, v is also a solution of the problem (6.11). Since the solution of (6.11) is unique, we conclude that $v(x, t) = u(x, t)$; that is,

$$-u(-x, t) = u(x, t)$$

Setting $x = 0$, we obtain $-u(0, t) = u(0, t)$, which implies that $u(0, t) = 0$, $t \geq 0$. Thus, the solution of the problem (6.11) provides a solution of the initial-boundary value problem (6.10) on a semi-infinite interval $x \geq 0$. Note that in order for the solution of the problem (6.11) to be twice continuously differentiable for all x and $t > 0$, the extended functions ϕ and ψ must be twice continuously differentiable and once continuously differentiable, respectively. This will be the case if f and g are themselves functions with these properties such that

$$f(0) = g(0) = f''(0) = 0$$

The foregoing discussion essentially shows that the solution of an initial value problem with initial data that are odd functions is an odd function in the variable x, and hence vanishes at $x = 0$ for $t \geq 0$. In an analogous manner it can be shown that if the initial data f and g are even functions, then the solution of the initial value problem is also even in x; that is,

$$u(-x, t) = u(x, t)$$

This implies that

$$-u_x(-x, t) = u_x(x, t)$$

from which we deduce $u_x(0, t) = 0$ for $t \geq 0$. This result provides a method for solving the initial-boundary value problem

$$u_{tt} - c^2 u_{xx} = 0 \qquad (x > 0, t > 0)$$

(6.12)
$$u(x, 0) = f(x), \qquad u_t(x, 0) = g(x) \qquad (x \geq 0)$$

$$u_x(0, t) = 0 \qquad (t \geq 0)$$

on a semi-infinite interval $x \geq 0$ with free boundary condition at $x = 0$. We need only extend f and g for $x < 0$ as even functions and solve the resulting initial value problem by d'Alembert's formula. Here, u is twice continuously differentiable if, in addition to the differentiability conditions to be satisfied by f and g as for (6.10), we assume that $f'(0) = g'(0) = 0$.

Example 6.1. Find the solution of the initial-boundary value problem

$$u_{tt} - u_{xx} = 0 \qquad (x > 0, t > 0)$$
$$u(x, 0) = \sin^2 x, \qquad u_t(x, 0) = 0 \qquad (x \geq 0)$$
$$u(0, t) = 0 \qquad (t \geq 0)$$

and evaluate $u(\pi/12, \pi/4)$.

Solution: We extend the function $f(x) = \sin^2 x$ as an odd function for $x < 0$. By d'Alembert's formula (2.8), we have

$$u(x, t) = \frac{f(x - t) + f(x + t)}{2}$$

$$= \frac{\sin^2(x - t) + \sin^2(x + t)}{2}$$

$$= \sin^2 x \, \cos^2 t + \cos^2 x \, \sin^2 t$$

for $x > t$ and

$$u(x, t) = \frac{-\sin^2(t - x) + \sin^2(x + t)}{2}$$

$$= 2 \cos x \, \sin x \, \cos t \, \sin t$$

$$= \frac{1}{2} \sin 2x \, \sin 2t$$

for $x < t$. Thus, at $(\pi/12, \pi/4)$ we have

$$u\left(\frac{\pi}{12}, \frac{\pi}{4}\right) = \frac{-\sin^2(\pi/6) + \sin^2(\pi/3)}{2}$$

$$= \frac{1}{2}\left(-\frac{1}{4} + \frac{3}{4}\right) = \frac{1}{4}$$

Example 6.2. Solve the problem in Example 6.1 when the boundary condition is replaced by the free boundary condition $u_x(0, t) = 0$, and evaluate $u(\pi/6, \pi/6)$.

Solution: Here we need to extend the initial data as even functions. Since $f(x) = \sin^2 x$ is already an even function, we immediately have for the solution of the problem

$$u(x, t) = \frac{\sin^2(x - t) + \sin^2(x + t)}{2}$$

$$= \sin^2 x \cos^2 t + \cos^2 x \sin^2 t \qquad (x \geq 0, t \geq 0)$$

Thus, $u(\pi/6, \pi/6) = \frac{3}{8}$.

Exercises 3.4

1. Let u be a solution of the wave equation

$$u_{tt} - c^2 u_{xx} = 0 \qquad\qquad (|x| < \infty, t > 0)$$

   which is twice continuously differentiable, and vanishes together with its first derivatives as $|x| \to \infty$ for $0 \leq t \leq t_1$. By differentiating under the integral sign and then integrating by parts, show that the "energy integral"

$$E(t) = \frac{1}{2} \int_{-\infty}^{\infty} (u_t^2 + c^2 u_x^2) \, dx$$

   is constant for $0 \leq t \leq t_1$.

2. Using the result of Problem 1, prove that the initial value problem (6.1), (6.2) has at most one solution, assuming that its solution vanishes together with the first-order derivative as $|x| \to \infty$.

3. Let u be a solution of the damped wave equation

$$u_{tt} - c^2 u_{xx} + hu = 0$$

   which is sufficiently smooth and vanishes together with its first derivatives as $|x| \to \infty$. Show, as in Problem 1, that the energy integral

$$E(t) = \frac{1}{2} \int_{-\infty}^{\infty} (u_t^2 + c^2 u_x^2 + hu^2) \, dx$$

   is constant for $0 \leq t \leq t_1$.

4. From the result of Problem 3 deduce that the initial value problem (6.3), (6.2) has at most one solution, assuming the same condition as in Problem 2.

5. Obtain the explicit solution of the problem (6.10) and verify that it satisfies the differential equation and the initial and boundary conditions.

6. Prove the statement in the text that if f and g are two even functions, then the solution u of the initial value problem (2.1), (2.2) is also even.

7. Find the solution of the initial-boundary value problem

$$u_{tt} - c^2 u_{xx} = 0 \qquad\qquad (x > 0, t > 0)$$
$$u(x, 0) = f(x), \qquad u_t(x, 0) = g(x) \qquad\qquad (x \geq 0)$$
$$u_x(0, t) = 0 \qquad\qquad (t \geq 0)$$

8. Find the solution of the initial-boundary value problem

$$u_{tt} - u_{xx} = 0 \qquad\qquad (x > 0, t > 0)$$
$$u(x, 0) = x^2, \qquad u_t(x, 0) = x(1 - x) \qquad\qquad (x \geq 0)$$
$$u(0, t) = 0 \qquad\qquad (t \geq 0)$$

and evaluate the solution at the points $(\frac{1}{4}, 1)$ and $(\frac{7}{8}, \frac{5}{8})$. (Use the solution formula of Problem 5.)

9. Solve the initial-boundary value problem

$$u_{tt} - u_{xx} = 0 \qquad\qquad (x > 0, t > 0)$$
$$u(x, 0) = \sin(\pi x/2), \qquad u_t(x, 0) = x \qquad\qquad (x \geq 0)$$
$$u(0, t) = 0 \qquad\qquad (t \geq 0)$$

10. Find the solution of the wave equation

$$u_{tt} - u_{xx} = 0 \qquad\qquad (x > 0, t > 0)$$

with the following conditions:
(a) $u(x, 0) = \cos(\pi x/2)$, $u_t(x, 0) = x^2$, $x \geq 0$; $u_x(0, t) = 0, t \geq 0$;
(b) $u(x, 0) = e^{-|x|}$, $u_t(x, 0) = \cos x$, $x \geq 0$; $u_x(0, t) = 0, t \geq 0$.

11. Show that if the function $F(x, t)$ is odd (or even) in x, then the same is true of the solution u of the initial value problem

$$u_{tt} - c^2 u_{xx} = F(x, t) \qquad\qquad (|x| < \infty, t > 0)$$
$$u(x, 0) = 0, \qquad u_t(x, 0) = 0 \qquad\qquad (|x| < \infty)$$

and thus deduce that u (or u_x) vanishes at $x = 0$.

12. Find the solution of the problem

$$u_{tt} - u_{xx} = x \qquad\qquad (x > 0, t > 0)$$
$$u(x, 0) = \sin x, \qquad u_t(x, 0) = 0 \qquad\qquad (x \geq 0)$$
$$u(0, t) = 0 \qquad\qquad (t \geq 0)$$

13. Find the solution of the problem

$$u_{tt} - u_{xx} = t \qquad\qquad (x > 0, t > 0)$$
$$u(x, 0) = 0, \qquad u_t(x, 0) = \cos x \qquad\qquad (x \geq 0)$$
$$u_x(0, t) = 0 \qquad\qquad (t \geq 0)$$

7. Initial-Boundary Value Problems

We have seen in the preceding section that the solution of an initial value problem for the wave equation with odd (or even) initial data, when restricted to $x \geq 0, t \geq 0$, provides a solution of the initial-boundary value problem on the semi-infinite interval $x \geq 0$ with fixed (or free) boundary condition at $x = 0$. The same idea can be used to solve an initial-boundary value problem on the finite interval $0 \leq x \leq L$ with either fixed or free boundary condition at either end point.

Let us consider the initial-boundary value problem

$$(7.1) \qquad\qquad \frac{\partial^2 u}{\partial t^2} - c^2 \frac{\partial^2 u}{\partial x^2} = 0 \qquad\qquad (0 < x < L, t > 0)$$

$$(7.2) \qquad u(x, 0) = f(x), \qquad u_t(x, 0) = g(x) \qquad\qquad (0 \leq x \leq L)$$

$$(7.3) \qquad u(0, t) = 0, \qquad u(L, t) = 0 \qquad\qquad (t \geq 0)$$

which corresponds physically to the problem of a vibrating string of finite length L with fixed ends and with no external force. We recall that the solution of an initial value problem with odd initial data (about $x = 0$) is again odd; that is, $u(-x, t) = -u(x, t)$. In a similar manner, we can show that if the initial data are odd about $x = L$—that is, $f(2L - x) = -f(x)$ and $g(2L - x) = -g(x)$— then so is the solution u. Consequently, if the initial data are odd about $x = 0$ and $x = L$, the solution u will then satisfy the relations

$$u(-x, t) = -u(x, t) \qquad \text{and} \qquad u(2L - x, t) = -u(x, t)$$

which, in particular, imply

$$u(0, t) = 0 \qquad \text{and} \qquad u(L, t) = 0 \qquad\qquad (t \geq 0)$$

Thus, the solution of the initial value problem with initial data that are odd about $x = 0$ and $x = L$, and which coincides with (7.2) on $[0, L]$, gives a solution of the initial-boundary value problem (7.1), (7.2), (7.3). Therefore, to find a solution of the problem (7.1), (7.2), (7.3), we extend the initial data f and g given for $0 \leq x \leq L$ as odd functions about $x = 0$ and $x = L$, and then substitute the extended functions in d'Alembert's formula (2.8). The restriction of this d'Alembert's solution to the region $0 \leq x \leq L$, $t \geq 0$ is a solution of our problem. In this connection, the solution obtained will be twice continuously differentiable if we require that the following compatibility conditions

$$f(0) = f(L) = 0, \qquad f''(0) = f''(L) = 0, \qquad g(0) = g(L) = 0$$

hold, in addition to the assumption that f and g have continuous second-order and first-order derivatives on $0 \leq x \leq L$, respectively. That such a solution is uniquely determined will be proved at the end of this section.

Example 7.1. Find the solution of the initial-boundary value problem

$$
\begin{aligned}
u_{tt} - u_{xx} &= 0 & (0 < x < 1, t > 0)\\
u(x, 0) &= \sin \pi x & (0 \leq x \leq 1)\\
u_t(x, 0) &= 0 & (0 \leq x \leq 1)\\
u(0, t) &= 0 & (u(1, t) = 0, t \geq 0)
\end{aligned}
$$

Solution: Since $\sin \pi(-x) = -\sin \pi x$ and $\sin \pi(2 - x) = -\sin \pi x$, the function $f(x) = \sin \pi x$ is already odd about $x = 0$ and $x = \pi$, and hence we immediately have

$$u(x, t) = \frac{\sin \pi(x - t) + \sin \pi(x + t)}{2}$$

$$= \sin \pi x \cos \pi t$$

as the solution valid for $0 \le x \le 1, t \ge 0$. This is easily verified.

Example 7.2. Solve the problem in Example 7.1 when the initial displacement is

$$u(x, 0) = x(x - 1) \qquad\qquad (0 \le x \le 1)$$

and evaluate $u(3/4, 1/2)$.

Solution: For points (x, t) such that $0 \le x - t < x + t \le 1$, the solution is given by

$$u(x, t) = \frac{(x - t)(x - t - 1) + (x + t)(x + t - 1)}{2}$$

$$= x^2 - x + t^2$$

For points (x, t) such that $x < t$ or $1 < x + t$, the solution is given by

$$u(x, t) = \frac{f(x - t) + f(x + t)}{2}$$

where f is the odd extension of $u(x, 0) = x(x - 1)$ about $x = 0$ and $x = 1$. Thus, at $(3/4, 1/2)$ we have

$$f(3/4 - 1/2) = f(1/4) = (1/4)(1/4 - 1) = -3/16$$

and

$$f(3/4 + 1/2) = f(5/4) = f(2 - 3/4) = -f(3/4)$$
$$= -(3/4)(3/4 - 1) = 3/16$$

so that $u(3/4, 1/2) = 0$.

Example 7.3. Find the solution of the problem

$$u_{tt} - u_{xx} = 0 \qquad\qquad (0 < x < 1, t > 0)$$
$$u(x, 0) = x^2(1 - x) \qquad\qquad (0 \le x \le 1)$$
$$u_t(x, 0) = x(x - 1) \qquad\qquad (0 \le x \le 1)$$
$$u(0, t) = 0, \qquad u(1, t) = 0 \qquad\qquad (t \ge 0)$$

at the point $(1/2, 5/4)$.

Solution: We extend the initial data here as odd functions about $x = 0$ and $x = 1$. Now, at $(1/2, 5/4)$, we have

$$f(-3/4) = -f(3/4) = -(3/4)^2(1 - 3/4) = -9/64$$
$$f(7/4) = f(2 - 1/4) = -f(1/4) = -(1/4)^2(1 - 1/4)$$
$$= -3/64$$

Further,

$$\int_{-3/4}^{7/4} g(x)\,dx = \int_{-3/4}^{3/4} g(x)\,dx + \int_{3/4}^{5/4} g(x)\,dx + \int_{5/4}^{7/4} g(x)\,dx$$

$$= 0 + 0 + \int_{5/4}^{7/4} g(x)\,dx$$

since $g(x)$ is an odd function about $x = 0$ and $x = 1$.
By the change of variable $x = 2 - s$, we have

$$\int_{5/4}^{7/4} g(x)\,dx = -\int_{1/4}^{3/4} s(s - 1)\,ds$$

$$= -\frac{s^2}{3} + \frac{s^2}{2}\Big|_{1/4}^{3/4} = \frac{11}{96}$$

Thus,

$$u\left(\frac{1}{2}, \frac{5}{4}\right) = \frac{-9 - 3}{2(64)} + \frac{1}{2} \cdot \frac{11}{96}$$

$$= \frac{-7}{192}$$

In the same way, we can show that the problem (7.1), (7.2) with free boundary conditions

(7.4) $$u_x(0, t) = 0, \qquad u_x(L, t) = 0 \qquad\qquad (t > 0)$$

at both ends can also be solved by using d'Alembert's formula (2.8), provided the initial data f and g are extended as even functions about $x = 0$ and $x = L$; that is, $f(-x) = f(x), g(-x) = g(x), f(2L - x) = f(x)$, and $g(2L - x) = g(x)$. Then d'Alembert's solution u is itself an even function about $x = 0$ and $x = L$, and hence satisfies the relations

$$u(-x, t) = u(x, t), \qquad u(2L - x, t) = u(x, t)$$

These imply that

$$u_x(-x, t) = -u_x(x, t), \qquad u_x(2L - x, t) = -u_x(x, t)$$

which, in particular, give

$$u_x(0, t) = 0 \qquad \text{and} \qquad u_x(L, t) = 0$$

showing that u satisfies the boundary conditions.

The same method can also be used to solve an initial-boundary value problem on the finite interval $0 \le x \le L$, which involves the nonhomogeneous wave equation

(7.5) $$\frac{\partial^2 u}{\partial t^2} - c^2 \frac{\partial^2 u}{\partial x^2} = F(x, t)$$

with fixed or free boundary conditions at either end point. In such a case, we extend the function F together with the initial data as odd or even function about an end point, according as the boundary condition prescribed at that point is fixed or free. Then the same will be true of the solution given by (5.6) and hence will satisfy the prescribed boundary conditions.

Example 7.4. Find the solution of the initial-boundary value problem

$$u_{tt} - u_{xx} = \sin \frac{\pi}{2} x \qquad\qquad (0 < x < 1, t > 0)$$

$$u(x, 0) = 0, \qquad u_t(x, 0) = 0 \qquad\qquad (0 \le x \le 1)$$

$$u(0, t) = 0, \qquad u_x(1, t) = 0 \qquad\qquad (t \ge 0)$$

Solution: Here we observe that the function $F(x, t) = \sin(\pi/2)x$ is already odd about $x = 0$ and is even about $x = 1$. Hence, by (5.7), our solution is

$$u(x, t) = \frac{1}{2} \int_0^t \int_{x-(t-\tau)}^{x+(t-\tau)} \sin \frac{\pi}{2} \xi \, d\xi \, d\tau$$

$$= \frac{1}{\pi} \int_0^t \left[\cos \frac{\pi}{2} (x - t + \tau) - \cos \frac{\pi}{2} (x + t - \tau) \right] d\tau$$

$$= \frac{2}{\pi^2} \left[\sin \frac{\pi}{2} (x - t + \tau) + \sin \frac{\pi}{2} (x + t - \tau) \right]_0^t$$

$$= \frac{4}{\pi^2} \sin \frac{\pi}{2} x \left(1 - \cos \frac{\pi}{2} t \right)$$

for $0 \le x \le 1, t \ge 0$.

The uniqueness of solution of the initial-boundary value problem (7.1), (7.2), (7.3) can, of course, be deduced from the uniqueness of d'Alembert's formula. However, it is worthwhile and not difficult to give a separate proof of uniqueness which is independent of the manner of derivation of the solution of the problem. We shall prove here the uniqueness of solution of the more general initial-boundary value problem

$$u_{tt} - c^2 u_{xx} = F(x, t) \qquad\qquad (0 < x < L, t > 0)$$

(7.6) $\qquad\qquad u(x, 0) = f(x), \qquad u_t(x, 0) = g(x) \qquad\qquad (0 \le x \le L)$

$$u(0, t) = h(t), \qquad u(L, t) = k(t) \qquad\qquad (t \ge 0)$$

where we assume that the functions $F, f, g, h,$ and k are sufficiently differentiable and compatible at the end points. An explicit solution of this problem when h and k are not both zero will be given in the next section.

Suppose u_1 and u_2 are two solutions of the problem (7.6) which are both twice continuously differentiable, and let $w = u_1 - u_2$. Then w is a solution of the homogeneous problem

(7.7)

$$w_{tt} - c^2 w_{xx} = 0 \qquad\qquad (0 < x < L, t > 0)$$

$$w(x, 0) = 0, \qquad w_t(x, 0) = 0 \qquad (0 \le x \le L)$$

$$w(0, t) = 0, \qquad w(L, t) = 0 \qquad (t \ge 0)$$

Consider the energy integral (see (6.9))

(7.8)
$$E(t) = \frac{1}{2} \int_0^L (w_t^2 + c^2 w_x^2) \, dx \qquad\qquad (t \ge 0)$$

for the function w on the interval $[0, L]$. Differentiating this with respect to t and integrating the second term by parts, we have

(7.9)
$$E'(t) = \int_0^L (w_t w_{tt} + c^2 w_x w_{xt}) \, dx$$

$$= \int_0^L w_t (w_{tt} - c^2 w_{xx}) \, dx + c^2 w_x w_t \Big|_0^L$$

Since w is a solution of the problem (7.7), we see that the integrand in the last integral above vanishes, $w_t(0, t) = 0$, and $w_t(L, t) = 0$, so that (7.9) reduces to $E'(t) = 0$ for $t \ge 0$. This means that the energy integral (7.8) is a constant for $t \ge 0$. But at $t = 0$, we see from (7.7) that $w_x(x, 0) = 0$ and $w_t(x, 0) = 0$, which imply that $E(0) = 0$. Hence, the integral (7.8) is identically zero, and since its integrand is nonnegative, it follows that

$$w_t^2 + c^2 w_x^2 = 0$$

for $0 \le x \le L, t \ge 0$. By the same argument as in the proof of Theorem 6.1 of Section 6, we therefore conclude that $w = 0$ identically, which shows that $u_1 = u_2$, as we wish to prove.

Exercises 3.5

1. Show that if f is odd (or even) about the points $x = 0$ and $x = L$, then f is periodic with period $2L$; that is, $f(x + 2L) = f(x)$.

2. Show that if f is odd (or even) about $x = 0$ and even (or odd) about $x = L$, then f is periodic with period $4L$.

3. Show that if f is periodic with period $2L$, then

$$\int_a^{a+2L} f(x) \, dx = \int_{-L}^L f(x) \, dx$$

(This means that the integral of f is the same over any interval of length $2L$.)

4. Let f and g be two odd functions about $x = 0$ and $x = L$. Verify that the solution of (2.1), (2.2) is also odd about $x = 0$ and $x = L$; thus, deduce that

$$u(0, t) = u(L, t) = 0$$

5. Let f and g be two even functions about $x = 0$ and $x = L$. Prove that the solution of (2.1), (2.2) is even about the same points and deduce $u_x(0, t) = u_x(L, t) = 0$.

6. Let f and g be two functions that are odd about $x = 0$ and even about $x = L$. Prove that the solution of (2.1), (2.2) is odd about $x = 0$ and even about $x = L$, and deduce that $u(0, t) = 0$, $u_x(L, t) = 0$.

In Problems 7 through 12, find the solution of (7.1) with the given initial and boundary conditions. Take $c = 1$ and $L = 1$.

7. $u(x, 0) = \sin \pi x$, $u_t(x, 0) = x(1 - x^2)$; $u(0, t) = u(1, t) = 0$.   Evaluate $u(5/8, 9/8)$.

8. $u(x, 0) = x(1 - x)$, $u_t(x, 0) = x^2(1 - x)$; $u(0, t) = u(1, t) = 0$.   Evaluate $u(3/4, 2)$.

9. $u(x, 0) = x^2(1 - x^2)$, $u_t(x, 0) = \cos \pi x/2$; $u_x(0, t) = 0$, $u(1, t) = 0$.

10. $u(x, 0) = \sin^2 \pi x$, $u_t(x, 0) = 0$; $u_x(0, t) = u_x(1, t) = 0$.

11.
$$u(x, 0) = \begin{cases} x & (0 \le x \le 1/4) \\ (-x + 1)/3 & (1/4 \le x \le 1) \end{cases}$$

$$u_t(x, 0) = 0 \qquad\qquad (0 \le x \le 1)$$

$$u(0, t) = u(1, t) = 0$$

12.
$$u(x, 0) = 0, \qquad u_t(x, 0) = \begin{cases} x & (0 \le x \le 1/2) \\ -x + 1 & (1/2 \le x \le 1) \end{cases}$$

$$u(0, t) = u_x(1, t) = 0$$

13. Evaluate $u(1/2, 3/2)$ if u satisfies

$$u_{tt} - u_{xx} = e^x \qquad\qquad (0 < x < 1, t > 0)$$
$$u(x, 0) = u_t(x, 0) = 0 \qquad (0 \le x \le 1)$$
$$u_x(0, t) = u_x(1, t) = 0 \qquad (t \ge 0)$$

14. Evaluate $u(1/4, 2)$ if

$$u_{tt} - u_{xx} = 1 - x \qquad\qquad (0 < x < 1, t > 0)$$
$$u(x, 0) = x^2(1 - x), \qquad u_t(x, 0) = 0 \qquad (0 \le x \le 1)$$
$$u_x(0, t) = u(1, t) = 0 \qquad (t \ge 0)$$

15. By using the energy integral (6.9) over $[0, L]$, prove that the initial-boundary value problem

$$u_{tt} - c^2 u_{xx} + hu = F(x, t) \qquad (0 < x < L, t > 0)$$
$$u(x, 0) = f(x), \qquad u_t(x, 0) = g(x) \qquad (0 \le x \le L)$$
$$u(0, t) = a(t), \qquad u(L, t) = b(t) \qquad (t \ge 0)$$

has at most one solution.

8. Nonhomogeneous Problems and Reflection of Waves

In the preceding two sections we showed how the solution of the initial value problem for the wave equation can be employed to obtain the solution of the initial-boundary value problem on a semi-infinite interval or on a finite interval when the boundary conditions are either fixed or free. When the boundary conditions are not homogeneous, the method does not apply, and we have to use a different approach. In this section we shall present a method for solving problems involving the wave equation with nonhomogeneous boundary conditions of the first kind.

First, let us consider the initial-boundary value problem

$$u_{tt} - c^2 u_{xx} = 0 \qquad\qquad\qquad (x > 0, t > 0)$$

(8.1)
$$u(x, 0) = f(x), \qquad u_t(x, 0) = g(x) \qquad\qquad (x \geq 0)$$

$$u(0, t) = h(t) \qquad\qquad\qquad (t \geq 0)$$

which corresponds to a vibrating semi-infinite string where the end point $x = 0$ is given a displacement described by $h(t)$ for $t \geq 0$. For each point (x, t) such that $x > ct$, we observe that the interval of dependence $[x - ct, x + ct]$ lies entirely on the positive x-axis. Hence, for $x > ct$, the solution of problem (8.1) is given by d'Alembert's formula

(8.2)
$$u(x, t) = \phi(x - ct) + \psi(x + ct)$$

where ϕ and ψ are defined by

(8.3)
$$\phi(x) = \frac{1}{2} f(x) - \frac{1}{2c} \int_0^x g(s)\, ds$$

$$\psi(x) = \frac{1}{2} f(x) + \frac{1}{2c} \int_0^x g(s)\, ds$$

This is true regardless of the boundary condition at $x = 0$. Physically, this says that at the point x on the string and at time t when no wave from the end point has yet arrived, the displacement $u(x, t)$ is caused simply by the initial disturbance on the interval $[x - ct, x + ct]$.

But when $x < ct$, the portion $[x - ct, 0]$ of the interval $[x - ct, x + ct]$ lies on the negative x-axis on which f and g are not defined (see Fig. 3.9). Hence, for $x < ct$ the value of ϕ is not known and so (8.2) is not valid. However, by using the boundary condition in (8.1), we see from (8.2) that

(8.4)
$$u(0, t) = h(t) = \phi(-ct) + \psi(ct)$$

which, on setting $s = ct$, gives

(8.5)
$$\phi(-s) = h\left(\frac{s}{c}\right) - \psi(s)$$

This furnishes the value of ϕ for negative values of its argument, and so for $x < ct$ we have

(8.6)
$$\phi(x - ct) = h\left(t - \frac{x}{c}\right) - \psi(ct - x)$$

Substituting this in (8.2), we obtain the formula

(8.7)
$$u(x, t) = h\left(t - \frac{x}{c}\right) - \psi(ct - x) + \psi(x + ct)$$

$$= h\left(t - \frac{x}{c}\right) + \frac{f(x + ct) - f(ct - x)}{2} + \frac{1}{2c} \int_{ct-x}^{x-ct} g(s)\, ds$$

for $x < ct$. Thus, our complete solution of the problem (8.1) is given by (8.2), (8.3) for $x > ct$ and by (8.7) for $x < ct$. In either case, we notice that the solution is the superposition of a forward wave $\phi(x - ct)$ and a backward wave $\psi(x + ct)$.

By direct differentiation it is easy to verify that the function u defined by (8.2) or (8.7) satisfies the wave equation and that (8.2) together with (8.3) satisfies the initial conditions, while (8.7) satisfies the boundary condition of the problem. In this connection, we assume that h has continuous second-order derivative for $t > 0$ and that f and g have continuous second- and first-order derivatives, respectively, for $x > 0$ such that $h(0) = f(0)$ and $h'(0) = g(0)$.

Formula (8.7) has an interesting and important physical interpretation. Let us consider (8.7) at the point (x_0, t_0) in the domain $x < ct$ of the xt-plane and draw the characteristics through this point (Fig. 3.9). We see that the first term in (8.7) is precisely the value of $h(t)$ at the t-intercept of the characteristic $x - ct = x_0 - ct_0$. It represents the displacement of the end point at time $t = t_0 - x_0/c$ and travels along the characteristic $x - ct = x_0 - ct_0$. The forward wave $-\psi(ct_0 - x_0)$ traveling along the same characteristic as

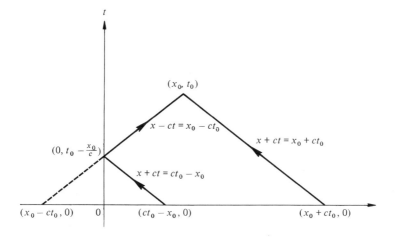

FIG. 3–9   *Reflection of wave from the end $x = 0$.*

$h(t_0 - x_0/c)$ represents the reflection of the backward wave that originated from the point $(ct_0 - x_0, 0)$ on the initial line. This backward wave first traveled along the characteristic $x + ct = ct_0 - x_0$ until it reached the end point and was reflected. The minus sign in front of ψ indicates that there is a 180-degree phase shift upon reflection. As a result of this phase shift, the contribution of the initial velocity from the interval $[0, ct_0 - x_0]$ canceled out. Thus, the interval of dependence of a point (x_0, t_0) in the domain $x < ct$ is

$$[ct_0 - x_0, x_0 + ct_0]$$

which is the interval cut off from the positive x-axis by the characteristic $x + ct = x_0 + ct_0$ and the reflection of the characteristic $x - ct = x_0 - ct_0$ at the end point $x = 0$.

The same method can be used to solve the initial-boundary value problem

$$u_{tt} - c^2 u_{xx} = 0 \qquad\qquad (0 < x < L, t > 0)$$

(8.8)

$$u(x, 0) = f(x), \qquad u_t(x, 0) = g(x) \qquad (0 \le x \le L)$$

$$u(0, t) = h(t), \qquad u(L, t) = k(t) \qquad (t \ge 0)$$

on a finite interval with nonhomogeneous boundary conditions. We note, as in the case of problem (8.1), that for points (x, t), $0 < x < L$, $t > 0$—for which the interval $[x - ct, x + ct]$ lies inside the interval $[0, L]$—d'Alembert's formula (8.2), (8.3) remains valid regardless of the boundary conditions. It is only when the interval $[x - ct, x + ct]$ extends beyond $[0, L]$ that we need to find for (8.2) the value of ϕ for negative argument and the value of ψ for positive argument.

Now, on the interval $-L < s < 0$, the value of ϕ is given by (8.5); that is,

(8.9)

$$\phi(-s) = h\left(\frac{s}{c}\right) - \psi(s) \qquad (0 < s < L)$$

To find the value of $\psi(s)$ for $L < s < 2L$, we note by the second boundary condition in (8.8) that

$$u(L, t) = k(t) = \phi(L - ct) + \psi(L + ct)$$

so that

(8.10)

$$\psi(s + L) = k\left(\frac{s}{c}\right) - \phi(L - s) \qquad (0 < s < L)$$

This gives the value of $\psi(x)$ for $L < x < 2L$. In this way the functions ϕ and ψ are then completely determined on the intervals $(-L, L)$ and $(0, 2L)$, respectively. Thus, it is possible to write down the solution of problem (8.8) at any point (x, t) such that $-L < x - ct < x + ct < 2L$ (see Example 8.1).

If we replace s by $s + L$ in (8.9) and use (8.10), we find

(8.11)

$$\phi(-s - L) = h\left(\frac{s + L}{c}\right) - \psi(s + L)$$

$$= h\left(\frac{s + L}{c}\right) - k\left(\frac{s}{c}\right) + \phi(L - s) \qquad (0 < s < L)$$

and this further extends $\phi(x)$ onto the interval $-2L < x < -L$. Similarly, by replacing s by $s + L$ in (8.10) and using (8.9), we have

(8.12) $$\psi(s + 2L) = k\left(\frac{s + L}{c}\right) - h\left(\frac{s}{c}\right) + \psi(s) \qquad (0 < s < L)$$

which defines $\psi(x)$ on the interval $2L < x < 3L$. Formulas (8.11) and (8.12) are recurrence relations that together with (8.9) and (8.10), determine the value of ϕ for any negative argument and the value of ψ for any positive argument. If we know the values of ϕ and ψ, it is possible to write down the solution of problem (8.8) at any point (x, t), for $0 < x < L$, $t > 0$.

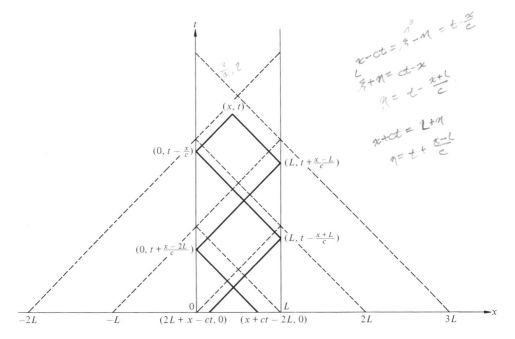

FIG. 3–10   *Repeated reflection of waves.*

For example, if (x, t) is a point such that $-2L < x - ct < -L$ and $2L < x + ct < 3L$ (see Fig. 3.10), then according to (8.11),

$$\phi(x - ct) = h\left(t - \frac{x}{c}\right) - k\left(t - \frac{x + L}{c}\right) + \phi(2L + x - ct)$$

where $0 < 2L + x - ct < L$ and, according to (8.12),

$$\psi(x + ct) = k\left(t + \frac{x - L}{c}\right) - h\left(t + \frac{x - 2L}{c}\right) + \psi(x + ct - 2L)$$

with $0 < x + ct - 2L < L$. Hence, by (8.2), the solution at this point is

(8.13) $u(x, t) = \phi(x - ct) + \psi(x + ct)$

$$= h\left(t - \frac{x}{c}\right) - h\left(t + \frac{x - 2L}{c}\right) + k\left(t + \frac{x - L}{c}\right)$$

$$- k\left(t - \frac{x + L}{c}\right) + \frac{f(x + ct - 2L) + f(2L + x - ct)}{2}$$

$$+ \frac{1}{2c} \int_{2L+x-ct}^{x+ct-2L} g(s)\, ds$$

where we have used (8.3) for $\phi(x)$ and $\psi(x)$ for $0 < x < L$.

It is interesting to note that the solution (8.13) can also be obtained geo-metrically by using the idea of reflection of characteristics, which is analogous to the reflection of waves. We draw the characteristics through the point (x, t) and their reflections at $x = 0$ and $x = L$, moving backward in time, until they intersect the initial line on the interval $0 < x < L$ (Fig. 3.10). Then the contribution of the boundary conditions to the displacement at (x, t) consists of the values of h at the t-intercepts and the values of k at the intercepts with $x = L$ of the characteristics, counting a change of sign following each reflection. Thus, from the end $x = 0$, we have $h(t - x/c)$ and $-h(t + (x - 2L)/c)$, in which the second term has a negative sign because the wave it represents is reflected once at $x = L$. Similarly, from the end $x = L$, we have

$$k(t + (x - L)/c) \quad \text{and} \quad -k(t - (x + L)/c)$$

where the wave represented by the second term is reflected once at $x = L$. The contribution from the initial displacement consists of the terms $f(2L + x - ct)$ and $f(x + ct - 2L)$, which represent waves that originated from the points $(2L + x - ct, 0)$ and $(x + ct - 2L, 0)$, respectively; these waves were re-flected twice, once at each end before arriving at the point (x, t). The net contribution from the initial velocity comes from the interval

$$[2L + x - ct, x + ct - 2L].$$

Needless to say, the method described above applies in particular to the case where the boundary conditions are homogeneous. In fact, in such case, formulas (8.11) and (8.12) imply that ϕ and ψ must be extended as periodic functions of period $2L$. Using this fact and the formulas given in (8.3), it can be established that the initial data f and g must then be extended as odd periodic functions of period $2L$. This is equivalent to extending f and g as odd functions about $x = 0$ and $x = L$ (see Problem 1, Exercises 3.5), which was the method we adopted in Section 7.

Example 8.1. Find the solution of the problem (8.8) at points (x, t) such that $-L < x - ct < 0$ and $L < x + ct < 2L$.

Solution: Since $-L < x - ct < 0$, we have by (8.9)

$$\phi(x - ct) = h\left(t - \frac{x}{c}\right) - \psi(ct - x)$$

and since $L < x + ct < 2L$, we have by (8.10)

$$\psi(x + ct) = k\left(t + \frac{x - L}{c}\right) - \phi(2L - x - ct)$$

Hence, by (8.2) and (8.3), the solution is given by

$$u(x, t) = h\left(t - \frac{x}{c}\right) + k\left(t + \frac{x - L}{c}\right) - \frac{f(ct - x) + f(2L - x - ct)}{2}$$

$$+ \frac{1}{2c}\int_{ct-x}^{2L-x-ct} g(s)\, ds$$

Exercises 3.6

1. Evaluate $u(5/8, 19/8)$ for Problem 8 of Exercises 3.5, using the method of wave reflection.

2. Evaluate $u(1/4, 3/2)$ for Problem 7 of Exercises 3.5, using the method of wave reflection.

3. Find the solution of the wave equation $u_{tt} - u_{xx} = 0$, $x > 0$, $t > 0$, satisfying the given conditions:
    (a) $u(x, 0) = e^{-x} - 1$, $u_t(x, 0) = 0$, $x \geq 0$; $u(0, t) = te^{-t}$, $t \geq 0$.
    (b) $u(x, 0) = \sin x$, $u_t(x, 0) = x$, $x \geq 0$; $u(0, t) = \sin 2t$, $t \geq 0$.

4. Find the solution at the indicated point of the wave equation

$$u_{tt} - u_{xx} = 0 \qquad\qquad (0 < x < 1, t > 0)$$

satisfying the given conditions
    (a) at $(1/4, 3/2)$ with $u(x, 0) = e^x - 1$, $u_t(x, 0) = 0$, $0 < x < 1$; $u(0, t) = te^{-t}$, $u(1, t) = t^2$, $t > 0$.
    (b) at $(3/4, 3/2)$ with $u(x, 0) = 0$, $u_t(x, 0) = x(1 - x)$, $0 < x < 1$; $u(0, t) = \sin \pi t$, $u(1, t) = \cos \pi t/2$, $t \geq 0$.

5. Show that the solution of the initial-boundary value problem (8.8) when $f = g = k = 0$ is given by

$$u(x, t) = \sum_{n \geq 0} h\left(t - \frac{x + 2nL}{c}\right) - \sum_{n \geq 1} h\left(t + \frac{x - 2nL}{c}\right)$$

where $h(t) = 0$ for $t < 0$ and h has continuous second-order derivative.

6. Find the solution of the problem (8.8) when $f = g = h = 0$.

7. Solve the initial-boundary value problem

$$u_{tt} - c^2 u_{xx} = 0 \qquad\qquad (x > 0, t > 0)$$
$$u(x, 0) = f(x), \qquad u_t(x, 0) = g(x) \qquad\qquad (x \geq 0)$$
$$u_x(0, t) = h(t) \qquad\qquad (t \geq 0)$$

8. Solve the initial-boundary value problem

$$u_{tt} - c^2 u_{xx} = 0 \qquad\qquad (x > 0, t > 0)$$
$$u(x, 0) = f(x), \qquad u_t(x, 0) = 0 \qquad\qquad (x \geq 0)$$
$$u_x(0, t) - ku(0, t) = 0 \qquad\qquad (k \text{ a constant}, t \geq 0)$$

Hint: Set $v(x, t) = u_x(x, t) - ku(x, t)$ and consider the initial-boundary problem for v.

9. Method of Separation of Variables

So far, we have been concerned with initial value and initial-boundary value problems for the wave equation. We have seen that by an appropriate extension of the initial data, it is possible to reduce an initial-boundary value problem to an initial value problem for which d'Alembert's formula can be employed. For a more general equation, however, we must use a different approach. In this section we shall describe a rather convenient and powerful method for solving initial value, initial-boundary value, or boundary value problems for a large class of partial differential equations of hyperbolic, parabolic, or elliptic types.

In order to establish the basic steps involved in the method, we shall solve the initial-boundary value problem

(9.1) $$u_{tt} - c^2 u_{xx} + hu = 0 \qquad (0 < x < L, t > 0)$$

where $h = \text{const} > 0$.

(9.2) $$u(x, 0) = f(x), \qquad u_t(x, 0) = 0 \qquad (0 \leq x \leq L)$$

(9.3) $$u(0, t) = 0, \qquad u(L, t) = 0 \qquad (t > 0)$$

for the damped-wave equation. The method consists in assuming a particular solution of (9.1) in the form

(9.4) $$u(x, t) = X(x)T(t)$$

where X is a function of x alone and T is a function of t alone. Moreover, the function (9.4) will be required to satisfy all homogeneous conditions of the problem, namely, the initial condition $u_t(x, 0) = 0$ and the boundary conditions (9.3). Now, substituting (9.4) in the differential equation (9.1), we have

$$X(x)T''(t) - c^2 X''(x)T(t) + hX(x)T(t) = 0$$

where the primes denote ordinary differentiation with respect to the argument of the function being differentiated. Dividing the last equation by $c^2 X(x)T(t)$ and "separating" variables, we find

(9.5)
$$\frac{T''(t)}{c^2 T(t)} + \frac{h}{c^2} = \frac{X''(x)}{X(x)}$$

Since the term on the left of equation (9.5) depends only on the variable t and the term on the right depends only on the variable x, it follows that the derivative with respect to t of the term on the left is zero; likewise, the derivative with respect to x of the term on the right is zero. Hence, both terms must be equal to a constant, which we denote by $-\lambda$. Thus,

$$\frac{X''(x)}{X(x)} = -\lambda, \qquad \frac{T''(t)}{c^2 T(t)} + \frac{h}{c^2} = -\lambda$$

which lead to the two ordinary differential equations

(9.6)
$$X''(x) + \lambda X(x) = 0$$
$$T''(t) + (\lambda c^2 + h)T(t) = 0$$

to be satisfied by the functions X and T, respectively. In this way we have replaced the partial differential equation (9.1) by two ordinary differential equations (9.6) involving a parameter λ. This is the essence of the method of separation of variables.

Since the function (9.4) is to satisfy the homogeneous conditions of the problem, we must have

(9.7)
$$X(x)T'(0) = 0$$
$$X(0)T(t) = 0, \qquad X(L)T(t) = 0$$

from which we conclude that $T'(0) = 0$, $X(0) = 0$, and $X(L) = 0$. The alternate choice $X(x) = 0$ or $T(t) = 0$ would each lead to the trivial solution $u(x, t) = 0$ of the differential equation. This, however, cannot be a solution of the problem unless $f = 0$, too, in which case the whole problem is trivial. Therefore, in order for (9.4) to be a nontrivial solution of equation (9.1) satisfying the homogeneous conditions (9.7), the functions X and T must be the solution of the problems

(9.8) $X'' + \lambda X = 0, \qquad X(0) = 0, \qquad X(L) = 0$

and

(9.9) $T' + (\lambda c^2 + h)T = 0, \qquad T'(0) = 0$

respectively.

The problem (9.8) is a special case of a more general boundary value problem in ordinary differential equations, known as the Sturm-Liouville problem, which is discussed in the next chapter. It will be seen that this type of problem has non-trivial solutions only for certain exceptional values of the parameter λ, called the eigenvalues of the problem. The corresponding nontrivial solutions are called eigenfunctions. For each eigenvalue λ, the product of the corresponding eigenfunction X and the corresponding function T determined from the problem (9.9) yields a particular solution of (9.1) satisfying the conditions (9.7).

We now proceed to the determination of nontrivial solutions of problem (9.8). We consider three separate cases according to whether λ is negative or zero or positive. Suppose first that $\lambda < 0$ and write $\lambda = -k^2$, where k is a nonzero real number. Then the differential equation in (9.8) has the general solution

$$X(x) = c_1 e^{-kx} + c_2 e^{kx}$$

Applying the boundary conditions $X(0) = X(L) = 0$, we have

$$c_1 + c_2 = 0$$

$$c_1 e^{-kL} + c_2 e^{kL} = 0$$

which can be regarded as a system of algebraic equations for c_1 and c_2. Since the determinant of coefficients

$$\begin{vmatrix} 1 & 1 \\ e^{-kL} & e^{kL} \end{vmatrix} = 2 \sinh kL$$

does not vanish for $k \neq 0$, the only solution of the system is $c_1 = c_2 = 0$. Thus (9.8) has only trivial solution when $\lambda < 0$; that is, the problem has no negative eigenvalues.

Next, suppose that $\lambda = 0$. Then the differential equation becomes $X'' = 0$, with general solution given by $X(x) = c_1 x + c_2$. Application of the boundary conditions readily shows that $c_1 = c_2 = 0$, leading again to the trivial solution. Hence, $\lambda = 0$ is not an eigenvalue of the problem.

Finally, we consider the case $\lambda > 0$. In this case the general solution of the differential equation is

$$X(x) = c_1 \sin \sqrt{\lambda}\, x + c_2 \cos \sqrt{\lambda}\, x$$

Applying the boundary condition $X(0) = 0$, we find $c_2 = 0$; therefore a non-trivial solution must be of the form $X(x) = c_1 \sin \sqrt{\lambda}\, x, c_1 \neq 0$. The boundary condition $X(L) = 0$ then requires that

$$\sin \sqrt{\lambda}\, L = 0$$

and this holds if and only if $\sqrt{\lambda}\, L = n\pi$, $n = 0, \pm 1, \pm 2, \pm 3, \ldots$. Since $\lambda > 0$, it follows that the eigenvalues of the problem (9.8) are

(9.10) $$\lambda_n = \frac{n^2 \pi^2}{L^2}$$ $(n = 1, 2, \ldots)$

and the corresponding eigenfunctions, apart from constant factors, are

(9.11)
$$X_n(x) = \sin \frac{n\pi x}{L}$$

Now, for each $\lambda_n = n^2\pi^2/L^2$, $n \geq 1$, the general solution of the differential equation in (9.9) is

$$T(t) = c_1 \sin \sqrt{\lambda_n c^2 + h}\, t + c_2 \cos \sqrt{\lambda_n c^2 + h}\, t$$

The initial condition $T'(0) = 0$ requires that $c_1 = 0$, thus leaving c_2 arbitrary. Hence, except for constant factors, we have

(9.12)
$$T_n(t) = \cos \left[\frac{n^2\pi^2 c^2}{L^2} + h\right]^{1/2} t \qquad (n = 1, 2, \ldots)$$

as the corresponding solution of the problem (9.9) for each eigenvalue λ_n. By forming the product of the functions (9.11) and (9.12) in accordance with (9.4), we obtain infinitely many particular solutions

(9.13)
$$u_n(x, t) = \sin \frac{n\pi x}{L} \cos \left[\frac{n^2\pi^2 c^2}{L^2} + h\right]^{1/2} t \qquad (n = 1, 2, \ldots)$$

of equation (9.1) satisfying the homogeneous conditions of (9.2) and (9.3). By the principle of superposition, any linear combination of these functions remains a solution of equation (9.1) and satisfies the same homogeneous initial and boundary conditions. Hence, if we can find a suitable linear combination of the functions (9.13) which satisfies as well the initial condition $u(x, 0) = f(x)$, then such a combination will be a solution of the problem (9.1), (9.2), (9.3).

However, it is clear that no (finite) linear combination of the functions (9.13) can satisfy (9.2) unless the initial datum f itself is a linear combination of the eigenfunctions (9.11). We therefore try an infinite linear combinaiton of the form

(9.14)
$$u(x, t) = \sum_{n=1}^{\infty} b_n \sin \frac{n\pi x}{L} \cos \left[\frac{n^2\pi^2 c^2}{L} + h\right]^{1/2} t$$

Clearly, if the constants b_n are such that the series (9.14) and its derivatives converge respectively to the function $u(x, t)$ and its derivatives for $0 < x < L$, $t > 0$, then by the extended principle of superposition the function u represented by the series (9.14) is a solution of equation (9.1) satisfying the homogeneous conditions in (9.2) and (9.3). There remains the problem of determining the constants b_n so that (9.14) also satisfies the nonhomogeneous initial condition in (9.2). Setting $t = 0$ in (9.14), we have

(9.15)
$$u(x, 0) = f(x) = \sum_{n=1}^{\infty} b_n \sin \frac{n\pi x}{L}$$

Thus, the constants b_n appear as the coefficients in the series expansion of f in terms of the eigenfunctions (9.11). To determine these coefficients, we make use of the following fundamental property of the eigenfunctions (9.11). If m and n are nonzero integers, then

$$(9.16) \qquad \int_0^L \sin\frac{m\pi x}{L} \sin\frac{n\pi x}{L}\, dx = \begin{cases} 0 & \text{(when } m \neq n\text{)} \\ \dfrac{L}{2} & \text{(when } m = n\text{)} \end{cases}$$

In the first case ($m \neq n$) we say that the functions $X_m(x) = \sin(m\pi x/L)$ and $X_n(x) = \sin(n\pi x/L)$ are orthogonal on the interval $0 \leq x \leq L$. This orthogonality property actually holds for every pair of eigenfunctions corresponding to distinct eigenvalues of any Sturm-Liouville problem and is established in Section 5 of the next chapter. In the present case, however, the validity of (9.16) follows immediately from the trigonometric identity

$$2 \sin\frac{m\pi x}{L} \sin\frac{n\pi x}{L} = \cos\frac{(m - n)\pi x}{L} - \cos\frac{(m + n)\pi x}{L}$$

We therefore multiply both sides of equation (9.15) by $\sin(m\pi x/L)$ and integrate the result from $x = 0$ to $x = L$. Assuming that the series can be integrated term by term, we obtain

$$(9.17) \qquad \int_0^L f(x) \sin\frac{m\pi x}{L}\, dx = \sum_{n=1}^{\infty} b_n \int_0^L \sin\frac{m\pi x}{L} \sin\frac{n\pi x}{L}\, dx$$

According to (9.16), each term on the right-hand side of (9.17), except the term corresponding to $n = m$, vanishes. Hence, equation (9.17) reduces to

$$\int_0^L f(x) \sin\frac{m\pi x}{L} = \frac{L}{2} b_m$$

which gives the formula

$$(9.18) \qquad b_n = \frac{2}{L} \int_0^L f(x) \sin\frac{n\pi x}{L}\, dx \qquad (n = 1, 2, \ldots)$$

only for n values appearing in $f(x)$ fcn.

for the coefficients in (9.15).

Thus, our formal solution of the problem (9.1), (9.2), (9.3) is given by (9.14), where the coefficients b_n are given by (9.18). The series (9.14) is called the eigenfunction expansion of the solution u.

The series in (9.15) for the function f with b_n given by (9.18) is called the Fourier sine series of f on the interval $0 \leq x \leq L$, and the constants b_n are known as the Fourier coefficients of f with respect to the eigenfunctions (9.11). It will be shown in Chapter 5 that when f is continuous and piecewise smooth on $0 \leq x \leq L$ with $f(0) = f(L) = 0$, the Fourier sine series of f converges uniformly and absolutely to f on $0 \leq x \leq L$. Under such conditions, the series (9.14) then converges uniformly to $u(x, t)$ for $0 \leq x \leq L$, $t \geq 0$. Since each term of the series is continuous for $0 \leq x \leq L$, $t \geq 0$, the same is true of u, and hence u satisfies the initial conditions (9.2) as well as the boundary conditions (9.3). However, in order for u to be twice continuously differentiable, we need more stringent conditions on f because otherwise the partial derivatives of u may fail to exist. In such a case, it is convenient to regard u as represented by (9.14) as a generalized solution of the problem in the sense described in Section 2. We illustrate these remarks by the following example.

Example 9.1. Find the solution of the problem

$$u_{tt} - u_{xx} + u = 0 \qquad (0 < x < \pi, t > 0)$$
$$u(x, 0) = f(x), \qquad u_t(x, 0) = 0 \qquad (0 \le x \le \pi)$$
$$u(0, t) = 0, \qquad u(\pi, t) = 0 \qquad (t \ge 0)$$

where

$$f(x) = \begin{cases} x & (0 \le x \le \pi/2) \\ \pi - x & (\pi/2 \le x \le \pi) \end{cases}$$

Solution: We compute the Fourier coefficients b_n of f. By (9.18), with $L = \pi$, we have

$$b_n = \frac{2}{\pi} \int_0^\pi f(x) \sin nx \, dx$$

$$= \frac{2}{\pi} \int_0^{\pi/2} x \sin nx \, dx + \frac{2}{\pi} \int_{\pi/2}^\pi (\pi - x) \sin nx \, dx$$

$$= \frac{2}{\pi} \left[\frac{-x \cos nx}{n} + \frac{\sin nx}{n^2} \right]_0^{\pi/2}$$

$$+ \frac{2}{\pi} \left[-(\pi - x) \frac{\cos nx}{n} - \frac{\sin nx}{n^2} \right]_{\pi/2}^\pi$$

$$= \frac{4}{\pi n^2} \sin \frac{n\pi}{2}$$

in which $\sin(n\pi/2) = 0$ when $n = 2k$, and $\sin(n\pi/2) = (-1)^{k+1}$ when $n = 2k - 1$, $k = 1, 2, \ldots$. Thus, by (9.14), our formal solution is

$$(9.19) \qquad u(x, t) = \frac{4}{\pi} \sum_{k=1}^{\infty} \frac{(-1)^{k+1}}{(2k - 1)^2} \sin(2k - 1)x \cos[(2k - 1)^2 + 1]^{1/2}t$$

The series solution (9.19) of the preceding example can be shown to converge uniformly for $0 \le x \le \pi, t \ge 0$ by the Weierstrass M-test, using the convergent series $\sum_{k=1}^{\infty} 1/(2k - 1)^2$. Hence, the limit function u is continuous for $0 \le x \le \pi$, $t \ge 0$, and satisfies the initial and boundary conditions of the problem. However, the second partial derivatives of u do not exist because the second derivatives of the series fail to converge. For this reason, u cannot be a solution of the differential equation. In this case, it is appropriate to regard (9.19) as a generalized solution of the problem in the sense of Section 2.

Indeed, for each integer $n \ge 1$, let us define

$$u_n(x, t) = \frac{4}{\pi} \sum_{k=1}^{n} \frac{(-1)^{k+1}}{(2k - 1)^2} \sin(2k - 1)x \cos[(2k - 1)^2 + 1]^{1/2}t$$

Then u is the limit of the uniformly convergent sequence u_n. Further, for each n, u_n is twice continuously differentiable for $0 \le x \le L$, $t \ge 0$, and satisfies the differential equation together with the initial conditions

$$u_n(x, 0) = f_n(x) = \frac{4}{\pi} \sum_{k=1}^{n} \frac{(-1)^{k+1}}{(2k-1)^2} \sin(2k-1)x$$

$$\frac{\partial u_n}{\partial t}(x, 0) = g_n(x) = 0$$

and the boundary conditions $u_n(0, t) = u_n(\pi, t) = 0$. Since the sequences f_n and g_n converge uniformly to the respective initial data f and g, it follows by definition that (9.19) is a generalized solution of our problem.

Exercises 3.7

In Problems 1 through 5, find the solution of the given problem by the method of separation of variables.

1. $u_{tt} - u_{xx} = 0$, $0 < x < \pi$, $t > 0$; $u(x, 0) = \sin^3 x$, $u_t(x, 0) = 0$, $0 \le x \le \pi$; $u(0, t) = 0$, $u(\pi, t) = 0$, $t \ge 0$.

2. $u_{tt} - u_{xx} + u = 0$, $0 < x < \pi$, $t > 0$; $u(x, 0) = 0$, $u_t(x, 0) = \sin^3 x$, $0 \le x \le \pi$; $u(0, t) = 0$, $u(\pi, t) = 0$, $t \ge 0$.

3. $u_{tt} - u_{xx} + u = 0$, $0 < x < \pi$, $t > 0$; $u(x, 0) = 0$, $u_t(x, 0) = 1 + \cos^3 x$, $0 \le x \le \pi$; $u_x(0, t) = 0$, $u_x(\pi, t) = 0$, $t \ge 0$.

4. $u_{tt} - u_{xx} - 2u_x = 0$, $0 < x < 1$, $t > 0$; $u(x, 0) = e^{-x}(2 \sin 2\pi x - 3 \sin 5\pi x)$, $0 \le x \le 1$; $u_t(x, 0) = 0$, $0 \le x \le 1$; $u(0, t) = 0$, $u(1, t) = 0$, $t \ge 0$.

5. $u_{tt} + u_t - u_{xx} = 0$, $0 < x < \pi$, $t > 0$; $u(x, 0) = 0$, $u_t(x, 0) = \sin^3 (x/2)$, $0 \le x \le \pi$; $u(0, t) = 0$, $u_x(\pi, t) = 0$, $t \ge 0$.

In Problems 6 through 9, find all particular solutions of each of the following partial differential equations satisfying the given initial and boundary conditions.

6. $u_{tt} - x^2 u_{xx} - x u_x = 0$, $1 < x < e$, $t > 0$; $u(x, 0) = 0$, $u(1, t) = 0$, $u_x(e, t) = 0$.

7. $u_{tt} - u_{xx} + 2u_t - 2u_x + u = 0$, $0 < x < \pi$, $t > 0$; $u_t(x, 0) = 0$, $u(0, t) = 0$, $u(\pi, t) = 0$.

8. $u_{tt} - x^2 u_{xx} = 0$, $1 < x < 2$, $t > 0$; $u(x, 0) = 0$, $u(1, t) = 0$, $u(2, t) = 0$.

9. $u_{tt} - [x^2/(1 + t)^2](u_{xx}) = 0$, $1 < x < 2$, $t > 0$; $u(x, 0) = 0$, $u(1, t) = 0$, $u(2, t) = 0$.

¥¹

$$C_m = \frac{\int_0^\pi f(x) \sin m x \, dx}{\int_0^\pi \sin^2 m x \, dx}$$

Chapter 4

Green's Function and Sturm-Liouville Problems

In Section 9 of Chapter 3 we introduced the method of separation of variables to solve an initial-boundary value problem for the damped wave equation. We saw that the method leads to the consideration of two ordinary differential equations, both involving a parameter λ. In contrast to an initial value problem in which values of the unknown function and its derivatives are prescribed at a single point, we found that the solution of the differential equation in the space variable has to satisfy conditions prescribed at each end of the interval in which the solution is sought. Such conditions are called boundary conditions, and problems of such a type are generally known as boundary value problems. In this chapter we shall study some of the properties of boundary value problems for linear second-order differential equations. Our discussion of these problems will lead us to some important concepts, such as Green's function and eigenfunction expansion of arbitrary functions, which play a fundamental role in the application and extension of the method of separation of variables to more general problems in partial differential equations.

1. Homogeneous Boundary Value Problems

Consider the general linear second-order differential equation

(1.1) $$A(x)u'' + B(x)u' + C(x)u = g(x)$$

on the interval $a \leq x \leq b$, where we assume the functions A, A', B, C, and g are continuous and $A(x) > 0$ for all x in the interval. If $A' = B$, then we can write the equation in the form

$$\frac{d}{dx}\left[A(x)\frac{du}{dx} \right] + C(x)u = g(x)$$

121

called the self-adjoint form. With our assumptions on the functions A, B, and C, it is always possible to transform equation (1.1) into an equivalent differential equation that is in self-adjoint form. Indeed, if we multiply both sides of equation (1.1) by the function

$$\frac{1}{A} \exp\left(\int \frac{B}{A} dx\right)$$

the equation becomes

(1.2) $$Lu \equiv \frac{d}{dx}\left[p(x)\frac{du}{dx}\right] + q(x)u = f(x)$$

where

$$p(x) = \exp\left(\int \frac{B}{A} dx\right), \qquad q(x) = \frac{C(x)}{A(x)} p(x), \qquad f(x) = \frac{g(x)}{A(x)} p(x)$$

Clearly, the functions p, p', q, and f are again continuous and $p(x) > 0$ on the interval $a \leq x \leq b$. The self-adjoint differential equation (1.2) is known as an equation of Sturm-Liouville type. For the most part in this chapter, we shall be concerned with this equation.

In this section we consider the problem of finding a solution of the homogeneous differential equation

(1.3) $$Lu \equiv \frac{d}{dx}\left[p(x)\frac{du}{dx}\right] + q(x)u = 0 \qquad (a \leq x \leq b)$$

which satisfies the homogeneous boundary conditions

(1.4)
$$B_1(u) \equiv \alpha u(a) + \beta u'(a) = 0$$
$$B_2(u) \equiv \gamma u(b) + \delta u'(b) = 0$$

The coefficients α, β, γ, and δ are real constants such that $\alpha^2 + \beta^2 \neq 0$ and $\gamma^2 + \delta^2 \neq 0$. Clearly, the problem (1.3), (1.4) has at least one solution, namely, the trivial solution $u = 0$. However, this solution has little practical importance. The significant question is whether the problem (1.3), (1.4) has any nontrivial solution and, if so, to find all such solutions.

Thus, let u_1 and u_2 be any two linearly independent solutions of equation (1.3) on the interval $a \leq x \leq b$. That such solutions exist follows from the theory of ordinary differential equations, with our assumptions on the functions p and q. Suppose that u is a nontrivial solution of the problem (1.3), (1.4). Then there exist constants c_1 and c_2, not both zero, such that

(1.5) $$u(x) = c_1 u_1(x) + c_2 u_2(x) \qquad (a \leq x \leq b)$$

Since u satisfies the boundary conditions (1.4) and because of the linearity of these conditions, we see that

(1.6)
$$B_1(u) \equiv c_1 B_1(u_1) + c_2 B_1(u_2) = 0$$
$$B_2(u) \equiv c_1 B_2(u_1) + c_2 B_2(u_2) = 0$$

a system of homogeneous algebraic equations in c_1 and c_2. The fact that c_1 and c_2 are not both zero requires that the determinant of coefficients must vanish; that is,

$$(1.7) \qquad \begin{vmatrix} B_1(u_1) & B_1(u_2) \\ B_2(u_1) & B_2(u_2) \end{vmatrix} = 0$$

Hence, if this condition does not hold, then problem (1.3), (1.4) has only the trivial solution.

On the other hand, if condition (1.7) is satisfied, then the two equations in (1.6) differ only by constant factor. Hence, we can use either one of the equations to derive a relationship between the constants c_1 and c_2, and in this way obtain a nontrivial solution of the problem. For instance, from the first equation we may take $c_1 = B_1(u_2)$ and $c_2 = -B_1(u_1)$. Then

$$(1.8) \qquad u(x) = B_1(u_2)u_1(x) - B_1(u_1)u_2(x)$$

is a nontrivial solution of the problem (1.3), (1.4). From the linear homogeneous nature of the problem it follows that $v(x) = Cu(x)$ is also a solution for any value of the constant C. Thus, we obtain an infinite family of nontrivial solutions. In fact, it is true that if the problem (1.3), (1.4) has a nontrivial solution u, then all other solutions of the problem are of the form $v(x) = Cu(x)$, where C is a constant.

To verify the last statement, suppose that v is any other solution of the problem. Since both u and v satisfy the first of boundary conditions (1.4), we have

$$\alpha u(a) + \beta u'(a) = 0$$
$$\alpha v(a) + \beta v'(a) = 0$$

which is a system of homogeneous equations for the constants α and β. By assumption, α and β are not both zero. Hence, the determinant of the system must vanish; that is,

$$(1.9) \qquad W(u, v; a) = \begin{vmatrix} u(a) & u'(a) \\ v(a) & v'(a) \end{vmatrix} = 0$$

This determinant is precisely the Wronskian of u and v evaluated at $x = a$. Now we recall that whenever the Wronskian of two solutions of equation (1.3) vanishes at a point in $a \le x \le b$, it vanishes identically on that interval. Therefore, (1.9) implies that $W(u, v; x) = 0$ for $a \le x \le b$, which in turn implies that u and v are linearly dependent; that is, $v(x) = Cv(x)$ for some constant C.

We summarize the results we have obtained above in the following theorem.

THEOREM 1.1.   *A necessary and sufficient condition for the problem (1.3), (1.4) to have a nontrivial solution is that for any two linearly independent solutions of (1.3), the condition (1.7) holds. In such a case, all solutions of the problem are given by $v(x) = Cu(x)$, where u is any nontrivial solution of the problem and C is an arbitrary constant.*

Example 1.1. Consider the boundary value problem

$$u'' + u = 0, \qquad u(0) = 0, \qquad u(\pi) = 0$$

The general solution of the differential equation is

$$u(x) = c_1 \sin x + c_2 \cos x$$

Since the determinant

$$\begin{vmatrix} \sin 0 & \cos 0 \\ \sin \pi & \cos \pi \end{vmatrix} = 0$$

the problem has nontrivial solutions. In fact, applying the boundary conditions to the general solution, we find that $c_2 = 0$ and c_1 is arbitrary. Hence, the solutions are given by

$$u(x) = C \sin x$$

where C is an arbitrary constant.

Example 1.2. Consider the problem

$$u'' + \tfrac{1}{4}u = 0, \qquad u(0) = 0, \qquad u(\pi) = 0$$

The general solution of the equation in this case is

$$u(x) = c_1 \sin \tfrac{1}{2}x + c_2 \cos \tfrac{1}{2}x$$

Since the determinant

$$\begin{vmatrix} \sin 0 & \cos 0 \\ \sin \dfrac{\pi}{2} & \cos \dfrac{\pi}{2} \end{vmatrix} = -1$$

the problem has only the trivial solution $u = 0$. In fact, if we apply the boundary conditions to the general solution, we find immediately that $c_1 = c_2 = 0$.

Exercises 4.1

In Problems 1 through 5, reduce the given differential equation to the self-adjoint form (1.2).

1. $u'' + bu' + cu = 0, 0 \le x \le 1$, b and c are real numbers.

2. $xu'' + 2u' + xu = 0, 0 < a \le x \le b$.

3. $xu'' + xu' + u = 0, 0 < a \le x \le b$.

4. $x^2u'' + xu' + u = 0, 0 < a \le x \le b$.

5. $xu'' + (1 - x)u' + u = 0, 0 < a \le x \le b$.

In Problems 6 through 14, determine if the problem has a nontrivial solution and, if so, find the solution.

6. $u'' = 0, \ 0 \le x \le 1$; (a) $u(0) + u'(0) = 0, \ u(1) = 0$; (b) $u(0) + u'(0) = 0, u'(1) = 0$.

7. $u'' + u = 0, 0 \le x \le \pi/2; u(0) = 0, u'(\pi/2) = 0$.

8. $u'' - u = 0, 0 \le x \le 1; u(0) + u'(0) = 0; u(1) = 0.$

9. $u'' - 4u = 0, 0 \le x \le 1; u(0) + u'(0), u(1) = 0.$

10. $u'' + 4u = 0, 0 \le x \le \pi; u'(0) = 0, u(\pi) = 0.$

11. $xu'' + u' = 0, 1 \le x \le 2; u(1) = 0, u(2) - (\ln 4)u'(2) = 0.$

12. $x^2u'' + xu' - 4u = 0, 1 \le x \le 2; 2u(1) + u'(1) = 0, u(2) + u'(2) = 0.$

13. $x^2u'' - 2xu' + 2u = 0, 1 \le x \le 2; u(1) - u'(1) = 0, u(2) - 2u'(2) = 0.$

14. $(d/dx)[(1 - x^2)u'] = 0, 0 \le x < 1; u(0) = 0, u(1)$ is finite.

15. (Nonhomogeneous boundary conditions.) Consider the boundary value problem $L(u) = 0, B_1(u) = c_1, B_2(u) = c_2$, where L is the operator (1.2) and B_1, B_2 are the boundary operators given in (1.3). Let u_1 and u_2 be two linearly independent solutions of the equation $L(u) = 0.$

    (a) Show that a necessary and sufficient condition for the problem to have a unique solution is that the determinant

    $$D = \begin{vmatrix} B_1(u_1) & B_1(u_2) \\ B_2(u_1) & B_2(u_2) \end{vmatrix} \ne 0$$

    (b) If $D = 0$, show that the problem has a solution only if the constants c_1 and c_2 satisfy the equations

    $$c_1 B_2(u_2) - c_2 B_1(u_2) = 0$$
    $$c_1 B_2(u_1) - c_2 B_1(u_1) = 0$$

In Problems 16 through 23, use the result of Problem 15 to determine if the problem has solution and, if so, find the solution.

16. $u'' + u = 0, 0 \le x \le \pi$; (a) $u(0) = 1, u(\pi) = -1$; (b) $u(0) + u'(0) = 1, u(\pi) = 1$; (c) $u(0) - u'(0) = 1, u(\pi) = 0.$

17. $u'' - u = 0, 0 \le x \le 1$; (a) $u(0) = 1, u(1) - u'(1) = 0$; (b) $u'(0) = 0, u(1) + u'(1) = 1$; (c) $u'(0) = -1, u(1) + u'(1) = 0$; (d) $u(0) - u'(0) = 2, u(1) + u'(1) = 0.$

18. $u'' - 4u = 0, 0 \le x \le 1$; (a) $u(0) = 1, u(1) = 0$; (b) $u(0) = 1, 2u(1) + u'(1) = 2e^2.$

19. $u'' + 4u = 0, 0 \le x \le \pi$; (a) $u(0) = -1, u(\pi) = 1$; (b) $u(0) = -1, u'(\pi) = 1$; (c) $u(0) + u'(0) = 1, u(\pi) - u'(\pi) = 0.$

20. $xu'' + u' = 0, 1 \le x \le 2$; (a) $u(1) = 0, u'(2) = 1$; (b) $u(1) = 1, u(2) - u'(2) = 0$; (c) $u'(1) = 1, u(2) = 0.$

21. $x^2u'' + xu' + u = 0, 1 \le x \le e$; (a) $u(1) = 1, u'(e) = 0$; (b) $u(1) - u'(1) = 1, u(e) = \cos 1$; (c) $u(1) + u'(1) = 1, u(e) = \sin 1.$

2. Nonhomogeneous Problems; Green's Function

We now consider the nonhomogeneous differential equation

(2.1) $$Lu \equiv \frac{d}{dx}\left[p(x) \frac{du}{dx} \right] + q(x)u = f(x)$$

where f is a given continuous function on the interval $a \leq x \leq b$. We seek a solution of this equation that satisfies the homogeneous boundary conditions

$$(2.2) \qquad u(a) = 0, \qquad u(b) = 0$$

We have taken here the simpler boundary conditions (2.2) mainly for convenience. The results that will be obtained remain valid for the general boundary conditions (1.4), as we shall indicate at the latter part of this section.

We first consider the problem (2.1), (2.2), assuming that the corresponding homogeneous problem

$$(2.3) \qquad Lu = 0, \qquad u(a) = 0, \qquad u(b) = 0$$

has only trivial solution. As we shall see in the next section, when the problem (2.3) has a nontrivial solution, (2.1), (2.2) either has no solution or has infinitely many solutions. Our procedure here is to find a particular solution of equation (2.1) by the method of variation of parameters and then to determine the constants of integration in such a way that the boundary conditions (2.2) are also satisfied. With this purpose in mind, we shall choose two linearly independent solutions of the homogeneous equation $Lu = 0$ in such a way that each satisfies one of the boundary conditions (2.2). Thus, let u_1 be a nontrivial solution of $Lu = 0$ that satisfies the condition $u_1(a) = 0$, and let u_2 be a nontrivial solution of the equation that satisfies the condition $u_2(b) = 0$. It is clear that such solutions exist. In fact, if y_1 and y_2 are any two linearly independent solutions of the equation $Lu = 0$, then we may take, for example, $u_1(x) = y_2(a)y_1(x) - y_1(a)y_2(x)$ and $u_2(x) = y_2(b)y_1(x) - y_1(b)y_2(x)$. Since the corresponding homogeneous problem (2.3) has only trivial solution, we have $u_1(b) \neq 0$, $u_2(a) \neq 0$ and the functions u_1 and u_2 are linearly independent. Hence, the Wronskian $W(u_1, u_2; x)$ of u_1 and u_2 does not vanish; that is,

$$(2.4) \qquad W(u_1, u_2; x) = u_1(x)u_2'(x) - u_1'(x)u_2(x) \neq 0$$

for $a \leq x \leq b$. Now let

$$(2.5) \qquad u(x) = v_1(x)u_1(x) + v_2(x)u_2(x)$$

where v_1 and v_2 are functions yet to be determined. Differentiating (2.5) and setting

$$(2.6) \qquad v_1'(x)u_1(x) + v_2'(x)u_2(x) = 0$$

we have

$$(2.7) \qquad u'(x) = v_1(x)u_1'(x) + v_2(x)u_2'(x)$$

Differentiating (2.7) and substituting the result together with (2.7) and (2.5) in the differential equation (2.1), we obtain

$$(2.8) \qquad v_1'(x)u_1'(x) + v_2'(x)u_2'(x) = \frac{f(x)}{p(x)}$$

for which we have used the fact that $Lu_1 = 0$ and $Lu_2 = 0$. In view of (2.4), we can solve for v'_1 and v'_2 from equations (2.6) and (2.8). We find

$$v'_1(x) = \frac{-u_2(x)f(x)}{p(x)W(u_1, u_2; x)}$$

$$v'_2(x) = \frac{u_1(x)f(x)}{p(x)W(u_1, u_2; x)}$$

and therefore

$$v_1(x) = -\int_{c_1}^x \frac{u_2(\xi)f(\xi)\,d\xi}{p(\xi)W(u_1, u_2; \xi)}$$

(2.9)

$$v_2(x) = \int_{c_2}^x \frac{u_1(\xi)f(\xi)\,d\xi}{p(\xi)W(u_1, u_2; \xi)}$$

where c_1 and c_2 are arbitrary constants. Substituting these functions in (2.5), we obtain a particular solution of (2.1) given by

(2.10) $$u(x) = u_1(x)\int_{c_1}^x \frac{-u_2(\xi)f(\xi)\,d\xi}{p(\xi)W(u_1, u_2; \xi)} + u_2(x)\int_{c_2}^x \frac{u_1(\xi)f(\xi)\,d\xi}{p(\xi)W(u_1, u_2; \xi)}$$

We now determine the constants c_1 and c_2 in (2.10) so that u satisfies also the boundary conditions (2.2). Setting $u = 0$ for $x = a$ and noting that $u_1(a) = 0$, we find $c_2 = a$. In the same way, setting $u = 0$ for $x = b$ and noting that $u_2(b) = 0$, we have $c_1 = b$. Substituting these values for c_1 and c_2 in (2.10), we finally have

(2.11) $$u(x) = \int_a^x \frac{u_1(\xi)u_2(x)f(\xi)}{p(\xi)W(u_1, u_2; \xi)}\,d\xi + \int_x^b \frac{u_1(x)u_2(\xi)f(\xi)}{p(\xi)W(u_1, u_2; \xi)}\,d\xi$$

for the solution of the problem (2.1), (2.2).

If we define

(2.12) $$G(x; \xi) = \begin{cases} \dfrac{u_1(x)u_2(\xi)}{p(\xi)W(u_1, u_2; \xi)} & (a \le x \le \xi) \\[2ex] \dfrac{u_1(\xi)u_2(x)}{p(\xi)W(u_1, u_2; \xi)} & (\xi \le x \le b) \end{cases}$$

then the solution (2.11) can be written simply as

(2.13) $$u(x) = \int_a^b G(x; \xi)f(\xi)\,d\xi$$

The function G defined in (2.12) is called the Green's function for the differential operator L, corresponding to the boundary conditions (2.2).

It is left as an exercise to verify that (2.13) with (2.12) indeed satisfies equation (2.1) and the boundary conditions (2.2). The uniqueness of this solution follows from the assumption that the corresponding homogeneous problem (2.3) has only trivial solution.

The definition of the Green's function given above holds for the general second-order differential equation (1.1). However, the fact that the operator L is self-adjoint leads to the important result that the quantity $p(x)W(u_1, u_2; x)$ is a constant. To see this, we note that

$$\frac{d}{dx}[p(x)W(u_1, u_2; x)] = \frac{d}{dx}\{p(x)[u_1(x)u_2'(x) - u_1'(x)u_2(x)]\}$$

$$= \frac{d}{dx}[p(x)u_1(x)u_2'(x)] - \frac{d}{dx}[p(x)u_1'(x)u_2(x)]$$

$$= u_1(x)\left\{\frac{d}{dx}[p(x)u_2'(x)] + q(x)u_2(x)\right\}$$

$$- u_2(x)\left\{\frac{d}{dx}[p(x)u_1'(x)] + q(x)u_1(x)\right\}$$

$$= u_1 L u_2 - u_2 L u_1$$

$$= 0$$

since both u_1 and u_2 satisfy the equation $Lu = 0$. Hence, for the self-adjoint operator L, the Green's function (2.12) becomes

(2.14)
$$G(x; \xi) = \begin{cases} \dfrac{u_1(x)u_2(\xi)}{K} & (a \le x \le \xi) \\[2mm] \dfrac{u_2(x)u_1(\xi)}{K} & (\xi \le x \le b) \end{cases}$$

where $K = p(x)W(u_1, u_2; x)$ is a constant.

As can be easily verified from (2.12) or (2.14), the Green's function possesses the following properties:

(i) For each ξ, the Green's function satisfies the equation

$$\frac{d}{dx}\left(p\frac{dG}{dx}\right) + qG = 0 \quad (a < x < b, x \ne \xi)$$

(ii) Green's function is continuous at $x = \xi$; that is,

(2.15)
$$G(\xi + 0; \xi) = G(\xi - 0; \xi)$$

(iii) Green's function satisfies the boundary conditions of the problem; that is, $G(a; \xi) = 0$, $G(b; \xi) = 0$.

(iv) The derivative of the Green's function is discontinuous at $x = \xi$, where it has a jump of magnitude

$$\frac{dG}{dx}(\xi + 0; \xi) - \frac{dG}{dx}(\xi - 0; \xi) = \frac{1}{p(\xi)}$$

(v) For a self-adjoint operator, Green's function is symmetric with respect to the variables x and ξ; that is,

$$G(x; \xi) = G(\xi; x)$$

Actually, properties (i) through (iv) determine the Green's function uniquely. This means that if we construct a function that satisfies all the properties (i)–(iv), the function will be of the form (2.12) or of the form (2.14) if the differential equation is self-adjoint.

Let us summarize in the following theorem the result we have obtained above.

THEOREM 2.1.   *If the homogeneous problem (2.3) has only the trivial solution, then the Green's function (2.12) exists and the nonhomogeneous problem (2.1), (2.2) has a unique solution given by the formula (2.13).*

Example 2.1.   Find Green's function and the solution of the problem

$$\frac{d^2u}{dx^2} = f(x) \qquad\qquad (0 \le x \le 1)$$

$$u(0) = 0, \qquad u(1) = 0$$

Solution: It is easily verified that the corresponding homogeneous problem has only the trivial solution, and so the Green's function exists. The differential equation $u'' = 0$ has the general solution

$$u(x) = Ax + B$$

A solution that satisfies the condition $u(0) = 0$ is easily found to be $u_1(x) = x$; and a solution that satisfies the condition $u(1) = 0$ is given by $u_2(x) = x - 1$. These two functions are linearly independent, with the Wronksian being equal to

$$W(u_1, u_2; x) = u_1 u_2' - u_1' u_2 = 1$$

Hence, by (2.12), Green's function is

$$G(x; \xi) = \begin{cases} x(\xi - 1) & (0 \le x \le \xi) \\ \xi(x - 1) & (\xi \le x \le 1) \end{cases}$$

and the solution of the problem is

$$u(x) = \int_0^1 G(x; \xi) f(\xi) \, d\xi$$

In particular, if $f(x) = 1$, we find $u(x) = x(x - 1)/2$, which is readily verified as the solution.

Example 2.2.   Find Green's function and the solution of the problem

$$\frac{d^2u}{dx^2} + u = f(x) \qquad\qquad (0 \le x \le 1)$$

$$u(0) = 0, \qquad u(1) = 0$$

Solution: The general solution of the corresponding homogeneous equation is

$$u(x) = A \cos x + B \sin x$$

For this solution to satisfy also the boundary conditions, we find $A = B = 0$; thus, the corresponding homogeneous problem has only trivial solution. To construct the Green's function, we take $u_1(x) = \sin x$ and $u_2(x) = \cos 1 \sin x - \sin 1 \cos x = \sin(x - 1)$ so that $u_1(x) = 0$ and $u_2(1) = 0$. The Wronskian of these functions is

$$W(u_1, u_2; x) = u_1(x)u_2'(x) - u_1'(x)u_2(x)$$
$$= \sin x \cos(x - 1) - \cos x \sin(x - 1)$$
$$= \sin[x - (x - 1)] = \sin 1$$

Hence, by (2.12), the Green's function is

$$G(x; \xi) = \begin{cases} \dfrac{\sin x \sin(\xi - 1)}{\sin 1} & (0 \le x \le \xi) \\[2em] \dfrac{\sin \xi \sin(x - 1)}{\sin 1} & (\xi \le x \le 1) \end{cases}$$

and the solution is

$$u(x) = \int_0^1 G(x; \xi) f(\xi) \, d\xi$$

In particular, if $f(x) = 1$, we find

$$u(x) = \frac{\sin(x - 1) - \sin x}{\sin 1} + 1$$

The solution of the boundary value problem consisting of equation (2.1) and the more general boundary conditions (1.4) can also be given in the form (2.13), where G is the corresponding Green's function for the problem, provided the related homogeneous problem has only trivial solution. In such a case, the Green's function can likewise be constructed from properties (i), (ii), and (iv) of (2.15) with property (iii) replaced by the conditions

$$\alpha G(a; \xi) + \beta G'(a; \xi) = 0$$
$$\gamma G(b; \xi) + \delta G'(b; \xi) = 0$$

Here we use prime to denote differentiation with respect to the variable x. Thus, the Green's function in this case is also defined by (2.12), provided u_1 and u_2 are linearly independent solutions of $Lu = 0$ such that u_1 satisfies the boundary condition at $x = a$ and u_2 satisfies the boundary condition at $x = b$.

Example 2.3.   Find the Green's function for the problem

$$\frac{d^2 u}{dx^2} = f(x) \qquad\qquad (0 \le x \le 1)$$

$$u(0) = 0, \qquad u(1) + u'(1) = 0$$

Solution: It is easy to verify that the related homogeneous problem has only the trivial solution $u = 0$. Now, from the general solution $u(x) = Ax + B$ of the homogeneous equation $u'' = 0$, we determine two linearly independent solutions

u_1 and u_2 that satisfy the boundary conditions of the problem at $x = 0$ and $x = 1$, respectively. We find $u_1(x) = x$ and $u_2(x) = x - 2$ for which

$$W(u_1, u_2; x) = 2$$

Hence, by (2.12), the Green's function is

$$G(x; \xi) = \begin{cases} \dfrac{x(\xi - 2)}{2} & (0 \le x \le \xi) \\[3mm] \dfrac{\xi(x - 2)}{2} & (\xi \le x \le 1) \end{cases}$$

It is easily seen that this function satisfies properties (i), (ii), and (iv) in (2.15) and the boundary conditions of the problem. Moreover, $G(x; \xi) = G(\xi; x)$, since $(d/dx)^2$ is self-adjoint.

The solution of the boundary value problem

$$(2.16) \qquad Lu = f(x), \qquad u(a) = A, \qquad u(b) = B$$

which involves nonhomogeneous differential equations and boundary conditions, can be found by combining the solution of problem (2.1), (2.2) and the solution of the problem

$$(2.17) \qquad Lu = 0, \qquad u(a) = A, \qquad u(b) = B$$

Thus, we need only to find the solution of problem (2.17). With the functions u_1 and u_2 used to construct the Green's function (2.12), let us assume a solution in the form

$$u(x) = c_1 u_1(x) + c_2 u_2(x)$$

where c_1 and c_2 are constants to be determined. Applying the boundary conditions and noting that $u_1(a) = 0$, $u_2(b) = 0$, we obtain

$$u(a) = c_2 u_2(a) = A, \qquad u(b) = c_1 u_1(b) = B$$

Since

$$u_1(b) \ne 0 \qquad \text{and} \qquad u_2(a) \ne 0$$

we find

$$c_1 = \frac{B}{u_1(b)}, \qquad c_2 = \frac{A}{u_2(a)}$$

Therefore, the solution of problem (2.16) is

$$(2.18) \qquad u(x) = \int_a^b G(x; \xi) f(\xi)\, d\xi + \frac{B}{u_1(b)} u_1(x) + \frac{A}{u_2(a)} u_2(x)$$

Example 2.4. Find the solution of the nonhomogeneous problem

$$\frac{d^2 u}{dx^2} + u = f$$

$$u(0) = A, \qquad u(1) = B$$

Solution: Referring to Example 2.2, we take $u_1(x) = \sin x$ and $u_2(x) = \sin(x - 1)$. Then, according to (2.18), the solution of the problem is

$$u(x) = \int_0^1 G(x; \xi) f(\xi) \, d\xi + \frac{B}{\sin 1} \sin x - \frac{A}{\sin 1} \sin(x - 1)$$

where G is the Green's function determined in Example 2.2.

Exercises 4.2

1. Find the Green's function for the operator $L = d^2/dx^2$, $0 \le x \le 1$, subject to the given boundary conditions: (a) $u(0) = 0$, $u'(0) = 0$; (b) $u'(0) = 0$, $u(1) - u'(1) = 0$; (c) $u(0) + u'(0) = 0$, $u'(1) = 0$.

2. Find the Green's function for the operator $L = (d^2/dx^2) + 1$, $0 \le x \le \pi$, subject to the given boundary conditions: (a) $u(0) = 0$, $u'(\pi) = 0$; (b) $u'(0) = 0$, $u(\pi) = 0$.

In Problems 3 through 6, find the Green's function for the problem and give the solution.

3. $u'' - 2u' + 2u = f(x)$, $0 \le x \le \pi/2$; $u(0) = 0$, $u(\pi/2) = 0$.

4. $x^2 u'' - 2xu' + 2u = f(x)$, $1 \le x \le 2$; $u(1) - u'(1) = 0$, $u(2) = 0$.

5. $x^2 u'' - xu' + u = f(x)$, $1 \le x \le 2$; $u(1) - u'(1) = 0$, $u(2) + 2u'(2) = 0$.

6. $(d/dx)[(x + 1)u'] = f(x)$, $0 \le x \le 1$; $u(0) = 0$, $u'(1) = 0$.

7. Verify that the function u defined by formula (2.13) satisfies the differential equation (2.1) and the boundary conditions (2.2).

8. Determine the Green's function (2.12) from the properties (i)–(iv) in (2.15). *Hint:* Let u_1 and u_2 be two linearly independent solutions of $Lu = 0$ such that $u_1(a) = 0$ and $u_2(b) = 0$, and set

$$G(x; \xi) = \begin{cases} C_1(\xi) u_1(x) & (a \le x \le \xi) \\ C_2(\xi) u_2(x) & (\xi \le x \le b) \end{cases}$$

9. Use the definition (2.12) and verify that

   (a) $(\partial G/\partial \xi)(x, a)$ satisfies the equation (2.1) and the conditions

$$\frac{\partial G}{\partial \xi}(a, a) = \frac{-1}{p(a)}, \qquad \frac{\partial G}{\partial \xi}(b, a) = 0$$

   (b) $(\partial G/\partial \xi)(x, b)$ satisfies the equation (2.1) and the conditions

$$\frac{\partial G}{\partial \xi}(b, b) = \frac{+1}{p(b)}, \qquad \frac{\partial G}{\partial \xi}(a, b) = 0$$

10. From the results of Problem 9 show that

$$u(x) = \int_a^b G(x, \xi) f(\xi) \, d\xi - Ap(a) \frac{\partial G}{\partial \xi}(x, a) + Bp(b) \frac{\partial G}{\partial \xi}(x, b)$$

   is a solution of the nonhomogeneous problem (2.16).

11. Verify that the solution given in Problem 10 agrees with (2.18).

12. Find the solution of the problem

$$u'' + 4u = f(x) \qquad\qquad (0 \le x \le 1)$$
$$u(0) = A, \qquad u(1) = B$$

13. Find the solution of the problem

$$u'' + k^2 u = f(x) \qquad\qquad (0 \le x \le 1)$$
$$u(0) - u'(0) = A, \qquad u(1) = B$$

where A and B are not both zero, and determine the values of k for which the problem has no solution.

In Problem 14 through 16, find the Green's function for the given operator subject to the given boundary conditions.

14. $L = x(d^2/dx^2) + (d/dx)$, $0 < x < 1$, $u(0)$ is finite, $u(1) = 0$.

15. $L = x^2(d^2/dx^2) + x(d/dx) - n^2$, $n > 0$, $0 < x < 1$; $u(0)$ is finite, $u(1) = 0$.

16. $(1 - x^2)(d^2/dx^2) - 2x(d/dx)$, $0 < x < 1$; $u(0) = 0$, $u(1)$ is finite.

17. Show that the Green's function for the operator

$$L = \frac{d^2}{dx^2} - s^2 \qquad (-\infty < x < \infty, \ (s \text{ real constant} > 0))$$

with the boundary conditions $u = 0$ as $|x| \to \infty$ is given by

$$G(x; \xi) = \frac{-1}{2s} e^{-s|x - \xi|}$$

3. Modified Green's Function

In the preceding section we were able to obtain a unique solution of the problem (2.1), (2.2) under the assumption that the related homogeneous problem (2.3) has only trivial solution. Under that assumption, the Green's function (2.12) for the problem is uniquely determined. We now consider the case when the homogeneous problem (2.3) has a nontrivial solution. In such a case, the Green's function (2.12) does not exist, since the functions u_1 and u_2 can no longer be linearly independent. In fact, we shall show that the problem (2.1), (2.2) in this case either has no solution or has infinitely many solutions. We first establish the following lemma.

LEMMA 3.1. (Green's Formula) *If u and v are twice continuously differentiable on the interval $a \le x \le b$, then*

(3.1) $$\int_a^b [uLv - vLu] \, dx = \left[p\left(u \frac{dv}{dx} - v \frac{du}{dx} \right) \right]_a^b$$

Proof: We have

$$
\begin{aligned}
\int_a^b uLv\,dx &= \int_a^b u\left[\frac{d}{dx}\left(p\frac{dv}{dx}\right) + qv\right]dx \\
&= \int_a^b u\frac{d}{dx}\left(p\frac{dv}{dx}\right)dx + \int_a^b quv\,dx
\end{aligned}
$$

(3.2)

Integrating by parts twice the first integral term on the right of (3.2), we find

$$
\begin{aligned}
\int_a^b u\frac{d}{dx}\left(p\frac{dv}{dx}\right)dx &= p\left[u\frac{dv}{dx}\right]_a^b - \int_a^b p\frac{du}{dx}\frac{dv}{dx}\,dx \\
&= \left[p\left(u\frac{dv}{dx} - v\frac{du}{dx}\right)\right]_a^b + \int_a^b v\frac{d}{dx}\left(p\frac{du}{dx}\right)dx
\end{aligned}
$$

Substituting this in (3.2) we obtain

$$
\begin{aligned}
\int_a^b uLv\,dx &= \int_a^b v\left[\frac{d}{dx}\left(p\frac{du}{dx}\right) + qu\right]dx + \left[p\left(u\frac{dv}{dx} - v\frac{du}{dx}\right)\right]_a^b \\
&= \int_a^b vLu\,dx + \left[p\left(u\frac{dv}{dx} - v\frac{du}{dx}\right)\right]_a^b
\end{aligned}
$$

which yields (3.1).

Now let u_0 be a nontrivial solution of the problem (2.3) and suppose that the problem (2.1), (2.2) has a solution u. Let us multiply both sides of equation (2.1) by u_0 and consider the integral

(3.3)
$$
\int_a^b u_0 Lu\,dx = \int_a^b u_0 f\,dx
$$

By Lemma (3.1) we have

(3.4)
$$
\int_a^b u_0 Lu\,dx = \int_a^b uLu_0\,dx + \left[p\left(u_0\frac{du}{dx} - u\frac{du_0}{dx}\right)\right]_a^b
$$

Since both u and u_0 vanish at $x = a$ and $x = b$, and $Lu_0 = 0$, the right-hand side of (3.4) reduces to zero and hence, by (3.3), we have

(3.5)
$$
\int_a^b u_0 f\,dx = 0
$$

This shows that when (2.3) has a nontrivial solution u_0, equation (3.5) must hold in order that the problem (2.1), (2.2) may have a solution. Therefore, if condition (3.5) is not satisfied, then the problem (2.1), (2.2) has no solution whatsoever. In other words, (3.5) is a necessary condition for the existence of a solution of the problem (2.1), (2.2) in the event that the related homogeneous problem (2.3) has a nontrivial solution u_0.

The condition (3.5) turns out to be also sufficient to ensure the existence of a solution of the problem (2.1), (2.2). As a matter of fact, if (3.5) holds, we can construct a modified Green's function analogous to (2.12) such that a solution of (2.1), (2.2) may be given in the form (2.13). Observe, however, that there is no longer uniqueness of solution, since we can always add to the solution any constant multiple of u_0. Before we proceed to the determination of a modified Green's function, let us consider a simple example to illustrate the various points pointed out above.

Example 3.1.   Find the solution of the nonhomogeneous problem

(3.6)
$$\frac{d^2u}{dx^2} + \pi^2 u = 1$$

$$u(0) = 0, \qquad u(1) = 0$$

Solution: A particular solution of the differential equation is easily seen to be $u_p(x) = 1/\pi^2$; therefore the general solution of the equation is

$$u(x) = \frac{1}{\pi^2} + c_1 \sin \pi x + c_2 \cos \pi x$$

Applying the boundary conditions of (3.6), we find

$$\frac{1}{\pi^2} + c_2 = 0, \qquad \frac{1}{\pi^2} - c_2 = 0$$

which yield contradictory results for c_2. This shows that the problem (3.6) has no solution. As a matter of fact, we observe that the corresponding homogeneous problem $u'' + \pi^2 u = 0$, $u(0) = 0$, $u(1) = 0$ has a nontrivial solution $u_0(x) = \sin \pi x$ for which $\int_0^1 1 \cdot \sin \pi x \, dx \neq 0$, violating condition (3.5).

On the other hand, if we take the nonhomogeneous term in (3.6) to be $f(x) = 2x - 1$ so that

$$\int_0^1 (2x - 1) \sin \pi x \, dx = 0$$

then by a similar elementary method we find infinitely many solutions given by

$$u(x) = \frac{1}{\pi^2} \cos \pi x + \frac{2x - 1}{\pi^2} + C \sin \pi x$$

where C is an arbitrary constant.

Incidentally, the preceding example showed that whenever a particular solution of the differential equation can be found by some other method, it is possible to treat a nonhomogeneous boundary value problem without resorting to Green's function.

We now proceed to the construction of a modified Green's function for the problem (2.1), (2.2) in the case that u_0 is a nontrivial solution of the related homogeneous problem (2.3). We assume that condition (3.5) holds. Let u_2 be a solution of the equation $Lu = 0$, which does not satisfy any of the boundary conditions (2.2). Then u_0 and u_2 are linearly independent (see Problem 7). Hence, by (2.10),

$$(3.7) \qquad u(x) = u_0(x) \int_{c_1}^x \frac{-u_2(\xi)f(\xi)\,d\xi}{K} + u_2(x) \int_{c_2}^x \frac{u_0(\xi)f(\xi)\,d\xi}{K}$$

is a solution of equation (2.1) for arbitrary constants c_1 and c_2. Here $K = p(x)W(u_0, u_2; x)$; this is a constant, since L is self-adjoint. Applying the boundary conditions (2.2) and noting that u_0 satisfies those conditions, we find

$$(3.8) \qquad u_2(a) \int_{c_2}^a \frac{u_0(\xi)f(\xi)\,d\xi}{K} = 0, \qquad u_2(b) \int_{c_2}^b \frac{u_0(\xi)f(\xi)\,d\xi}{K} = 0$$

Since $u_2(a) \neq 0$ and $u_2(b) \neq 0$, equations (3.8) will hold if and only if the integral terms vanish for some value of c_2. In view of condition (3.5), it suffices to take $c_2 = a$ or $c_2 = b$, leaving the other constant c_1 arbitrary. Let us choose $c_1 = c_2 = a$. Then the solution (3.7) becomes

$$(3.9) \qquad u(x) = \int_a^x \frac{u_0(\xi)u_2(x) - u_0(x)u_2(\xi)}{K} f(\xi)\,d\xi$$

It is easy to verify that (3.9) is a solution of the problem (2.1), (2.2), subject to the condition (3.5). This solution is not unique because we can add to (3.9) any constant multiple of u_0. In fact, if we add the term

$$u_0(x) \int_a^b \frac{u_2(\xi)f(\xi)}{K}\,d\xi \equiv u_0(x) \int_a^x \frac{u_2(\xi)f(\xi)}{K}\,d\xi$$

$$+ u_0(x) \int_x^b \frac{u_2(\xi)f(\xi)}{K}\,d\xi$$

to the solution (3.9), we obtain

$$(3.10) \qquad \begin{aligned} u(x) &= \int_a^x \frac{u_0(\xi)u_2(x)}{K} f(\xi)\,d\xi + \int_x^b \frac{u_0(x)u_2(\xi)}{K} f(\xi)\,d\xi \\ &= \int_a^b G^*(x; \xi)f(\xi)\,d\xi \end{aligned}$$

where

$$(3.11) \qquad G^*(x; \xi) = \begin{cases} \dfrac{u_0(x)u_2(\xi)}{K} & (a \leq x \leq \xi) \\[2ex] \dfrac{u_0(\xi)u_2(x)}{K} & (x \leq \xi \leq b) \end{cases}$$

The function G^* defined in (3.11) is called a modified Green's function. It is easily seen that G^* possesses all the properties of a regular Green's function listed in (2.15), except property (iii). Here, L must be self-adjoint, and hence K is a constant. It is clear that G^* is symmetric with respect to x and ξ.

Let us summarize the result we have obtained above in the following theorem.

THEOREM 3.1. *If the homogeneous problem* (2.3) *has a nontrivial solution* u_0, *then the nonhomogeneous problem* (2.1), (2.2) *has a solution if and only if condition* (3.5) *holds. If* (3.5) *holds, then a solution of the problem* (2.1), (2.2) *is given by* (3.10).

Example 3.2. Find the solution of the problem $u'' + \pi^2 u = f(x)$, $u(0) = 0$, $u(1) = 0$, assuming that

$$\int_0^1 f(x) \sin \pi x \, dx = 0$$

Solution: The function $u_0(x) = \sin \pi x$ is clearly a nontrivial solution of the corresponding homogeneous problem $u'' + \pi^2 u = 0$, $u(0) = u(1) = 0$. Let us seek a solution of the homogeneous differential equation that does not vanish at $x = 0$ and $x = 1$. We find $u_2(x) = \cos \pi x$, for which we have $K = u_0 u_2' - u_0' u_2 = -\pi$. Hence, according to (3.11),

$$G^*(x; \xi) = \begin{cases} -\dfrac{1}{\pi} \sin \pi x \cos \pi \xi & (0 \leq x \leq \xi) \\[2mm] -\dfrac{1}{\pi} \sin \pi \xi \cos \pi x & (\xi \leq x \leq 1) \end{cases}$$

and the solution of the problem is

$$u(x) = \int_0^1 G^*(x; \xi) f(\xi) \, d\xi + C \sin \pi x$$

for any constant C.

Exercises 4.3

In Problems 1 through 5, find a modified Green's function for the given operator L subject to the given boundary conditions.

1. $L = d^2/dx^2$, $0 \leq x \leq 1$; $u'(0) = 0$, $u'(1) = 0$.
2. $L = d^2/dx^2$, $0 \leq x \leq 1$; $u(0) + u'(0) = 0$, $u(1) = 0$.
3. $L = d^2/dx^2 + 1$, $0 \leq x \leq \pi/2$; $u(0) = 0$, $u'(\pi/2) = 0$.
4. $L = x(d^2/dx^2) + (d/dx)$, $0 < x < 1$; $u(0)$ is finite, $u'(1) = 0$.
5. $L = (1 - x^2)(d^2/dx^2) - 2x(d/dx)$, $-1 < x < 1$; u is finite at $x = 1$ and $x = -1$.
6. Suppose the problem $Lu = 0$, $u(a) = 0$, $u(b) = 0$ has a nontrivial solution. Let u_1 and u_2 be two nontrivial solutions of $Lu = 0$ such that $u_1(a) = 0$ and $u_2(b) = 0$. Show that u_1 and u_2 must be linearly dependent.
7. Let u_0 be a nontrivial solution of the problem $L(u) = 0$, $u(a) = 0$, $u(b) = 0$, and let u be any solution of the equation $L(u) = 0$. Prove that u and u_0 are linearly dependent if and only if u satisfies one of the conditions $u(a) = 0$, $u(b) = 0$.
8. Verify that for the modified Green's function given in (3.11), G^* satisfies properties (i), (ii), and (iv) of (2.15) but not property (iii).

9. Let u_0 be a nontrivial solution of the problem $Lu = 0$, $u(a) = 0$, $u(b) = 0$ $(a \leq x \leq b)$ such that $\int_a^b u_0^2(x)\,dx = 1$. Show that the problem $Lu = u_0$, $u(a) = 0$, $u(b) = 0$ has no solution.

10. Determine whether the problem $u'' - 2u' + u = 1$, $0 < x < 1$; $u(0) = 0$, $2u(1) - u'(1) = 0$ has a solution.

11. Obtain the necessary condition for a solution of the problem

$$A(x)u'' + B(x)u' + C(x)u = f(x) \qquad (a \leq x \leq b)$$
$$u(a) = 0, \qquad u(b) = 0$$

to exist, assuming that the related homogeneous problem has a nontrivial solution.

4. Sturm-Liouville Problems

In Section 9 of Chapter 3 we introduced the method of separation of variables to find particular solutions of type $X(x)T(t)$ of the damped-wave equation that satisfy homogeneous initial boundary conditions. The method leads to the boundary value problem

$$(4.1) \qquad X''(x) + \lambda X(x) = 0, \qquad X(0) = 0, \qquad X(L) = 0$$

involving a parameter λ for the function X. We saw that nontrivial solutions of this problem exist only for certain exceptional values of the parameter λ.

When the method is applied to more general boundary value problems in partial differential equations, there frequently arise boundary value problems involving ordinary differential equations of the type

$$(4.2) \qquad \frac{d}{dx}\left[p(x)\frac{du}{dx} \right] + [q(x) + \lambda r(x)]u \equiv Lu + \lambda r(x)u = 0$$

together with the boundary conditions

$$(4.3) \qquad \alpha u(a) + \beta u'(a) = 0, \qquad \gamma u(b) + \delta u'(b) = 0$$

Here, λ is a parameter and r is a function that is assumed continuous and positive on the interval $a \leq x \leq b$. As before, the functions p, p', and q are assumed continuous, and p is positive on this interval. Under these conditions, the boundary value problem (4.2), (4.3) is known as a regular Sturm-Liouville problem. This is distinguished from the case when p or r vanishes at some point in the interval $[a, b]$ or when the interval is of infinite length, in which case the problem is called a singular Sturm-Liouville problem.

Other important boundary conditions that may also arise with the differential equation (4.2) are

$$(4.4) \qquad u(a) - u(b) = 0, \qquad u'(a) - u'(b) = 0$$

These are called periodic boundary conditions, since both the solution u and its derivative are required to have the same value at the end points of the interval $[a, b]$.

In this discussion we shall be concerned mainly with regular Sturm-Liouville problems. We shall establish several important though elementary results in the general theory, which will be useful in later discussion. As will be seen in the exercises, some of these results hold also in the singular case and in the case when the boundary conditions are periodic.

We note that problem (4.2), (4.3) constitutes a homogeneous boundary value problem of the type considered in Section 1 and is therefore satisfied by the trivial solution $u = 0$ for any value of the parameter λ. However, as we saw in the special case (4.1), the existence of nontrivial solutions depends on the particular value of λ. Indeed, let $u_1 = u_1(x, \lambda)$ and $u_2 = u_2(x, \lambda)$ be two linearly independent solutions of equation (4.2). Notice that u_1 and u_2 depend on both x and λ. Then, by Theorem 1.1, nontrivial solutions of (4.2), (4.3) exist if and only if the determinant of coefficients (1.7) vanishes; that is,

(4.5)
$$\begin{vmatrix} \alpha u_1(a, \lambda) + \beta u_1'(a, \lambda) & \alpha u_2(a, \lambda) + \beta u_2'(a, \lambda) \\ \gamma u_1(b, \lambda) + \delta u_1'(b, \lambda) & \gamma u_2(b, \lambda) + \delta u_2'(b, \lambda) \end{vmatrix} = 0$$

Hence, the problem (4.2), (4.3) has nontrivial solutions if and only if λ satisfies the determinantal equation (4.5). The values of λ satisfying equation (4.5) are called eigenvalues of the problem (4.2), (4.3) and the corresponding nontrivial solutions are called eigenfunctions. It follows from Theorem 1.1 that an eigenfunction corresponding to an eigenvalue is uniquely determined up to a constant factor. This means that to each eigenvalue there corresponds only one linearly independent eigenfunction. An eigenvalue having this property is said to be simple.

It is possible to show that a regular Sturm-Liouville problem has infinitely many real and simple eigenvalues λ_n, $n = 1, 2, \ldots$, which can be arranged in a monotonic increasing sequence $\lambda_1 < \lambda_2 < \cdots < \lambda_n$ such that $\lim \lambda_n = \infty$ as n tends to ∞. These properties are clearly exemplified in the particular problem (4.1) for which we found infinitely many real and increasing eigenvalues

$$\frac{\pi^2}{L^2} < \frac{4\pi^2}{L^2} < \cdots < \frac{n^2\pi^2}{L^2} < \cdots$$

which are all simple. We consider two more examples as further exhibits of these properties.

Example 4.1. Find the eigenvalues and eigenfunctions of the problem

$$u''(x) + \lambda u(x) = 0$$
$$u(0) = 0, \qquad u'(\pi) = 0$$

Solution: As in problem (4.1), it is readily shown that the present problem has only trivial solution when $\lambda \leq 0$. When $\lambda > 0$, the differential equation has the general solution

$$u(x) = c_1 \sin \sqrt{\lambda}\, x + c_2 \cos \sqrt{\lambda}\, x$$

Applying the first boundary condition, we obtain $c_2 = 0$. Thus, any eigenfunction of the problem must be of the form $u(x) = c_1 \sin \sqrt{\lambda}\, x$.

Applying the second boundary condition, we find $c_1 \sqrt{\lambda} \cos \sqrt{\lambda} \pi = 0$. Since we do not want $c_1 = 0$ and since $\lambda > 0$, we must then have $\cos \sqrt{\lambda} \pi = 0$. This implies that

$$\sqrt{\lambda} = \frac{2n - 1}{2} \qquad (n = 1, 2, \ldots)$$

Hence, the eigenvalues of the problem are

$$\lambda_n = \left(\frac{2n - 1}{2}\right)^2$$

which are real and increasing, and the corresponding eigenfunctions are

$$u_n(x) = \sin\left(\frac{2n - 1}{2}\right) x \qquad (n = 1, 2, \ldots)$$

except for constant factors.

Example 4.2. Find the eigenvalues and eigenfunctions of the problem $u''(x) + \lambda u(x) = 0$, $u(0) = 0$, $u(\pi) - u'(\pi) = 0$.

Solution: The reader can easily verify that the problem has only trivial solution when $\lambda \le 0$. Let $\lambda > 0$ and write $\lambda = k^2$, where k is a real nonzero number. Then the general solution of the differential equation is

$$u(x) = c_1 \sin kx + c_2 \cos kx$$

The first boundary condition requires $c_2 = 0$; therefore an eigenfunction of the problem must be of the form

$$u(x) = c_1 \sin kx$$

Since we do not want $c_1 = 0$, application of the second boundary condition leads to $\sin k\pi - k \cos k\pi = 0$. Thus, the eigenvalues of the problem are square of the roots of the preceding transcendental equation. Let us write the equation in the form

$$\tan k\pi = k \qquad\qquad (k \ne 0)$$

Then the roots can be determined approximately by a graphical method in the following manner: We plot the graph of the functions $y = \tan k\pi$ and $y = k$ in the same k, y coordinate system and determine the abscissas of the points of intersection of the two curves (see Fig. 4.1). We exclude $k = 0$ in this consideration because we have assumed k to be nonzero. Thus, from the figure, we see that $k_1 \cong 1.3$ so that the first eigenvalue is approximately $\lambda_1 \cong 1.69$. For very large n, we see that k_n is approximated reasonably well by $(2n + 1)/2$; hence, $\lambda_n \cong (2n + 1)^2/4$. The corresponding eigenfunctions are given by $u_n(x) = \sin \lambda_n x$. Note that while the eigenvalues λ_n may also be determined from the negative values of k_n, no new eigenfunctions are derived by considering $-k_n$, since the eigenfunctions are determined to within a constant factor.

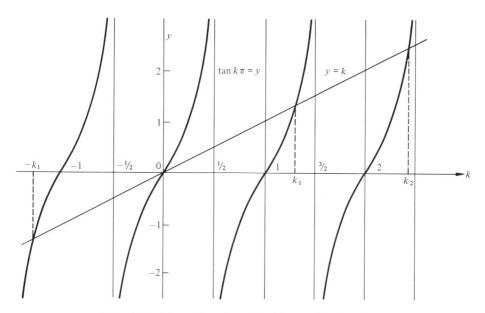

FIG. 4–1 *Eigenvalues determined by graphical method.*

Exercises 4.4

In Problems 1 through 5, find the eigenvalues and eigenfunctions of each of the given Sturm-Liouville problems.

1. $u'' + \lambda u = 0, 0 \le x \le L; u'(0) = 0, u(L) = 0.$
2. $u'' + \lambda u = 0, 0 \le x \le \pi; u'(0) = 0, u'(\pi) = 0.$
3. $u'' + \lambda u = 0, 0 \le x \le \pi; u(0) + u'(0) = 0, u(\pi) + u'(\pi) = 0.$
4. $u'' + \lambda u = 0, 0 \le x \le \pi; u(0) - u'(0) = 0, u(\pi) - u'(\pi) = 0.$
5. $u^{(iv)} - \lambda u = 0, 0 \le x \le L; u(0) = u''(0) = 0, u(L) = u''(L) = 0.$

For each of Problems 6 through 10, find the equation (4.5) and estimate graphically the eigenvalues for sufficiently large n and give the form of the eigenfunctions.

6. $u'' + \lambda u = 0, 0 \le x \le 1; u(0) + u'(0) = 0, u(1) = 0.$
7. $u'' + \lambda u = 0, 0 \le x \le \pi; u(0) = 0, u(\pi) + u'(\pi) = 0.$
8. $u'' + \lambda u = 0, 0 \le x \le 1; u'(0) = 0, u(1) - u'(1) = 0.$
9. $u'' + \lambda u = 0, 0 \le x \le \pi; u(0) + u'(0) = 0, u'(\pi) = 0.$
10. $u'' + \lambda u = 0, 0 \le x \le \pi; u(0) + u'(0) = 0, u(\pi) - u'(\pi) = 0.$
11. Find the eigenvalues and eigenfunctions of the Sturm-Liouville equation

$$\frac{d}{dx}(xu') + \frac{\lambda}{x}u = 0 \qquad (1 \le x \le e)$$

for each of the boundary conditions (a) $u(1) = 0$, $u(e) = 0$; (b) $u(1) = 0$, $u'(e) = 0$; (c) $u'(1) = 0$, $u'(e) = 0$.

12. Find the eigenvalues and eigenfunctions of the Sturm-Liouville problem

$$x^2u'' + 2xu' + \lambda u = 0 \qquad\qquad (1 \le x \le e)$$

$$u(1) = 0, \qquad u(e) = 0$$

13. Find the eigenvalues and eigenfunctions of the Sturm-Liouville problem

$$\frac{d}{dx}(x^3u') + \lambda xu = 0 \qquad\qquad (1 \le x \le e^\pi)$$

$$u(1) = 0, \qquad u(e^\pi) = 0$$

14. Find the eigenvalues and eigenfunctions of the Sturm-Liouville problem

$$\frac{d}{dx}\left(\frac{1}{x}u'\right) + \frac{\lambda}{x^3}u = 0 \qquad\qquad (1 \le x \le e)$$

$$u(1) = 0, \qquad u(e) = 0$$

15. Consider the boundary value problem

$$u'' + \lambda u = 0 \qquad\qquad (-L \le x \le L)$$

$$u(-L) - u(L) = 0, \qquad u'(-L) - u'(L) = 0$$

with periodic boundary conditions. Find the eigenvalues of the problem and show that to each eigenvalue $\lambda \ne 0$, there corresponds two linearly independent eigenfunctions.

16. Find the eigenvalues and eigenfunctions of the problem

$$u'' + \lambda u = 0 \qquad\qquad (0 \le x \le L)$$

$$u(0) - u(L) = 0, \qquad u'(0) - u'(L) = 0$$

with periodic boundary conditions.

17. The function

$$J_p(t) = \sum_{k=0}^{\infty} \frac{(-1)^k(t/2)^{2k+p}}{k!\,\Gamma(k + p + 1)}$$

is known as Bessel's function of the first kind, of order p, and satisfies the differential equation

$$\frac{d}{dt}(ty') + \left(t - \frac{p^2}{t}\right)y = 0 \qquad\qquad (p \text{ a real number})$$

called Bessel's equation.

(a) By introducing the new variable x defined by $t = \sqrt{\lambda}\,x$, show that the equation becomes

$$Mu \equiv \frac{d}{dx}(xu') + \left(\lambda x - \frac{p^2}{x}\right)u = 0$$

where $u(x) = y(\sqrt{\lambda}\,x)$.

(b) Thus, show that $u_n(x) = J_p(\sqrt{\lambda_n}\, x)$ is an eigenfunction of the Sturm-Liouville problem

$$Mu = 0, \qquad u(0) = 0, \qquad u(1) = 0 \qquad (p > 0, 0 < x < 1)$$

when λ_n is a root of the equation $J_p(\sqrt{\lambda}) = 0$.

18. What are the eigenvalues and eigenfunctions of the singular Sturm-Liouville problem

$$xu'' + u' + \lambda xu = 0 \qquad\qquad (0 < x < 1)$$
$$u'(0) = 0, \qquad u(1) = 0$$

19. Let $J_{1/2}(t)$ be the Bessel's function of order $p = \tfrac{1}{2}$ and let $u(x) = xJ_{1/2}((\sqrt{\lambda}/2)x^2)$. Show that u satisfies the differential equation

$$Lu \equiv \frac{d}{dx}\left(\frac{1}{x}u'\right) + \frac{\lambda}{x}u = 0 \qquad\qquad (x > 0)$$

and thus determine the eigenvalues and eigenfunctions of the singular Sturm-Liouville problem $Lu = 0$, $u(0) = 0$, $u(1) = 0$.

5. Orthogonality of Eigenfunctions

In relation to their corresponding eigenvalues, the eigenfunctions of a regular Sturm-Liouville problem possess a basic property that is of fundamental importance in application. We have observed this in Section 9 of the preceding chapter in connection with the eigenfunctions $X(x) = \sin(n\pi x)/L$ and eigenvalues $\lambda_n = (n\pi)^2/L^2$, $n \geq 1$. In this section we shall establish this property in the general case and in later sections consider some of its implications.

We now introduce the definition of orthogonal functions. Let u and v be two functions that are integrable on the interval $a \leq x \leq b$, and let σ be a positive continuous function on this interval. The functions u and v are said to be orthogonal on $[a, b]$ with respect to the weight function σ if and only if

(5.1) $$\int_a^b \sigma(x)u(x)v(x)\, dx = 0$$

Thus, the functions $u(x) = \sin x$ and $v(x) = \cos x$ are orthogonal on the interval $[-\pi, \pi]$ with respect to the weight function $\sigma(x) = 1$, since the integral of their product over this integral vanishes. Whenever (5.1) holds for the functions u and v with $\sigma(x) = 1$, we shall simply say that u and v are orthogonal on $[a, b]$.

When $u = v$, the quantity

(5.2) $$\|u\| = \left\{\int_a^b \sigma(x)u^2(x)\, dx\right\}^{1/2}$$

is called the norm of the function u. Notice that $\|u\| = 0$ if and only if $u(x) = 0$ for $a \leq x \leq b$. If $\|u\| = 1$, then the function u is said to be normalized. It is easy to see that a given function that is not identically zero can always be normalized. Thus, if u is a function such that $\|u\| \neq 0$, then the function $v = u/\|u\|$ has a unit norm. Indeed, we see that

$$\int_a^b \sigma(x)v^2(x) \, dx = \frac{1}{\|u\|^2} \int_a^b \sigma(x)u^2(x) \, dx$$

$$= \frac{\|u\|^2}{\|u\|^2} = 1$$

We now establish the orthogonal property of eigenfunctions of the Sturm-Liouville problem (4.2), (4.3).

THEOREM 5.1.　*Let u and v be two eigenfunctions of the Sturm-Liouville problem (4.2), (4.3) corresponding to the eigenvalues μ and v. If μ and v are distinct, then u and v are orthogonal on $[a, b]$ with respect to the weight function r; that is,*

$$\int_a^b r(x)u(x)v(x) \, dx = 0$$

Proof:　Since u and v satisfy equation (4.2) corresponding to $\lambda = \mu$ and $\lambda = v$, we have

$$Lu = -\mu r u, \qquad Lv = -v r v$$

If we multiply the first equation by v and the second equation by u, and then subtract one result from the other, we obtain

$$(\mu - v)ruv = uLv - vLu$$

Let us integrate both sides of the last equation from $x = a$ to $x = b$ and use Lemma 3.1. We find

$$\textbf{(5.3)} \qquad (\mu - v) \int_a^b r(x)u(x)v(x) \, dx = \left[p \left(u \frac{dv}{dx} - v \frac{du}{dx} \right) \right]_a^b$$

$$= p(b)W(u, v; b) - p(a)W(u, v; a)$$

where $W(u, v; x) = u(x)v'(x) - u'(x)v(x)$ is the Wronskian of u and v. From (1.9) we know that $W(u, v; a) = 0$, and in a similar manner we find $W(u, v; b) = 0$. Therefore, the right-hand side of equation (5.3) reduces to zero and we obtain

$$\textbf{(5.4)} \qquad (\mu - v) \int_a^b r(x)u(x)v(x) \, dx = 0$$

Since $\mu - v \neq 0$, we conclude that

$$\int_a^b r(x)u(x)v(x) \, dx = 0$$

and the theorem is proved.

It follows from this theorem that the eigenfunctions of the Sturm-Liouville problem (4.2), (4.3) form a set of mutually orthogonal functions on the interval

$a \leq x \leq b$ with weight function r. Such a set of functions is called an ortho-gonal system on the interval $[a, b]$ with respect to the weight function r. If $r = 1$, then the system is simply said to be orthogonal on $[a, b]$. Thus, the set of functions $X_n(x) = \sin(n\pi x)/L$, $n = 1, 2, \ldots$ forms an orthogonal system over the interval $0 \leq x \leq L$.

If each eigenfunction u_n of (4.2), (4.3) is normalized—that is, if we replace each u_n by $\phi_n = u_n/\|u_n\|$—then the alternate set of eigenfunctions ϕ_n, $n \geq 1$, satisfies the relation

(5.5)
$$\int_a^b r(x)\phi_m(x)\phi_n(x)\,dx = \begin{cases} 1 & \text{(if } m = n) \\ 0 & \text{(if } m \neq n) \end{cases}$$

In such a case the set of functions ϕ_n, $n \geq 1$, is called an orthonormal system over $[a, b]$ with respect to the weight function r. Equation (5.5) is oftentimes written as

(5.6)
$$\int_a^b r(x)\phi_m(x)\phi_n(x)\,dx = \delta_{mn}$$

where the symbol δ_{mn}, known as the Kronecker delta, is defined by the equation

(5.7)
$$\delta_{mn} = \begin{cases} 1 & \text{(if } m = n) \\ 0 & \text{(if } m \neq n) \end{cases}$$

Example 5.1. Determine the normalized eigenfunctions of the problem (4.1).

Solution: The eigenfunctions of problem (4.1) are $X_n(x) = \sin(n\pi x)/L$, $n \geq 1$, for which we find

$$\|X_n\|^2 = \int_0^L \sin^2\left(\frac{n\pi x}{L}\right)\,dx$$

$$= \int_0^L \frac{1 - \cos(2n\pi x)/L}{2}\,dx = \frac{L}{2}$$

Thus, $\|X_n\| = \sqrt{L/2}$ and the normalized eigenfunctions are given by

$$\phi_n(x) = \left(\frac{2}{L}\right)^{1/2} \sin\frac{n\pi x}{L} \qquad (n \geq 1)$$

We stated in the preceding section that the Sturm-Liouville problem (4.2), (4.3) has only real eigenvalues. This fact can be established by using the proof of Theorem 5.1.

THEOREM 5.2. *The eigenvalues of the Sturm-Liouville problem (4.2), (4.3) are all real and the corresponding eigenfunctions are real except for a constant (possibly complex) factor.*

Proof: Suppose $\lambda = s + it$ is an eigenvalue of the problem (4.2), (4.3) and suppose $\psi = U + iV$ is the corresponding eigenfunction. Then ψ satisfies the differential equation

$$(5.8) \qquad\qquad L\psi + \lambda r\psi = 0$$

Since the function r and the coefficients of the differential operator L are real-valued, it follows by taking the complex conjugate of each term in (5.8) that

$$(5.9) \qquad\qquad L\bar{\psi} + \bar{\lambda} r\bar{\psi} = 0$$

Similarly, by taking the complex conjugate of each of the boundary conditions

$$(5.10) \qquad \alpha\psi(a) + \beta\psi'(a) = 0, \qquad \gamma\psi(b) + \delta\psi'(b) = 0$$

we obtain

$$(5.11) \qquad \alpha\bar{\psi}(a) + \beta\bar{\psi}'(a) = 0, \qquad \gamma\bar{\psi}(b) + \delta\bar{\psi}'(b) = 0$$

since α, β, γ, and δ are real constants. Now equation (5.9) and (5.11) imply that $\bar{\psi}$ is also an eigenfunction of (4.2), (4.3) and $\bar{\lambda}$ is the corresponding eigenvalue. Hence, letting $u = \psi$ and $v = \bar{\psi}$ in the proof of Theorem 5.1, from (5.4) we have

$$(5.12) \qquad\qquad (\lambda - \bar{\lambda}) \int_a^b r(x)\psi(x)\bar{\psi}(x) \, dx = 0$$

Since $\psi(x)\bar{\psi}(x) = U^2(x) + V^2(x) > 0$ and $r(x) > 0$ for $a \le x \le b$, the integral in (5.12) is always positive. Therefore, we must have $\lambda - \bar{\lambda} = 2it = 0$; in other words, $t = 0$. Thus, $\lambda = s$, a real number.

If we consider the real and imaginary parts of equations (5.8) and (5.10), we see that both U and V are eigenfunctions corresponding to the eigenvalue $\lambda = s$. Hence, $U = cV$ for some constant c so that

$$\psi = U + iV = (c + i)V$$

Thus, ψ is a real-valued function except for a multiplicative (possibly complex) factor. This completes the proof of the theorem.

Theorems 5.1 and 5.2 can also be shown to hold in the case when the boundary conditions (4.3) are replaced by the periodic boundary conditions (4.4), provided $p(a) = p(b)$ (Problems 10 and 13.)

Exercises 4.5

1. Determine the normalized eigenfunctions of Problem 3, Exercises 4.4.

2. Determine the normalized eigenfunctions of Problem 5, Exercises 4.4.

3. Determine the normalized eigenfunctions of Problem 15, Exercises 4.4. (See Problem 11 below.)

4. By applying Theorem 5.1 to the eigenfunctions of the problem $u'' + \lambda u = 0$, $0 \le x \le \pi$; $u(0) = 0$, $u(\pi) - u'(\pi) = 0$, show that

$$\int_0^\pi \sin \lambda_1 x \sin \lambda_2 x \, dx = 0$$

when λ_1 and λ_2 are roots of the equation $\tan \lambda\pi = \lambda$.

5. Verify by direct integration that the eigenfunctions of Problem 11(a), Exercises 4.4, are mutually orthogonal; that is,

$$\int_1^e \frac{1}{x} \sin(m\pi \ln x) \sin(n\pi \ln x) \, dx = 0$$

when m and n are distinct integers.

6. Verify that Theorem 5.1 holds for the singular Sturm-Liouville problem

$$\frac{d}{dx}(xu') + \left(\lambda x - \frac{p^2}{x}\right) u = 0 \qquad (0 < x < 1, p > 0)$$

$$u(0) = 0, \qquad u(1) = 0$$

and thus deduce that

$$\int_0^1 x J_p(\sqrt{\lambda_1} \, x) J_p(\sqrt{\lambda_2} \, x) \, dx = 0$$

when λ_1 and λ_2 are distinct roots of the equation $J_p(\sqrt{\lambda}) = 0$. (See Problem 17, Exercises 4.4.)

7. Do as in Problem 6 for the singular Sturm-Liouville problem

$$\frac{d}{dx}\left(\frac{1}{x} u'\right) + \frac{\lambda}{x} u = 0 \qquad (0 < x < 1)$$

$$u(0) = 0, \qquad u(1) = 0$$

and deduce that

$$\int_0^1 x J_{1/2}\left(\frac{\mu^{1/2}}{2} x^2\right) J_{1/2}\left(\frac{\nu^{1/2}}{2} x^2\right) dx = 0$$

when μ and ν are distinct roots of $J_{1/2}(\lambda^{1/2}/2) = 0$. (See Problem 19, Exercises 4.4.)

8. The singular Sturm-Liouville problem

$$(1 - x^2)u'' - 2xu' + \lambda u = 0 \qquad (-1 < x < 1)$$

$$u \text{ finite at } x = \pm 1$$

has eigenvalues $\lambda_n = n(n + 1)$, $n = 0, 1, 2, \ldots$ with the corresponding eigenfunctions

$$P_n(x) = \frac{1}{2^n n!} \frac{d^n}{dx^n} (x^2 - 1)^n \qquad (n = 0, 1, 2, \ldots)$$

called Legendre's polynomials. Verify that Theorem 5.1 holds in this case, and thus deduce that

$$\int_{-1}^{1} P_m(x)P_n(x)\, dx = 0$$

when $m \neq n$.

9. A sequence of functions $\phi_1, \phi_2, \ldots, \phi_n, \ldots$ defined on $[a, b]$ is said to be linearly independent if, for each n, any linear combination $\sum_{k=1}^{n} c_k \phi_k(x)$ cannot vanish identically on $[a, b]$ unless $c_k = 0$ for each k, $1 \leq k \leq n$. Show that a sequence of eigenfunctions is necessarily linearly independent.

10. Show that Theorem 5.1 remains valid when the boundary conditions (4.3) are replaced by the periodic boundary conditions (4.4) with $p(a) = p(b)$.

11. Verify the result of Problem 9 for the eigenfunctions of Problem 15, Exercises 4.4, and then obtain the orthogonal system of eigenfunctions

$$\left\{ 1,\ \sin\frac{n\pi x}{L},\quad \cos\frac{n\pi x}{L} \right\} \qquad\qquad (n \geq 1)$$

12. Do as in Problem 10 for the eigenfunctions of Problem 16, Exercises 4.4, and obtain an orthogonal system of eigenfunctions.

13. Show that Theorem 5.2 remains valid when the boundary conditions (4.3) are replaced by (4.4), provided $p(a) = p(b)$.

14. Show that if q is nonpositive on the interval $a \leq x \leq b$, then the eigenvalues of equation (4.2) are nonnegative under each of the following boundary conditions:

(i) $u(a) = 0$, $u(b) = 0$.
(ii) $u'(a) = 0$, $u'(b) = 0$.
(iii) $u'(a) - c_1 u(a) = 0$, $u'(b) + c_2 u(b) = 0$, $c_1 \geq 0$, $c_2 \geq 0$.

Hint: Multiply the differential equation (4.2) by u and integrate from $x = a$ to $x = b$.

15. Show that if u and v are eigenfunctions of the boundary value problem

$$u^{(iv)} - \lambda u = 0 \qquad\qquad (0 \leq x \leq L)$$
$$u(0) = u''(0) = 0, \qquad u(L) = u''(L) = 0$$

corresponding to distinct eigenvalues, then u and v are orthogonal on $[0, L]$. (Problem 5, Exercises 4.4.) Note that

$$uv^{(iv)} - vu^{(iv)} = \frac{d}{dx}(uv''' - u''v - u'v'' + u''v')$$

6. Eigenfunction Expansions; Mean Convergence

In Section 9 of the preceding chapter we were faced with the problem of expanding a given function f in an infinite series of the form

$$(6.1) \qquad\qquad f(x) = \sum_{n=1}^{\infty} b_n \sin\frac{n\pi x}{L}$$

where the functions $X_n(x) = \sin(n\pi x/L)$, $(n \geq 1)$, are eigenfunctions of the particular Sturm-Liouville problem (4.1). We found that in order for the expansion (6.1) to hold, the coefficients b_n must be given by the formula

(6.2)
$$b_n = \frac{2}{L} \int_0^L f(x) \sin \frac{n\pi x}{L} \, dx \qquad (n = 1, 2, \ldots)$$

This formula was derived by making use of the orthogonal property of the eigenfunctions $X_n(x) = \sin(n\pi x/L)$, $n \geq 1$.

The series (6.1) is actually just a special case of the problem of expanding a function f in an infinite series of eigenfunctions of the more general Sturm-Liouville problem (4.2), (4.3). For if f satisfies appropriate conditions, it is possible to expand the function in a series of the form

(6.3)
$$f(x) = \sum_{n=1}^{\infty} c_n \phi_n(x) \qquad (a \leq x \leq b)$$

where ϕ_n, $n \geq 1$, are the eigenfunctions of the problem (4.2), (4.3). Here we assume that the eigenfunctions ϕ_n have already been normalized. If the expansion (6.3) is possible, the coefficients c_n can then be determined in the same way we determined b_n for the series (6.1). We multiply both sides of equation (6.3) by $r(x)\phi_m(x)$ and integrate the result over the interval $[a, b]$. Assuming that the series can be integrated term by term, we obtain

(6.4)
$$\int_a^b r(x)f(x)\phi_m(x) \, dx = \sum_{n=1}^{\infty} c_n \int_a^b r(x)\phi_m(x)\phi_n(x) \, dx$$
$$= \sum_{n=1}^{\infty} c_n \delta_{mn}$$

where we have used equation (5.6). Since $\delta_{mn} = 0$ when $m \neq n$ and $\delta_{mn} = 1$ when $m = n$, equation (6.4) yields the formula

(6.5)
$$c_n = \int_a^b r(x)f(x)\phi_n(x) \, dx$$

The series in (6.3) with the coefficients c_n given by (6.5) is called the generalized Fourier series of the function f with respect to the orthonormal system $\{\phi_n\}$. The coefficients c_n are called the Fourier coefficients. We observe that the series in (6.3) can always be formed for a given function f whenever the coefficients (6.5) can be determined. However, there is no guarantee that the series obtained will converge at any point in the interval $a \leq x \leq b$. In fact, even when the series does converge, there is no assurance that it will converge to the function f on that interval. Until the question of convergence has been established, we shall simply regard the series in (6.3) as the formal eigenfunction expansion of f with respect to the orthonormal system $\{\phi_n\}$ and write

$$f(x) \sim \sum_{n=1}^{\infty} c_n \phi_n(x)$$

For reference, we present a basic theorem that gives sufficient conditions for the pointwise convergence of the series in (6.3) to f. The theorem will be proved in the next chapter in the special case where $L = (d/dx)^2$ for which the orthonormal system $\{\phi_n\}$ consists of trigonometric functions.

THEOREM 6.1. *Let* $\{\phi_n\}$, $n \geq 1$, *be an orthonormal system of eigenfunctions of the Sturm-Liouville problem (4.2), (4.3), and let f be a function that is piecewise smooth on the interval* $a \leq x \leq b$. *Then the series in (6.3), whose coefficients* c_n *are given by (6.5), converges to the value*

$$\frac{f(x + 0) + f(x - 0)}{2}$$

at each point x for $a < x < b$. *If, in addition, f is continuous on* $a \leq x \leq b$ *and satisfies the boundary conditions (4.3), then the series (6.3) converges uniformly and absolutely to f for all x,* $a \leq x \leq b$.

Example 6.1. Determine the series (6.3) for the function $f(x) = x$, $0 \leq x \leq \pi$ with respect to the orthonormal system $\{(2/\pi)^{1/2} \sin nx\}$.

Solution: By (6.5) we find

$$c_n = (2/\pi)^{1/2} \int_0^\pi x \sin nx \, dx = (2/\pi)^{1/2} \left[\frac{-x \cos nx}{n} + \frac{\sin nx}{n^2} \right]_0^\pi$$

$$= -\sqrt{2\pi} \, \frac{\cos n\pi}{n} = \frac{\sqrt{2\pi}}{n} (-1)^{n+1} \qquad (n \geq 1)$$

Thus, we have

$$x \sim 2 \sum_{n=1}^{\infty} (-1)^{n+1} \frac{\sin nx}{x}$$

According to Theorem 6.1, the series converges to the function $f(x) = x$ for $0 < x < \pi$. At $x = \pi$, we notice that the series converges to zero while $f(\pi) \neq 0$. At $x = 0$ both the series and the function converge to zero. Hence, the series expansion above is valid for $0 \leq x < \pi$.

In the study of convergence of the series in (6.3) or, for that matter, of any series involving orthogonal functions, there is a different kind of convergence that is often more convenient and appropriate to use, especially when pointwise convergence can nowhere be attained. We refer to the notion of convergence in the mean square sense or, briefly, convergence in the mean. We say that the series

(6.6) $$f(x) \sim \sum_{n=1}^{\infty} c_n \phi_n(x)$$

with coefficients given by (6.5) converges to f in the mean if and only if

(6.7) $$\lim_{m \to \infty} \int_a^b r(x) \left[f(x) - \sum_{n=1}^{m} c_n \phi_n(x) \right]^2 dx = 0$$

Here, we shall continue to regard the system $\{\phi_n\}$ as the set of normalized eigenfunctions of the Sturm-Liouville problem (4.2), (4.3), although it can be any given set of orthonormal continuous functions on $a \leq x \leq b$ relative to a weight function r, $r(x) > 0$.

The integral

$$(6.8) \qquad E_m = \int_a^b r(x) \left[f(x) - \sum_{n=1}^m c_n \phi_n(x) \right]^2 dx$$

is a measure of the average error in approximating f over the interval $a \leq x \leq b$ by the mth partial sum

$$(6.9) \qquad S_m(x) = \sum_{n=1}^m c_n \phi_n(x)$$

and is called the mean square deviation of S_m from f. The vanishing of (6.8) as m tends to infinity implies that S_m is close to f for all points in $[a, b]$ except possibly for points in a set of intervals whose total length is small. Thus, it is possible for the series (6.6) to converge in the mean to f without actually converging at every point in the interval $[a, b]$. This indicates that convergence in the mean does not imply pointwise convergence. It is also true that pointwise convergence does not imply mean convergence.

It is significant that if we are to approximate the function f by any linear combination $\sum_{n=1}^m a_n \phi_n(x)$ of the normalized eigenfunctions $\phi_1, \ldots, \phi_m$ in the sense that the mean square deviation (6.8) is minimum, the coefficients a_n must be chosen precisely as the Fourier coefficients (6.5) of f with respect to the system $\{\phi_n\}$ relative to the weight function r. Indeed, since the integral

$$(6.10) \qquad E(a_1, \ldots, a_m) = \int_a^b r(x) \left[f(x) - \sum_{n=1}^m a_n \phi_n(x) \right]^2 dx$$

is a function of the coefficients $a_1, \ldots, a_m$, we see that in order for $E(a_1, \ldots, a_m)$ to be minimum, it must satisfy the equation

$$\frac{\partial E}{\partial a_i} = 2 \int_a^b r(x) \left[f(x) - \sum_{n=1}^m a_n \phi_n(x) \right] \phi_i(x) \, dx = 0$$

$1 \leq i \leq m$. Now, in view of the orthonormality of the system $\{\phi_n\}$, this gives

$$a_i = \int_a^b r(x) f(x) \phi_i(x) \, dx$$

$$= c_i \qquad\qquad\qquad (i = 1, \ldots, m)$$

which are the Fourier coefficients of f relative to the system $\{\phi_n\}$ with weight function r.

To see that these coefficients render the integral (6.10) minimum, let us expand the integrand in (6.10) and integrate the terms. We obtain

$$E(a_1, \ldots, a_m) = \int_a^b r(x)f^2(x)\, dx$$

$$- 2 \sum_{n=1}^m a_n \int_a^b r(x)f(x)\phi_n(x)\, dx$$

(6.11)
$$+ \sum_{n=1}^m \sum_{k=1}^m a_n a_k \int_a^b r(x)\phi_n(x)\phi_k(x)\, dx$$

$$= \int_a^b r(x)f^2(x)\, dx - 2 \sum_{n=1}^m a_n c_n + \sum_{n=1}^m a_n^2$$

$$= \int_a^b r(x)f^2(x)\, dx + \sum_{n=1}^m (a_n - c_n)^2 - \sum_{n=1}^m c_n^2$$

where we have again used the orthonormality of the system $\{\phi_n\}$. It is now apparent from the last expression above that $E(a_1, \ldots, a_m)$ has minimum value when $a_i = c_i$ for $i = 1, \ldots, m$. Thus, the $m$thpartial sum (6.9) really provides the best approximation to f with the eigenfunctions $\phi_1, \ldots, \phi_m$ in the mean square sense.

When $a_n = c_n$, we see from (6.8) and (6.11) that

(6.12)
$$E_m = E(c_1, \ldots, c_m) = \int_a^b r(x)f^2(x)\, dx - \sum_{n=1}^m c_n^2$$

Since by its definition, $E_m \geq 0$, it follows that

(6.13)
$$\sum_{n=1}^m c_n^2 \leq \int_a^b r(x)f^2(x)\, dx$$

for any m. This important result is known as Bessel's inequality. We notice that as m increases, the sum on the left is always bounded above by the integral of rf^2 over $[a, b]$. Hence, if we assume that f is a function such that the integral on the right of (6.12) exists (e.g., f is piecewise continuous), then on letting m tend to infinity, Bessel's inequality becomes

(6.14)
$$\sum_{n=1}^\infty c_n^2 \leq \int_a^b r(x)f^2(x)\, dx$$

This implies that the series $\sum_{n=1}^\infty c_n^2$ converges and therefore

(6.15)
$$\lim_{n \to \infty} c_n = \lim_{n \to \infty} \int_a^b r(x)f(x)\phi_n(x)\, dx = 0$$

Now suppose that for a given function f the series (6.6) converges in the mean.

Then, in view of (6.12), it follows that

$$\lim_{m \to \infty} E_m = \int_a^b r(x)f^2(x) \, dx - \sum_{n=1}^{\infty} c_n^2 = 0$$

or

(6.16) $$\sum_{n=1}^{\infty} c_n^2 = \int_a^b r(x)f^2(x) \, dx$$

This is a particular case of the inequality (6.14) and is called Parseval's equation. It is readily seen that if Parseval's equation holds, then the series (6.6) converges in the mean. Therefore, Parseval's equation is a necessary and sufficient condition for the mean convergence of the series (6.6).

We say that the system of orthonormal functions $\{\phi_n\}$ with weight function r is complete with respect to a class of functions (e.g., the class of piecewise continuous functions) if for every function f in this class, the series (6.6) converges in the mean, or equivalently, Parseval's equation (6.16) holds. In terms of this notion of completeness, it is known that the set of eigenfunctions of the Sturm-Liouville problem (4.2), (4.3) is complete with respect to the class of functions that is square integrable on $a \le x \le b$. (A function f is said to be square integrable on $a \le x \le b$ if both f and f^2 are integrable on $[a, b]$.) Thus, if f is a square integrable function on $[a, b]$ (e.g., f is piecewise continuous), then its expansion in series of eigenfunctions of the problem (4.2), (4.3) with coefficients given by (6.5) converges in the mean. In this connection, it is interesting to note that a function satisfies significantly much weaker condition for mean convergence than it ordinarily does for pointwise convergence.

Exercises 4.6

1. If a_n $(n \ge 1)$ are constants such that the series of eigenfunctions $\sum_{n=1}^{\infty} a_n \phi_n(x)$ converges to $f(x)$, where $f(x) = 0$ for each x on the interval $a \le x \le b$, show that $a_n = 0, n \ge 1$.

2. Let u_n $(n \ge 1)$ be a sequence of eigenfunctions not necessarily normalized and suppose that

    $$f(x) = \sum_{n=1}^{\infty} a_n u_n(x) \qquad\qquad (a \le x \le b)$$

    Obtain formally the formula for the coefficients a_n, $n \ge 1$.

3. Find the formal eigenfunction expansion of the function $f(x) = x^2, 0 \le x < \pi$, with respect to the system of orthonormal functions $\{(2/\pi)^{1/2} \sin nx\}$.

4. Find the formal eigenfunction expansion of $f(x) = x, 0 \le x \le L$, with respect to the eigenfunctions of Problem 1, Exercises 4.4.

5. Find the formal eigenfunction expansion of $f(x) = x, 0 \le x \le \pi$, with respect to the eigenfunctions of Problem 2, Exercises 4.4.

6. Find the formal eigenfunction expansion of $f(x) = 1, 1 \le x \le e$, with respect to the eigenfunctions of Problem 11(a), Exercises 4.4.

7. Obtain the formal eigenfunction expansion of a function f with respect to the eigenfunctions of Problem 3, Exercises 4.4.

8. Show that the series

$$\sum_{n=1}^{\infty} \frac{\phi_n(x)}{\sqrt{n}}$$

cannot be the eigenfunction expansion of any square integrable function. (Use Bessel's inequality.)

9. Show that Parseval's equation can be obtained formally from equation (6.3) by squaring both sides, multiplying by $r(x)$, and then integrating term by term.

10. Let $\{\phi_n\}$ be a complete orthonormal system on $a \leq x \leq b$ relative to a positive weight function r. Show that any continuous function f that is orthogonal to all functions of the system must be identically zero. (Use Parseval's equation.)

11. Let $\{\phi_n\}$ be a complete orthonormal system of continuous functions on $a \leq x \leq b$ (relative to the weight function $r = 1$). Show that if f is a continuous function that is orthogonal to all functions of the set $\{\phi_1 + \phi_2, \phi_2 + \phi_3, \phi_3 + \phi_4, \ldots\}$, then f must be identically zero.

12. Let $\{\phi_n\}$ be a complete orthonormal system of continuous functions on $a \leq x \leq b$, where $|\phi_n| \leq M$ for all n. Find a continuous function f, not identically zero, that is orthogonal to all the functions $\phi_1 + \phi_2, \phi_2 + 2\phi_3, \phi_3 + 3\phi_4, \ldots,$ $\phi_n + n\phi_{n+1}, \ldots.$

7. Nonhomogeneous Sturm-Liouville Problems; Bilinear Expansion

One important application of eigenfunction expansions concerns finding solutions of boundary value problems for nonhomogeneous differential equations. We consider here the nonhomogeneous Sturm-Liouville problem

$$(7.1) \qquad\qquad Lu + \lambda r(x)u = f(x)$$

where f is a given function on the interval $a \leq x \leq b$, together with the boundary conditions

$$(7.2) \qquad\qquad \begin{aligned} \alpha u(a) + \beta u'(a) &= 0 \\ \gamma u(b) + \delta u'(b) &= 0 \end{aligned}$$

We suppose that the normalized eigenfunctions ϕ_n corresponding to the eigenvalues λ_n ($n \geq 1$) of the related homogeneous Sturm-Liouville problem (4.2), (4.3) are known. Then, for each $n \geq 1$, we have

$$(7.3) \qquad\qquad L\phi_n = -\lambda_n r(x)\phi_n$$

We assume that a solution u of the problem (7.1), (7.2) exists and can be expressed as a series of the form

$$(7.4) \qquad\qquad u(x) = \sum_{n=1}^{\infty} c_n\phi_n(x) \qquad\qquad (a \leq x \leq b)$$

If the series in (7.4) converges suitably for appropriate values of the coefficients c_n, then the function u represented by the series automatically satisfies the boundary conditions (7.2), since each of the eigenfunctions ϕ_n does. It remains, then, for us to determine the constants c_n such that the series in (7.4) satisfies the differential equation (7.1). Proceeding rather formally, we substitute (7.4) in the differential equation (7.1) and use (7.3) to obtain

$$Lu + \lambda r(x)u = \sum_{n=1}^{\infty} c_n L\phi_n(x) + \lambda r(x) \sum_{n=1}^{\infty} c_n \phi_n(x)$$

$$= \sum_{n=1}^{\infty} c_n[-\lambda_n r(x)\phi_n(x)]$$

$$+ \lambda r(x) \sum_{n=1}^{\infty} c_n \phi_n(x)$$

$$= r(x) \sum_{n=1}^{\infty} c_n(\lambda - \lambda_n)\phi_n(x)$$

$$= f(x)$$

This can be written as

(7.5)
$$\sum_{n=1}^{\infty} c_n(\lambda - \lambda_n)\phi_n(x) = F(x)$$

where we have set $F(x) = f(x)/r(x)$. Let us further assume that the function F can also be expressed in a series of the eigenfunctions ϕ_n. Then

(7.6)
$$F(x) = \sum_{n=1}^{\infty} b_n \phi_n(x)$$

where, by (6.5),

(7.7)
$$b_n = \int_a^b r(x)F(x)\phi_n(x)\, dx = \int_a^b f(x)\phi_n(x)\, dx$$

Substituting (7.6) in (7.5) and combining terms, we obtain

(7.8)
$$\sum_{n=1}^{\infty} [c_n(\lambda - \lambda_n) - b_n]\phi_n(x) = 0$$

Since this holds for all x in the interval $[a, b]$, each coefficient of the series must vanish; hence, we have

(7.9)
$$c_n(\lambda - \lambda_n) = b_n \qquad\qquad (n = 1, 2, \ldots)$$

Therefore, if the parameter λ in the differential equation (7.1) is not equal to an eigenvalue of the corresponding homogeneous problem (4.2), (4.3), we can solve for c_n from (7.9) to obtain

$$c_n = \frac{b_n}{(\lambda - \lambda_n)} \qquad\qquad (n = 1, 2, \ldots)$$

Substituting this in (7.4), we finally have

$$(7.10) \qquad u(x) = \sum_{n=1}^{\infty} \frac{b_n}{(\lambda - \lambda_n)} \phi_n(x)$$

where the constants b_n are given by (7.7). This is our formal solution of the boundary value problem (7.1), (7.2). The series in (7.10) is called the eigenfunction expansion of the solution of u. If the function $f(x)/r(x)$ is continuous and piecewise smooth on $[a, b]$, it is possible to show that (7.10) is the one and only solution of the problem (7.1), (7.2).

Now, if λ is equal to an eigenvalue of the corresponding homogeneous problem (4.2), (4.3)—say, $\lambda = \lambda_k$ for some fixed integer k—then when $n = k$, equation (7.9) becomes $c_k \cdot 0 = b_k$. If $b_k \neq 0$, then the coefficient c_k cannot be determined. This means that the problem (7.1), (7.2) has no solution in this case. On the other hand, if $b_k = 0$, that is, if

$$(7.11) \qquad b_k = \int_a^b f(x)\phi_k(x)\, dx = 0$$

then c_k becomes arbitrary and a formal solution of the problem (7.1), (7.2) is given by

$$(7.12) \qquad u(x) = \sum_{\substack{n=1 \\ n \neq k}}^{\infty} \frac{b_n}{(\lambda - \lambda_n)} \phi_n(x) + C\phi_k(x)$$

for any constant C.

Hence, if λ is equal to an eigenvalue λ_k of the homogeneous problem (4.2), (4.3), then a necessary and sufficient condition for the nonhomogeneous problem (7.1), (7.2) to have a solution is that condition (7.11) holds. This result is in agreement with our discussion in Section 3.

Let us summarize in the following theorem the results we have obtained above. (Compare with Theorems 2.1 and 3.1.)

THEOREM 7.1. *The nonhomogeneous Sturm-Liouville problem* (7.1), (7.2) *has a unique solution given by* (7.10), *if and only if λ is not an eigenvalue of the corresponding homogeneous problem* (4.2), (4.3). *If λ is equal to an eigenvalue λ_k, for some fixed k, then the nonhomogeneous problem* (7.1), (7.2) *has a solution if and only if f is orthogonal to the corresponding eigenfunction ϕ_k, in which case a solution is given by* (7.12), *which is not unique.*

Example 7.1. Find the solution of the nonhomogeneous problem $u'' + \lambda u = x$, $0 < x < \pi$; $u(0) = 0$, $u(\pi) = 0$; where $\lambda \neq n^2$, $n = 1, 2, \ldots$.

Solution: We recall from Example 5.1 that the related homogeneous boundary value problem has the normalized eigenfunctions $\varphi_n(x) = \sqrt{2/\pi} \sin nx$ corresponding to the eigenvalues $\lambda_n = n^2$, $n \geq 1$. From Example 6.1, the Fourier coefficients of the function $f(x) = x$ with respect to the orthonormal system $\{\varphi_n\}$ are given by

$$b_n = \frac{\sqrt{2\pi}}{n} (-1)^{n+1} \qquad\qquad (n = 1, 2, \ldots)$$

Since λ is not an eigenvalue, by (7.10) the solution is

$$u(x) = 2 \sum_{n=1}^{\infty} \frac{(-1)^{n+1}}{n(\lambda - n^2)} \sin nx$$

We have described above the method of eigenfunction expansions for solving nonhomogeneous boundary value problems. It is, of course, also possible to approach such problems from the standpoint of our discussion in Section 2 and Section 3, which uses the concept of Green's function. Indeed, let us write

$$L^* = L + \lambda r = \frac{d}{dx}\left(p\,\frac{d}{dx}\right) + q^*$$

where $q^* = q + \lambda r$, and note that L^* is also self-adjoint, thus possessing properties similar to those of the operator L. Suppose that λ is not an eigenvalue of the homogeneous problem (4.2), (4.3). Then, according to Theorem 2.1, the Green's function corresponding to the operator L^* and boundary conditions (7.2) exists. This function can be determined by using the formula (2.14) with u_1 and u_2, now depending on both x and λ, being two linearly independent solutions of the equation $L^*u = 0$ such that they satisfy the boundary conditions at $x = a$ and $x = b$, respectively. If $G(x; \xi; \lambda)$ denotes the Green's function so determined, then by Theorem 2.1 the solution of the nonhomogeneous problem (7.1), (7.2) is given by

(7.13) $$u(x) = \int_a^b G(x; \xi; \lambda)f(\xi)\, d\xi$$

Thus, in the case where λ is not an eigenvalue, the solution of the problem (7.1), (7.2) has the representations (7.10) and (7.13). If we substitute the formula (7.7) for b_n in (7.10) and formally interchange the order of summation and integration, (7.10) becomes

(7.14) $$u(x) = \int_a^b \sum_{n=1}^{\infty} \frac{\phi_n(x)\phi_n(\xi)}{\lambda - \lambda_n} f(\xi)\, d\xi$$

In view of the uniqueness of the solution u in the present case, we conclude that the representations (7.13) and (7.14) are identical. Hence, we formally deduce that

(7.15) $$G(x; \xi; \lambda) = \sum_{n=1}^{\infty} \frac{\phi_n(x)\phi_n(\xi)}{\lambda - \lambda_n} \qquad\qquad (a \leq x \leq b)$$

The series on the right-hand side of (7.15) gives the eigenfunction expansion of the Green's function G and is called the bilinear expansion of G. In this form, we have a composite expression for the Green's function on the whole interval $a \leq x \leq b$, and its symmetric property with respect to the variables x and ξ becomes apparent.

It is natural to expect that the bilinear expansion in (7.15) can be established from Theorem 6.1, it being the generalized Fourier series of G with respect to the orthonormal system $\{\phi_n\}$, with coefficients depending on ξ and λ. In fact, from the properties of a Green's function, we know that G is continuous, has piecewise continuous derivative, and satisfies the boundary conditions (7.2). Hence, according to Theorem 6.1, G can be expressed in generalized Fourier series of the form

$$\textbf{(7.16)} \qquad G(x; \xi; \lambda) = \sum_{n=1}^{\infty} c_n \phi_n(x)$$

where

$$\textbf{(7.17)} \qquad c_n = \int_a^b r(x) G(x; \xi; \lambda) \phi_n(x)\, dx \qquad (n \geq 1)$$

Thus, the bilinear expansion (7.15) will be established if we can show that

$$\textbf{(7.18)} \qquad c_n = \frac{\phi_n(\xi)}{\lambda - \lambda_n} \qquad (n \geq 1)$$

Now, from their definitions we have

$$L\phi_n = -\lambda_n r(x) \phi_n(x) \qquad (n \geq 1)$$

and

$$LG = -\lambda r(x) G(x; \xi; \lambda) \qquad (x \neq \xi)$$

If we multiply the first equation above by G and the second equation by ϕ_n, and then subtract one result from the other, we obtain

$$\textbf{(7.19)} \qquad (\lambda - \lambda_n) r(x) G(x; \xi; \lambda) \phi_n(x) = GL\phi_n - \phi_n LG$$

Let us integrate both sides of equation (7.19) over the interval $a \leq x \leq b$, making an intermediate stop at the point $x = \xi$ because of the discontinuity of dG/dx at that point, to obtain

$$\textbf{(7.20)} \qquad (\lambda - \lambda_n) \int_a^b r(x) G(x; \xi; \lambda) \phi_n(x)\, dx = \int_a^{\xi - 0} (GL\phi_n - \phi_n LG)\, dx$$

$$+ \int_{\xi + 0}^b (GL\phi_n - \phi_n LG)\, dx$$

Applying Lemma 3.1 to each of the integrals on the right side of (7.20), we find

(7.21)
$$(\lambda - \lambda_n) \int_a^b r(x)G(x; \xi; \lambda)\phi_n(x) \, dx$$

$$= \left[p \left(G \frac{d\phi_n}{dx} - \phi_n \frac{dG}{dx} \right) \right]_a^{\xi-0} + \left[p \left(G \frac{d\phi_n}{dx} - \phi_n \frac{dG}{dx} \right) \right]_{\xi+0}^b$$

$$= p(b)W(G, \phi_n; b) - p(a)W(G, \phi_n; a)$$

$$+ p(\xi)\phi_n(\xi) \left[\frac{dG}{dx} (\xi + 0; \xi; \lambda) - \frac{dG}{dx} (\xi - 0; \xi; \lambda) \right]$$

where we have noted that the functions p, $d\phi_n/dx$, and G are all continuous at $x = \xi$. Since both G and ϕ_n satisfy the boundary conditions (7.2), it follows (as in the proof of Theorem 5.1) that the Wronskian $W(G, \phi_n; x)$ vanishes at $x = a$ and $x = b$. Moreover, by property (iv) of (2.15),

$$\frac{dG}{dx} (\xi + 0; \xi; \lambda) - \frac{dG}{dx} (\xi - 0; \xi; \lambda) = \frac{1}{p(\xi)}$$

Hence, (7.21) reduces to

$$(\lambda - \lambda_n) \int_a^b r(x)G(x; \xi; \lambda)\phi_n(x) \, dx = \phi_n(\xi)$$

which yields (7.18) in view of (7.17). This completes the derivation of the expansion (7.15) from Theorem 6.1.

It follows from (7.15) that if $\lambda = 0$ is not an eigenvalue of the homogeneous problem (4.2), (4.3), then the Green's function $G(x; \xi)$ for the operator L corresponding to the boundary conditions (4.3) has the bilinear expansion

(7.22)
$$G(x; \xi) = - \sum_{n=1}^{\infty} \frac{\phi_n(\xi)\phi_n(x)}{\lambda_n}$$

In the case where λ is equal to an eigenvalue (say, $\lambda = \lambda_k$ for some integer $k > 0$) for which condition (7.11) holds, it is possible to construct a modified Green's function $G^*(x; \xi; \lambda)$ along the procedure described in Section 3 so that a solution of the problem (7.1), (7.2) may also be given in the form (7.13). However, we shall not discuss this possibility.

Example 7.2.   Find the Green's function and its bilinear expansion for the operator $L^* = (d/dx)^2 + \lambda$ with boundary conditions $u(0) = 0$, $u(\pi) = 0$, where λ is not an eigenvalue.

Solution: We recall that the eigenvalues of the problem $L^*u = 0$, $u(0) = 0$, $u(\pi) = 0$ are $\lambda_n = n^2$, with the corresponding normalized eigenfunctions

$\phi_n(x) = \sqrt{2/\pi} \sin nx$, $n \geq 1$. Hence, if $\lambda \neq n^2$ and G is the Green's function sought, then by (7.15) we have the bilinear expansion

$$G(x; \xi; \lambda) = \frac{2}{\pi} \sum_{n=1}^{\infty} \frac{\sin n\xi \sin nx}{\lambda - n^2}$$

On the other hand, using formula (2.14), we find

$$G(x; \xi; \lambda) = \begin{cases} \dfrac{\sin \sqrt{\lambda}\, x \sin \sqrt{\lambda}(\xi - \pi)}{\sqrt{\lambda} \sin \sqrt{\lambda}\, \pi} & (0 \leq x \leq \xi) \\[2ex] \dfrac{\sin \sqrt{\lambda}\, \xi \sin \sqrt{\lambda}(x - \pi)}{\sqrt{\lambda} \sin \sqrt{\lambda}\, \pi} & (\xi \leq x \leq \pi) \end{cases}$$

For $\lambda = 0$, which is not an eigenvalue, the Green's function for the operator $L = (d/dx)^2$ can be obtained from $G(x; \xi; \lambda)$ by letting λ tend to zero. In fact, for $0 \leq x \leq \xi$, we see that

$$\lim_{\lambda \to 0} \frac{\sin \sqrt{\lambda}\, x \sin \sqrt{\lambda}(\xi - \pi)}{\sqrt{\lambda} \sin \sqrt{\lambda}\, \pi} = \lim_{\lambda \to 0} \frac{\sin \sqrt{\lambda}\, x}{\sqrt{\lambda}} \frac{[\sin \sqrt{\lambda}(\xi - \pi)]/\sqrt{\lambda}}{(\sin \sqrt{\lambda}\, \pi)/\sqrt{\lambda}}$$

$$= \frac{x(\xi - \pi)}{\pi}$$

Similarly, for $\xi \leq x \leq \pi$, we have

$$\lim_{\lambda \to 0} \frac{\sin \sqrt{\lambda}\, \xi \sin \sqrt{\lambda}(x - \pi)}{\sqrt{\lambda} \sin \sqrt{\lambda}\, \pi} = \frac{\xi(x - \pi)}{\pi}$$

Hence, the Green's function corresponding to $\lambda = 0$ is

$$G(x; \xi) = \begin{cases} \dfrac{x(\xi - \pi)}{\pi} & (0 \leq x \leq \xi) \\[2ex] \dfrac{\xi(x - \pi)}{\pi} & (\xi \leq x \leq \pi) \end{cases}$$

which has the bilinear expansion

$$G(x; \xi) = -\frac{2}{\pi} \sum_{n=1}^{\infty} \frac{\sin n\xi \sin nx}{n^2}$$

Exercises 4.7

In Problems 1 through 7, find a formal eigenfunction expansion of the solution of each of the following problems and state the values of λ for which the solution exists.

1.
$$u'' + \lambda u = 2 \sin x - 4 \sin 3x \qquad (0 \leq x \leq \pi)$$
$$u(0) = 0, \qquad u(\pi) = 0$$

2.
$$u'' + \lambda u = 2 \cos 2x - 3 \cos 5x \qquad (0 \le x \le \pi)$$
$$u'(0) = 0, \qquad u'(\pi) = 0$$

3.
$$u'' + \lambda u = 3 \cos \frac{\pi x}{2} + 2 \cos \frac{7\pi x}{2} \qquad (0 \le x \le 1)$$
$$u'(0) = 0, \qquad u(1) = 0$$

4.
$$u'' + \lambda u = \sum_{k=1}^{n} \frac{1}{k} \sin \left(\frac{2k-1}{2} \right) x \qquad (0 \le x \le \pi)$$
$$u(0) = 0, \qquad u'(\pi) = 0$$

5.
$$u'' + \lambda u = f(x) \qquad (0 \le x \le \pi)$$
$$u(0) + u'(0) = 0, \qquad u(\pi) + u'(\pi) = 0$$

(See Problem 3, Exercises 4.4.)

6.
$$\frac{d}{dx}(xu') + \frac{\lambda}{x} u = f(x) \qquad (1 \le x \le e)$$
$$u(1) = 0, \qquad u(e) = 0$$

(See Problem 11, Exercises 4.4.)

7.
$$\frac{d}{dx}\left(\frac{1}{x} u' \right) + \frac{\lambda}{x^3} u = [3 \sin(\pi \ln x) - 4 \sin(3\pi \ln x)]/x^3 \quad (1 \le x \le e)$$
$$u(1) = 0, \qquad u(e) = 0$$

(See Problem 14, Exercises 4.4.)

8. Obtain the bilinear expansion of the Green's function for the problem

$$u'' + \lambda u = f(x) \qquad (0 \le x \le L)$$
$$u(0) = 0, \qquad u(L) = 0$$

when λ is not an eigenvalue.

9. Find the Green's function for the operator $L = (d^2/dx^2) + \lambda$ subject to the boundary conditions $u(0) = 0$, $u'(1) = 0$, and obtain its bilinear expansion. In particular, show that

$$\frac{2}{\pi^2} \sum_{n=1}^{\infty} \frac{\sin(n - \tfrac{1}{2})\pi\xi \, \sin(n - \tfrac{1}{2})\pi x}{(n - \tfrac{1}{2})^2} = \begin{cases} x & (x \le \xi) \\ \xi & (\xi \le x) \end{cases}$$

10. By using formula (7.15), show that the Green's function for the operator

$$L = \frac{d}{dx}\left(x \frac{d}{dx} \right) + \lambda^2 u \qquad (0 < x < 1)$$

subject to the conditions $u(0)$ is finite and $u(1) = 0$ has the bilinear expansion

$$\sum_{n=1}^{\infty} \frac{\phi(\lambda_n x)\phi(\lambda_n \xi)}{\lambda^2 - \lambda_n^2}$$

where

$$\phi(\lambda_n x) = \frac{J_0(\lambda_n x)}{\| J_0(\lambda_n x) \|} \qquad \text{and} \qquad J_0(\lambda_n) = 0$$

(See Problem 17, Exercises 4.4.)

11. Find the Green's function $G(x; \xi; \lambda)$ for the operator

$$L = \frac{d}{dx}\left(x\frac{d}{dx}\right) + \frac{\lambda^2}{x} \qquad (1 \le x \le e)$$

subject to the boundary conditions $u(1) = 0$, $u'(e) = 0$, and by (7.15) show that it has the bilinear expansion

$$G(x; \xi; \lambda) = \sum_{n=1}^{\infty} \frac{\phi_n(\xi)\phi_n(x)}{\lambda^2 - \lambda_n^2}$$

where

$$\phi_n(x) = \frac{\sin[(n - \tfrac{1}{2})\pi \ln x]}{\|\sin(n - \tfrac{1}{2})\pi \ln x\|}$$

provided $\lambda \ne (n - 1/2)\pi$. In particular, show that

$$\frac{1}{\pi^2}\sum_{n=1}^{\infty} \frac{\phi_n(\xi)\phi_n(x)}{(n - \tfrac{1}{2})^2} = \begin{cases} \ln x & (1 \le x \le \xi) \\ \ln \xi & (\xi \le x \le e) \end{cases}$$

12. Find the bilinear expansion of the Green's function for the operator

$$L = \frac{d}{dx}\left(x\frac{d}{dx}\right) - \frac{n^2}{x} + \lambda^2 x \qquad (n \text{ positive integer})$$

subject to the boundary conditions $u(0) = u(1) = 0$, and show in particular

$$\sum_{k=1}^{\infty} \frac{\phi(\lambda_k\xi)\phi(\lambda_k x)}{\lambda_k^2} = \begin{cases} \dfrac{1}{2n}[(x/\xi)^n - (x\xi)^n] & (0 \le x \le \xi) \\ \dfrac{1}{2n}[(\xi/x)^n - (x\xi)^n] & (\xi \le x \le 1) \end{cases}$$

where

$$\phi(\lambda_k x) = \frac{J_n(\lambda_k x)}{\|J_n(\lambda_k x)\|} \qquad \text{and} \qquad J_n(\lambda_k) = 0$$

13. Find the bilinear expansion of the Green's function for the operator

$$L = \frac{d}{dx}\left(\frac{1}{x}\frac{d}{dx}\right) + \frac{\lambda^2}{x}$$

subject to the boundary conditions $u(0) = 0$, $u(1) = 0$, and show in particular

$$\sum_{k=1}^{\infty} \frac{\phi_n(x)\phi_n(\xi)}{\lambda_n^2} = \begin{cases} \tfrac{1}{2}x^2(1 - \xi^2) & (0 \le x \le \xi) \\ \tfrac{1}{2}\xi^2(1 - x^2) & (\xi \le x \le 1) \end{cases}$$

where

$$\phi_n(x) = \frac{xJ_{1/2}(\lambda_n/2)(x^2)}{\|xJ_{1/2}(\lambda_n/2)(x^2)\|} \qquad \text{and} \qquad J_{1/2}\left(\frac{\lambda_n}{2}\right) = 0$$

(See Problem 19, Exercises 4.4.)

Chapter 5

Fourier Series and Fourier Integral

In this chapter we shall be concerned with expansion of functions on finite intervals in series of orthogonal trigonometric functions. This represents an extremely important special case of the eigenfunction expansions, which we discussed rather formally in Section 6 of the preceding chapter. We shall establish here conditions under which such an expansion is possible. We shall also be interested in the representation of functions on infinite intervals in terms of eigenfunctions of certain singular eigenvalue problems.

1. Orthogonal Trigonometric Functions

We recall that the Sturm-Liouville problem

(1.1) $$u'' + \lambda u = 0, \qquad u(0) = 0, \qquad u(L) = 0$$

has the eigenfunctions

(1.2) $$u_n(x) = \sin \frac{n\pi x}{L}$$

corresponding to the eigenvalues

$$\lambda_n = \frac{n^2 \pi^2}{L^2} \qquad\qquad (n = 1, 2, \ldots)$$

If we replace the boundary conditions in (1.1) by $u'(0) = 0$ and $u'(L) = 0$, then the new Sturm-Liouville problem has the eigenfunctions

(1.3) $$u_n(x) = \cos \frac{n\pi x}{L}$$

which correspond to the eigenvalues

$$\lambda_n = \frac{n^2\pi^2}{L^2} \qquad (n = 0, 1, 2, \ldots)$$

According to Theorem 5.1 of the preceding chapter, each of the sets of eigen-functions given by (1.2) and by (1.3) forms an orthogonal system on the interval $0 \le x \le L$. That is,

$$\int_0^L \sin\frac{m\pi x}{L} \sin\frac{n\pi x}{L}\, dx = 0 \qquad (m \ne n)$$

and

$$\int_0^L \cos\frac{m\pi x}{L} \cos\frac{n\pi x}{L}\, dx = 0 \qquad (m \ne n)$$

Now let us consider the set of functions

(1.4) $\qquad\qquad 1, \qquad \cos\frac{n\pi x}{L}, \qquad \sin\frac{n\pi x}{L} \qquad (n = 1, 2, \ldots)$

which is the collection of the eigenfunctions (1.2) and (1.3). These functions are all periodic and have the common period $2L$; that is,

$$\cos\frac{n\pi}{L}(x + 2L) = \cos\frac{n\pi x}{L}$$

$$\sin\frac{n\pi}{L}(x + 2L) = \sin\frac{n\pi x}{L}$$

for all n. We shall show that these functions also form an orthogonal system on the larger interval $-L \le x \le L$. Indeed, for each integer $n \ge 1$, it is clear that

(1.5) $\qquad\qquad \int_{-L}^L 1 \cdot \cos\frac{n\pi x}{L}\, dx = \int_{-L}^L 1 \cdot \sin\frac{n\pi x}{L}\, dx = 0$

which shows that the function 1 is orthogonal to the functions $\cos(n\pi x/L)$ and $\sin(n\pi x/L)$ for $n \ge 1$ on the interval $[-L, L]$.

Next, let m and n be two distinct integers. From the trigonometric identities

$$\cos\frac{m\pi x}{L} \cos\frac{n\pi x}{L} = \frac{1}{2}\left[\cos\frac{(m - n)\pi x}{L} + \cos\frac{(m + n)\pi x}{L}\right]$$

$$\sin\frac{m\pi x}{L} \sin\frac{n\pi x}{L} = \frac{1}{2}\left[\cos\frac{(m - n)\pi x}{L} - \cos\frac{(m + n)\pi x}{L}\right]$$

we immediately obtain

(1.6) $\qquad\qquad \int_{-L}^L \cos\frac{m\pi x}{L} \cos\frac{n\pi x}{L}\, dx = 0$

(1.7) $\qquad\qquad \int_{-L}^L \sin\frac{m\pi x}{L} \sin\frac{n\pi x}{L}\, dx = 0$

Formulas (1.6) and (1.7) show respectively that orthogonality of the eigenfunctions (1.3) and (1.2) remain valid on the extended interval $-L \leq x \leq L$.
    Finally, from the identities

$$\sin \frac{m\pi x}{L} \cos \frac{n\pi x}{L} = \frac{1}{2} \left[\sin \frac{(m-n)\pi x}{L} + \sin \frac{(m+n)\pi x}{L} \right]$$

we see that for all integers m and n

(1.8)
$$\int_{-L}^{L} \sin \frac{m\pi x}{L} \cos \frac{n\pi x}{L} \, dx = 0$$

This shows that each of the functions in (1.2) is orthogonal to each of the
functions in (1.3) on the interval $-L \leq x \leq L$, and vice versa. Therefore, by
definition, it follows that the functions in (1.4) form an orthogonal system on the
interval $-L \leq x \leq L$.
    Note that because of the periodicity of the functions (1.4), formulas (1.5)–(1.8)
also hold over any other interval of integration that is of length $2L$. Thus, the
set (1.4) is also orthogonal on the interval $a \leq x \leq a + 2L$ for arbitrary
constant a.
    It is worthwhile to note that the functions in (1.4) actually constitute a set of
eigenfunctions for the eigenvalue problem

(1.9) $u'' + \lambda u = 0;$ $u(-L) - u(L) = 0;$ $u'(-L) - u'(L) = 0$

whose orthogonality property can be deduced from Theorem 5.1, Chapter 4.
Indeed, we observe that although the problem (1.9) is not of the Sturm-Liouville
type because its boundary conditions are periodic, nevertheless it has real eigenvalues given by $\lambda_n = n^2 \pi^2 / L^2$, $n = 0, 1, 2, \ldots$. (Problem 15, Exercises 4.4.)
For each integer $n \geq 1$, the functions $u_n(x) = \cos(n\pi x/L)$ and $v_n(x) =$
$\sin(n\pi x/L)$ constitute two linearly independent eigenfunctions, corresponding
to the same eigenvalue $\lambda_n = n^2 \pi^2 / L^2$, which are orthogonal on the interval
$-L \leq x \leq L$. The function $u_0 = 1$ is the only eigenfunction associated with
the smallest eigenvalue $\lambda_0 = 0$. Now, for the differential equation in (1.9), we
have $p(x) = 1$. Hence, by Problem 10, Exercises 4.5, the orthogonality of these
eigenfunctions corresponding to distinct eigenvalues follows from Theorem 5.1,
Chapter 4. Thus, the set (1.4) is an orthogonal system of eigenfunctions for the
problem (1.9). Notice that except for $\lambda_0 = 0$, the eigenvalues of the problem
are not simple, as is the case with a regular Sturm-Liouville.
    The orthonormal system corresponding to the set (1.4) is given by

(1.10)
$$\frac{1}{\sqrt{2L}}, \qquad \frac{1}{\sqrt{L}} \cos \frac{n\pi x}{L}, \qquad \frac{1}{\sqrt{L}} \sin \frac{n\pi x}{L} \qquad (n \geq 1)$$

2. Fourier Series

    We now consider the problem of expanding an arbitrary function in infinite
series of the form considered in Section 6 of Chapter 4, using the orthonormal
system (1.10).

Let f be a function defined on the interval $-L \le x \le L$. Then the formal eigenfunction expansion of f with respect to the system (1.10) is given by

$$(2.1) \qquad f(x) \sim \frac{c_0}{\sqrt{2L}} + \sum_{n=1}^{\infty} \left(\frac{c_n}{\sqrt{L}} \cos \frac{n\pi x}{L} + \frac{c_n'}{\sqrt{L}} \sin \frac{n\pi x}{L} \right)$$

where the Fourier coefficients are given by

$$c_0 = \frac{1}{\sqrt{2L}} \int_{-L}^{L} f(x)\, dx$$

$$(2.2) \qquad c_n = \frac{1}{\sqrt{L}} \int_{-L}^{L} f(x) \cos \frac{n\pi x}{L}\, dx$$

$$c_n' = \frac{1}{\sqrt{L}} \int_{-L}^{L} f(x) \sin \frac{n\pi x}{L}\, dx$$

for $n = 1, 2, \dots$. If we incorporate in the formulas (2.2) the common factor $1/\sqrt{L}$ appearing in the series (2.1), then we can write the series in the convenient form

$$(2.3) \qquad f(x) \sim \frac{a_0}{2} + \sum_{n=1}^{\infty} \left(a_n \cos \frac{n\pi x}{L} + b_n \sin \frac{n\pi x}{L} \right)$$

where the coefficients a_n and b_n are now given by

$$a_0 = \frac{1}{L} \int_{-L}^{L} f(x)\, dx$$

$$(2.4) \qquad a_n = \frac{1}{L} \int_{-L}^{L} f(x) \cos \frac{n\pi x}{L}\, dx \qquad (n = 0, 1, 2, \dots)$$

$$b_n = \frac{1}{L} \int_{-L}^{L} f(x) \sin \frac{n\pi x}{L}\, dx \qquad (n = 1, 2, \dots)$$

The series in (2.3), with its coefficients given by (2.4), is called the Fourier series of f on the interval $-L \le x \le L$. We notice that this series is precisely the eigenfunction expansion of f with respect to the set (1.4) of eigenfunctions, with the constant 1 replaced by $\frac{1}{2}$; hence, the coefficients (2.4) are the Fourier coefficients of f with respect to that set.

If f is periodic, of period $2L$, then the integrands in the integrals (2.4) are also periodic, of period $2L$. Hence, the interval of integration $[-L, L]$ can be replaced by any other interval of length $2L$; that is, (2.4) can also be written as

$$a_n = \frac{1}{L} \int_{a}^{a+2L} f(x) \cos \frac{n\pi x}{L}\, dx \qquad (n = 0, 1, 2, \dots)$$

$$(2.5)$$

$$b_n = \frac{1}{L} \int_{a}^{a+2L} f(x) \sin \frac{n\pi x}{L}\, dx \qquad (n = 1, 2, \dots)$$

for any choice of the constant a.

In Section 5 of the present chapter, we shall show that if f satisfies certain restrictions, then its Fourier series converges pointwise to f on $-L \le x \le L$.

In such case, the function can then be represented by its Fourier series, and thus the symbol $\sim$ in (2.3) can be replaced by the equality sign.

We observe that whenever the series in (2.3) converges on the interval $-L \le x \le L$, it converges for all x to a periodic function of period $2L$. This is so because each term of the series is periodic, of period $2L$. Therefore, if the series converges to f on $-L \le x \le L$, it will converge to the periodic extension of f for all x with period $2L$. Consequently, if f is defined for all x and is not periodic, it cannot have a Fourier series representation that is valid for all x.

Example 2.1. Find the Fourier series of the function

$$f(x) = \begin{cases} 0 & (-\pi \le x \le 0) \\ x & (0 < x \le \pi) \end{cases}$$

Solution: We compute the Fourier coefficients a_n and b_n according to the formulas (2.4), noting that here $L = \pi$. We find

$$a_0 = \frac{1}{\pi} \int_{-\pi}^{\pi} f(x)\, dx = \frac{1}{\pi} \left[0 + \int_0^{\pi} x\, dx \right] = \frac{\pi}{2}$$

$$a_n = \frac{1}{\pi} \int_0^{\pi} x \cos nx\, dx$$

$$= \frac{1}{\pi} \left(\frac{x \sin nx}{n} + \frac{\cos nx}{n^2} \right) \Bigg|_0^{\pi}$$

$$= \frac{1}{\pi} \frac{\cos n\pi - 1}{n^2} = \frac{(-1)^n - 1}{\pi n^2}$$

$$b_n = \frac{1}{\pi} \int_0^{\pi} x \sin nx\, dx$$

$$= \frac{1}{\pi} \left(\frac{-x \cos nx}{n} + \frac{\sin nx}{n^2} \right) \Bigg|_0^{\pi}$$

$$= \frac{-\cos n\pi}{n} = \frac{(-1)^{n+1}}{n}$$

for $n = 1, 2, \dots$. Thus, the Fourier series of f is

$$f(x) \sim \frac{\pi}{4} + \sum_{n=1}^{\infty} \left[\frac{(-1)^n - 1}{\pi n^2} \cos nx + \frac{(-1)^{n+1}}{n} \sin nx \right]$$

$$\sim \frac{\pi}{4} - \sum_{n=1}^{\infty} \left[\frac{2}{\pi(2n - 1)^2} \cos(2n - 1)x + \frac{(-1)^n}{n} \sin nx \right]$$

In Section 5 it will be shown that this Fourier series does converge to the function on the interval $-\pi < x < \pi$. Hence, outside this interval, the series converges to the periodic extension of f with period 2π. The graph of that extension is shown in Figure 5.1, where it is seen that the extension is discontinuous at the points $x = \pm(2n - 1)\pi$, $n = 1, 2, \dots$. At these points, the series will be seen to converge to the value $\pi/2$, which is the average of the left-hand and right-hand limits of the extended function at the points of discontinuity.

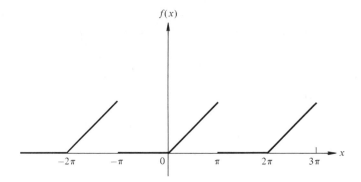

FIG. 5–1   *Periodic function.*

Example 2.2.   Find the Fourier series of the function $f(x) = |x|$, $-\pi \le x \le \pi$.

Solution: Computing for the Fourier coefficients of the function, we find

$$a_0 = \frac{1}{\pi}\left[\int_{-\pi}^{0} -x\,dx + \int_{0}^{\pi} x\,dx\right] = \frac{\pi}{2} + \frac{\pi}{2} = \pi$$

$$a_n = \frac{1}{\pi}\left[\int_{-\pi}^{0} -x\cos nx\,dx + \int_{0}^{\pi} x\cos nx\,dx\right]$$

$$= -\left.\frac{nx\sin nx + \cos nx}{n^2\pi}\right|_{-\pi}^{0} + \left.\frac{nx\sin nx + \cos nx}{n^2\pi}\right|_{0}^{\pi}$$

$$= \frac{2}{n^2\pi}[(-1)^n - 1]$$

$$b_n = \frac{1}{\pi}\left[\int_{-\pi}^{0} -x\sin nx\,dx + \int_{0}^{\pi} x\sin nx\,dx\right]$$

$$= \left.\frac{nx\cos nx - \sin nx}{n^2\pi}\right|_{-\pi}^{0} - \left.\frac{nx\cos nx - \sin nx}{n^2\pi}\right|_{0}^{\pi}$$

$$= 0$$

for $n = 1, 2, \ldots$. Hence,

$$|x| \sim \frac{\pi}{2} + \frac{2}{\pi}\sum_{n=1}^{\infty} \frac{(-1)^n - 1}{n^2}\cos nx$$

$$\sim \frac{\pi}{2} - \frac{4}{\pi}\sum_{n=1}^{\infty} \frac{\cos(2n-1)x}{(2n-1)^2} \qquad (-\pi \le x \le \pi)$$

It will follow from Section 5 that this series converges to the function $|x|$ on the interval indicated and hence to the periodic extension of that function with period 2π for all x outside that interval (Fig. 5.2). Notice that here the periodic extension is continuous at all points.

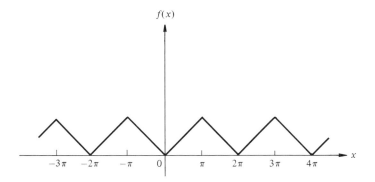

$f(x)$

FIG. 5-2   *Periodic extension of $f(x) \sim |x|$.*

The Fourier series in (2.3), with coefficients given by (2.4), can be written in the equivalent form

(2.6)
$$f(x) \sim \sum_{n=-\infty}^{\infty} c_n e^{in\pi x/L}$$

where the coefficients c_n are given by

(2.7)
$$c_n = \frac{1}{2L} \int_{-L}^{L} f(x) e^{-in\pi x/L} \, dx \quad (n = 0, \pm 1, \pm 2, \ldots)$$

Indeed, (2.6) implies that

(2.8)
$$f(x) \sim c_0 + \sum_{n=1}^{\infty} c_n e^{in\pi x/L} + \sum_{n=1}^{\infty} c_{-n} e^{-in\pi x/L}$$

By the Euler's formula, $e^{it} = \cos t + i \sin t$; this becomes

(2.9)
$$
\begin{aligned}
f(x) \sim &\; c_0 + \sum_{n=1}^{\infty} c_n \left(\cos \frac{n\pi x}{L} + i \sin \frac{n\pi x}{L} \right) \\
&+ \sum_{n=1}^{\infty} c_{-n} \left(\cos \frac{n\pi x}{L} - i \sin \frac{n\pi x}{L} \right) \\
\sim &\; c_0 + \sum_{n=1}^{\infty} \left[(c_n + c_{-n}) \cos \frac{n\pi x}{L} + i(c_n - c_{-n}) \sin \frac{n\pi x}{L} \right]
\end{aligned}
$$

Now, by (2.7), we see that for $n \geq 1$,

$$
\begin{aligned}
c_n + c_{-n} &= \frac{1}{2L} \int_{-L}^{L} f(x)(e^{-in\pi x/L} + e^{in\pi x/L}) \, dx \\
&= \frac{1}{L} \int_{-L}^{L} f(x) \frac{e^{in\pi x/L} + e^{-in\pi x/L}}{2} \, dx \\
&= \frac{1}{L} \int_{-L}^{L} f(x) \cos \frac{n\pi x}{L} \, dx \\
&= a_n
\end{aligned}
$$

and

$$i(c_n - c_{-n}) = \frac{i}{2L} \int_{-L}^{L} f(x)(e^{-in\pi x/L} - e^{in\pi x/L}) \, dx$$

$$= \frac{1}{L} \int_{-L}^{L} f(x) \frac{e^{in\pi x/L} - e^{-in\pi x/L}}{2i} \, dx$$

$$= \frac{1}{L} \int_{-L}^{L} f(x) \sin \frac{n\pi x}{L} \, dx$$

$$= b_n$$

and

$$c_0 = \frac{1}{2L} \int_{-L}^{L} f(x) \, dx = \frac{a_0}{2}$$

So the series in (2.6), with its coefficients given by (2.7), is precisely the Fourier series of f. This series is known as the complex form of Fourier series.

Exercises 5.1

In Problems 1 through 7, find the Fourier series of the given function on the interval indicated and describe graphically the periodic function to which the series can converge.

1. $f(x) = \begin{cases} -\pi & (-\pi < x < 0) \\ x & (0 \le x < \pi) \end{cases}$

2. $f(x) = \begin{cases} 0 & (-\pi \le x \le 0) \\ x & (0 \le x \le \pi/2) \\ \pi - x & (\pi/2 \le x \le \pi) \end{cases}$

3. $f(x) = \begin{cases} x + \frac{1}{2} & (-1 \le x \le 0) \\ \frac{1}{2} - x & (0 \le x \le 1) \end{cases}$

4. $f(x) = e^{ax}$ $(-L < x < L)$

5. $f(x) = \begin{cases} 0 & (-\pi \le x \le 0) \\ \sin x & (0 \le x \le \pi) \end{cases}$

6. $f(x) = x \cos \dfrac{\pi x}{L}$ $(-L \le x \le L)$

7. $f(x) = x + x^2$ $(-L < x < L)$

8. Using the result of Problem 4, find the Fourier series of the function $\cosh ax = (e^{ax} + e^{-ax})/2$ on the interval $[-\pi, \pi]$.

9. As in Problem 8, find the Fourier series of the function $\sinh ax = (e^{ax} - e^{-ax})/2$ on the interval $(-\pi, \pi)$.

10. Let f be a periodic function with period $2L$ and set $g(x) = f(x - L)$ for all x. Show that

$$g(x) \sim \frac{a_0}{2} + \sum_{n=1}^{\infty} (-1)^n \left(a_n \cos \frac{n\pi x}{L} + b_n \sin \frac{n\pi x}{L} \right)$$

where a_n and b_n are the Fourier coefficients of $f(x)$.

11. Using the result of Problem 10, obtain from Problem 5 the Fourier series of the function

$$f(x) = \begin{cases} -\sin x & (-\pi \le x \le 0) \\ 0 & (0 \le x \le \pi) \end{cases}$$

$$f(x) = f(x + 2\pi)$$

12. As in Problem 11, obtain from the result in Example 2.2 the Fourier series of the function

$$f(x) = \begin{cases} x + \pi & (-\pi \le x \le 0) \\ -x + \pi & (0 \le x \le \pi) \end{cases}$$

$$f(x) = f(x + 2\pi)$$

13. If $f(x - L) = f(x)$, show that $a_{2n-1} = b_{2n-1} = 0$ for $n \ge 1$ and that

$$a_{2n} = \frac{2}{L} \int_0^L f(x) \cos \frac{2n\pi x}{L} \, dx \qquad (n = 0, 1, \ldots)$$

$$b_{2n} = \frac{2}{L} \int_0^L f(x) \sin \frac{2n\pi x}{L} \, dx \qquad (n = 1, 2, \ldots)$$

14. Apply the result of Problem 13 to obtain the Fourier series of the function

$$f(x) = x, \qquad 0 \le x < \pi, \qquad f(x - \pi) = f(x)$$

15. Using the complex form of Fourier series (2.6), show that the function in Problem 4 has the expansion

$$e^{ax} \sim \sinh aL \sum_{n=-\infty}^{\infty} (-1)^n \frac{aL + in\pi}{a^2 L^2 + n^2 \pi^2} e^{in\pi x/L}$$

3. Fourier Cosine and Sine Series

We recall that a function defined on an interval $-L \le x \le L$ is said to be even if

(3.1) $$f(-x) = f(x)$$

and odd if

(3.2) $$f(-x) = -f(x)$$

for all x in the interval. If f is an odd function, then it follows from the definition that $f(0) = 0$. Geometrically, the graph of an even function is symmetric with respect to the y-axis, and that of an odd function is symmetric with respect to the origin (Fig. 5.3).

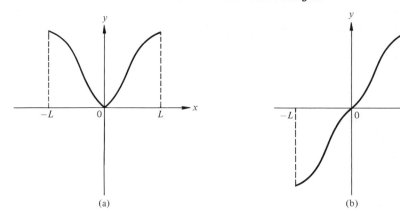

FIG. 5-3 (a) *Even function.* (b) *Odd function.*

If f is even and integrable on $[-L, L]$, then

(3.3)
$$\int_{-L}^{L} f(x)\, dx = 2 \int_{0}^{L} f(x)\, dx$$

This follows readily from the geometrical interpretation of the integral as the area under the curve $y = f(x)$ bounded by the lines $x = \pm L$. Analytically, it is easily proved by writing

$$\int_{-L}^{L} f(x)\, dx = \int_{-L}^{0} f(x)\, dx + \int_{0}^{L} f(x)\, dx$$

and setting $x = -t$ in the first integral on the right. Using the definition (3.1), we thus obtain

$$\int_{-L}^{L} f(x)\, dx = \int_{L}^{0} f(-t)(-dt) + \int_{0}^{L} f(x)\, dx$$

$$= \int_{0}^{L} f(t)\, dt + \int_{0}^{L} f(x)\, dx$$

$$= 2 \int_{0}^{L} f(x)\, dx$$

On the other hand, if f is odd and integrable on $[-L, L]$, then by a similar argument we have

(3.4)
$$\int_{-L}^{L} f(x)\, dx = 0$$

It is easily shown from the definition that the product of two even or two odd functions is an even function and that the product of an even and an odd function is an odd function. For example, if both f and g are even and if we set $h(x) = f(x)g(x)$, then

$$h(-x) = f(-x)g(-x) = f(x)g(x) = h(x)$$

which shows that h is even. On the other hand, if f is even and g is odd, then

$$h(-x) = f(-x)g(-x) = f(x)[-g(x)] = -f(x)g(x) = -h(x)$$

so that h is odd. Similarly, the ratio of two functions that are both even or both odd is an even function, and the ratio of two functions of which one is even and the other odd is an odd function. Here it is assumed, of course, that the function in the denominator never vanishes.

Now suppose that f is an even function on the interval $-L \le x \le L$. Let us consider its Fourier series

$$f(x) \sim \frac{a_0}{2} + \sum_{n=1}^{\infty} \left(a_n \cos \frac{n\pi x}{L} + b_n \sin \frac{n\pi x}{L} \right)$$

where

$$a_n = \frac{1}{L} \int_{-L}^{L} f(x) \cos \frac{n\pi x}{L} \, dx \qquad (n = 0, 1, 2, \ldots)$$

$$b_n = \frac{1}{L} \int_{-L}^{L} f(x) \sin \frac{n\pi x}{L} \, dx \qquad (n = 1, 2, \ldots)$$

For each integer n, we note that $\cos(n\pi x/L)$ is even and $\sin(n\pi x/L)$ is odd; hence, $f(x) \cos(n\pi x/L)$ is even and $f(x) \sin(n\pi x/L)$ is odd. Therefore, according to (3.3) and (3.4), we have

$$a_n = \frac{1}{L} \int_{-L}^{L} f(x) \cos \frac{n\pi x}{L} \, dx$$

$$= \frac{2}{L} \int_{0}^{L} f(x) \cos \frac{n\pi x}{L} \, dx \qquad (n = 0, 1, 2, \ldots)$$

and

$$b_n = \frac{1}{L} \int_{-L}^{L} f(x) \sin \frac{n\pi x}{L} \, dx = 0 \qquad (n = 1, 2, \ldots)$$

respectively. Thus, if f is an even function on $[-L, L]$, its Fourier series reduces to

(3.5) $$f(x) \sim \frac{a_0}{2} + \sum_{n=1}^{\infty} a_n \cos \frac{n\pi x}{L}$$

where

(3.6) $$a_n = \frac{2}{L} \int_{0}^{L} f(x) \cos \frac{n\pi x}{L} \, dx \qquad (n = 0, 1, 2, \ldots)$$

This series is called the Fourier cosine series of f on the interval $0 \le x \le L$.

We note that formula (3.6) for the coefficients a_n involves only the values of f in the interval $0 \le x \le L$. Hence, even when f is defined only on the interval $[0, L]$, one can formally form the Fourier cosine series of f. If the series converges to the function on $[0, L]$, then the series automatically extends the function into the interval $-L \le x \le 0$ as an even function, and extends it outside the interval $[-L, L]$ as an even periodic function with period $2L$.

In terms of the idea of eigenfunction expansion, we observe that the Fourier cosine series (3.5) on $[0, L]$ is precisely the eigenfunction expansion of the function f with respect to the system of eigenfunctions $\{1/2, \cos(n\pi x/L)\}$ of the Sturm-Liouville problem

$$u'' + \lambda u = 0, \qquad u'(0) = 0, \qquad u'(L) = 0$$

On the other hand, if f is an odd function on the interval $-L \le x \le L$, then $f(x) \cos(n\pi x/L)$ is odd and $f(x) \sin(n\pi x/L)$ is even for each integer n. Accordingly, we have

$$a_n = \frac{1}{L} \int_{-L}^{L} f(x) \cos \frac{n\pi x}{L} \, dx = 0 \qquad (n = 0, 1, 2, \ldots)$$

and

$$b_n = \frac{1}{L} \int_{-L}^{L} f(x) \sin \frac{n\pi x}{L} \, dx$$

$$= \frac{2}{L} \int_{0}^{L} f(x) \sin \frac{n\pi x}{L} \, dx \qquad (n = 1, 2, \ldots)$$

Therefore, for an odd function f defined on $[-L, L]$, the Fourier series reduces to

$$(3.7) \qquad f(x) \sim \sum_{n=1}^{\infty} b_n \sin \frac{n\pi x}{L}$$

where

$$(3.8) \qquad b_n = \frac{2}{L} \int_{0}^{L} f(x) \sin \frac{n\pi x}{L} \, dx \qquad (n = 1, 2, \ldots)$$

This is called the Fourier sine series of f on the interval $0 \le x \le L$.

The sine series extends f into the interval $-L \le x \le 0$ as an odd function whenever it converges to f on the interval $0 \le x \le L$. Outside the interval $-L \le x \le L$, the series represents the odd periodic extension of the function with period $2L$. Here we notice that the Fourier sine series (3.7) is the eigenfunction expansion of f with respect to the eigenfunctions (1.2) of the Sturm-Liouville problem (1.1).

In summary, given a function f on the interval $0 \le x \le L$, it is possible to represent the function on that interval by either a Fourier cosine series or a Fourier sine series. In the former case, the function is extended as an even function into the interval $-L \le x \le 0$ and as an even periodic function for all x with period $2L$. In the latter case, the function is extended as an odd function into $[-L, 0]$ and as an odd periodic function for all x with period $2L$.

Example 3.1. Find the Fourier cosine and sine series of the function $f(x) = x$, $0 \leq x \leq \pi$.

Solution: The Fourier coefficients for the cosine series are

$$a_0 = \frac{2}{\pi} \int_0^\pi x \, dx = \pi$$

$$a_n = \frac{2}{\pi} \int_0^\pi x \cos nx \, dx$$

$$= \frac{2}{\pi} \left(\frac{nx \sin nx + \cos nx}{n^2} \right) \Big|_0^\pi$$

$$= \frac{2}{\pi} \frac{(-1)^n - 1}{n^2}$$

Hence, the Fourier cosine series is

$$x \sim \frac{\pi}{2} + \frac{2}{\pi} \sum_{n=1}^\infty \frac{(-1)^n - 1}{n^2} \cos nx \qquad (0 \leq x \leq \pi)$$

This series is the same as the series we obtained in Example 2.2, as should be expected. (Why?) The series converges to the function x on $[0, \pi]$ and represents the even periodic extension of the function for all x with periodic 2π. The periodic extension coincides with the extension of the function considered in Example 2.2.
The Fourier coefficients for the sine series are

$$b_n = \frac{2}{\pi} \int_0^\pi x \sin nx \, dx$$

$$= \frac{2}{\pi} \left(\frac{-nx \cos nx + \sin nx}{n^2} \right) \Big|_0^\pi$$

$$= 2 \frac{(-1)^{n+1}}{n}$$

so that we have

$$x \sim 2 \sum_{n=1}^\infty \frac{(-1)^{n+1}}{n} \sin nx$$

It will be seen that this series converges to the function x for $0 \leq x < \pi$. For all x outside the interval $[0, \pi]$, the series extends the function as an odd periodic function with period 2π (Fig. 5.4). The periodic function is discontinuous at the points $x = \pm n\pi$, $n = 1, 3, 5, \ldots$, at which the series has the value zero. We note in passing that on the interval $0 \leq x \leq \pi$, the function $f(x) = x$ can also be represented by the Fourier series obtained in Example 2.1.

Example 3.2. Find the Fourier cosine series of the function

$$f(x) = \begin{cases} \cos x & (0 \leq x \leq \pi/2) \\ 0 & (\pi/2 \leq x \leq \pi) \end{cases}$$

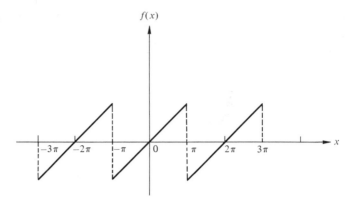

FIG. 5–4   *Odd periodic extension of $f(x)$.*

Solution: The Fourier coefficients for $n = 0$ and $n = 1$ are

$$a_0 = \frac{2}{\pi} \int_0^{\pi/2} \cos x \; dx = \frac{2}{\pi} \sin x \Big|_0^{\pi/2} = \frac{2}{\pi}$$

$$a_1 = \frac{2}{\pi} \int_0^{\pi/2} \cos^2 x \; dx$$

$$= \frac{1}{\pi} \int_0^{\pi/2} (\cos 2x + 1) \; dx = \frac{1}{2}$$

For $n > 1$, we have

$$a_n = \frac{2}{\pi} \int_0^{\pi/2} \cos x \cos nx \; dx$$

$$= \frac{1}{\pi} \int_0^{\pi/2} [\cos(n + 1)x + \cos(n - 1)x] \; dx$$

$$= \frac{1}{\pi} \left\{ \frac{\sin(n + 1)x}{n + 1} + \frac{\sin(n - 1)x}{n - 1} \right\} \Big|_0^{\pi/2}$$

Since

$$\sin(n \pm 1)\frac{\pi}{2} = \sin \frac{n\pi}{2} \cos \frac{\pi}{2} \pm \cos \frac{n\pi}{2} \sin \frac{\pi}{2}$$

$$= \pm \cos \frac{n\pi}{2}$$

and $\cos(n\pi/2) = 0$ when n is odd, and $\cos(n\pi/2) = (-1)^k$ when $n = 2k$, $k = 1, 2, \ldots$, we obtain

$$a_{2k} = \frac{(-1)^k}{\pi} \left[\frac{1}{2k + 1} - \frac{1}{2k - 1} \right] = \frac{2(-1)^{k+1}}{\pi(4k^2 - 1)}$$

Thus, we have

$$f(x) \sim \frac{1}{\pi} + \frac{1}{2} \cos x + \frac{2}{\pi} \sum_{k=1}^{\infty} \frac{(-1)^{k+1}}{(4k^2 - 1)} \cos 2kx$$

If we assume that the series converges to f on $0 \le x \le \pi$, then outside this interval the series converges to the continuous even periodic extension of f for all x. The graph of f and its periodic extension is shown in Figure 5.5.

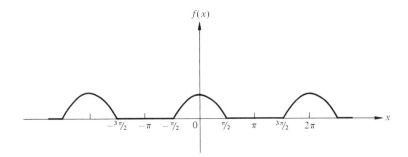

FIG. 5–5 *Even periodic extension of $f(x)$.*

Exercises 5.2

In Problems 1 through 5, find the Fourier cosine and sine series of the given function, and graph the periodic function to which the series can converge outside the given interval.

1. $f(x) = \begin{cases} x, & 0 \le x \le \frac{1}{2} \\ 1 - x, & \frac{1}{2} \le x \le 1 \end{cases}$.

2. $f(x) = \pi^2 - x^2, \quad 0 \le x < \pi$.

3. $f(x) = 1 - x, \quad 0 < x < 2$.

4. $f(x) = \begin{cases} x, & 0 \le x \le 1 \\ 1, & 1 \le x < 2 \end{cases}$.

5. $f(x) = e^x, \quad 0 < x < \pi$.

In Problems 6 through 10, find the Fourier cosine series of the function on the given interval.

6. $f(x) = \cos 2x, \quad 0 \le x \le \pi$.

7. $f(x) = \begin{cases} \sin \pi x, & 0 \le x \le \frac{1}{2} \\ 1 & \frac{1}{2} \le x \le 1 \end{cases}$.

8. $f(x) = \sinh x, \quad 0 \le x \le \pi$.

9. $f(x) = \begin{cases} x, & 0 \le x < 1 \\ 0, & 1 < x < 2 \end{cases}$.

10. $f(x) = \sin x, \quad 0 \le x \le \pi$.

In Problems 11 through 15, find the Fourier sine series of the function on the given interval.

11. $f(x) = \begin{cases} \sin x, & 0 \le x < \pi/2 \\ 0, & \pi/2 < 0 \le \pi \end{cases}$.

12. $f(x) = x(1 - x), \quad 0 \le x \le 1.$

13. $f(x) = \begin{cases} x^2, & 0 \le x \le 1 \\ 1, & 1 \le x \le 2 \end{cases}.$

14. $f(x) = \cosh x, \quad 0 \le x < \pi.$

15. $f(x) = \cos \pi x, \quad 0 \le x \le 1.$

4. Bessel's Inequality; Riemann-Lebesgue Theorem

In preparation for proving pointwise convergence of Fourier series, to be presented in the next section, we derive here Bessel's inequality for the Fourier coefficients a_n and b_n given in (2.4) of a function f with respect to the orthogonal system

(4.1)
$$\left\{ \frac{1}{2}, \ \cos \frac{n\pi x}{L}, \ \sin \frac{n\pi x}{L} \right\}$$

on $-L \le x \le L$. We shall assume throughout this discussion that f is a function that is piecewise continuous on the interval $-L \le x \le L$. Then, clearly, the Fourier coefficients a_n and b_n of f exist. Now, by using (2.4), we see from (2.2) that

$$c_0^2 = \frac{L}{2} \left[\frac{1}{L} \int_{-L}^{L} f(x) \, dx \right]^2 = L \frac{a_0^2}{2}$$

$$c_n^2 = L \left[\frac{1}{L} \int_{-L}^{L} f(x) \cos \frac{n\pi x}{L} \, dx \right]^2 = L a_n^2$$

$$c_n'^2 = L \left[\frac{1}{L} \int_{-L}^{L} f(x) \sin \frac{n\pi x}{L} \, dx \right]^2 = L b_n^2$$

for $n = 1, 2, \dots$. Hence, by the Bessel's inequality (6.13) of Chapter 4, we have

$$c_0^2 + \sum_{n=1}^{m} (c_n^2 + c_n'^2) = L \left[\frac{a_0^2}{2} + \sum_{n=1}^{m} (a_n^2 + b_n^2) \right]$$

$$\le \int_{-L}^{L} f^2(x) \, dx$$

or

(4.2)
$$\frac{a_0^2}{2} + \sum_{n=1}^{m} (a_n^2 + b_n^2) \le \frac{1}{L} \int_{-L}^{L} f^2(x) \, dx$$

for any m. This is the form of the Bessel's inequality we seek for the coefficients a_n and b_n.

By assumption, f and hence also f^2 is piecewise continuous on $[-L, L]$ so that the integral on the right of (4.2) exists. Since the integral is independent of m and (4.2) is true for any m, no matter how large, we find on letting $m \to \infty$,

$$(4.3) \qquad \frac{a_0^2}{2} + \sum_{n=1}^{\infty} (a_n^2 + b_n^2) \leq \frac{1}{L} \int_{-L}^{L} f^2(x)\, dx$$

This says, in particular, that the series

$$(4.4) \qquad \frac{a_0^2}{2} + \sum_{n=1}^{\infty} (a_n^2 + b_n^2)$$

converges. Thus we have established the following result.

THEOREM 4.1. *If f is a piecewise continuous function on the interval $-L \leq x \leq L$, then the series (4.4) of squares of the Fourier coefficients of f with respect to the system (4.1) converges and the inequality (4.3) holds.*

The fact that (4.4) converges implies that

$$(4.5) \qquad \lim_{n \to \infty} a_n = \lim_{n \to \infty} b_n = 0$$

that is, the Fourier coefficients of a piecewise continuous function approach zero as $n \to \infty$. This result is actually a special case of the following theorem, which is due to Riemann and Lebesgue.

THEOREM 4.2. (Riemann-Lebesgue) *If g is a piecewise continuous function on the interval $a \leq t \leq b$, then*

$$(4.6) \qquad \lim_{\lambda \to \infty} \int_a^b g(t) \sin \lambda t\, dt = 0$$

Proof: We first prove the theorem in the case where g is continuous on the interval $a \leq t \leq b$. Set

$$(4.7) \qquad I = \int_a^b g(t) \sin \lambda t\, dt$$

and make the change of variable $t = \tau + (\pi/\lambda)$, assuming that λ is so large that $b - \pi/\lambda > a$. Since $\sin \lambda t = \sin \lambda(\tau + (\pi/\lambda)) = -\sin \lambda\tau$, the integral (4.7) becomes

$$(4.8) \qquad I = -\int_{a-\pi/\lambda}^{b-\pi/\lambda} g\left(\tau + \frac{\pi}{\lambda}\right) \sin \lambda\tau\, d\tau$$

Using again t as the variable of integration in (4.8), and adding the equation to (4.7), we obtain

$$I = \frac{1}{2} \left[\int_a^b g(t) \sin \lambda t \, dt - \int_{a-\pi/\lambda}^{b-\pi/\lambda} g\left(t + \frac{\pi}{\lambda}\right) \sin \lambda t \, dt \right]$$

(4.9)
$$= \frac{1}{2} \left\{ \int_a^{b-\pi/\lambda} \left[g(t) - g\left(t + \frac{\pi}{\lambda}\right) \right] \sin \lambda t \, dt \right.$$

$$\left. + \int_{b-\pi/\lambda}^b g(t) \sin \lambda t \, dt - \int_{a-\pi/\lambda}^a g\left(t + \frac{\pi}{\lambda}\right) \sin \lambda t \, dt \right\}$$

Let M denote the maximum value of $|g(t)|$ on the interval $a \le t \le b$. Then the last two integrals on the right in (4.9) yield

(4.10)
$$\left| \frac{1}{2} \int_{b-\pi/\lambda}^b g(t) \sin \lambda t \, dt \right| \le \frac{M\pi}{2\lambda}$$

and

(4.11)
$$\left| \frac{1}{2} \int_{a-\pi/\lambda}^a g\left(t + \frac{\pi}{\lambda}\right) \sin \lambda t \, dt \right| = \left| \frac{1}{2} \int_a^{a+\pi/\lambda} g(t) \sin \lambda t \, dt \right| \le \frac{M\pi}{2\lambda}$$

respectively.

Now let $\varepsilon > 0$ be any given small number. Since g is continuous on the closed interval $a \le t \le b$, it is uniformly continuous there; that is, corresponding to the given ε, there exists a number δ such that

$$\left| g(t) - g\left(t + \frac{\pi}{\lambda}\right) \right| < \frac{\varepsilon}{b-a} \qquad \left(\text{whenever } \frac{\pi}{\lambda} < \delta\right)$$

where t is any point in the interval $[a, b]$. Then the first term on the right of (4.9) gives

$$\left| \frac{1}{2} \int_a^{b-\pi/\lambda} \left[g(t) - g\left(t + \frac{\pi}{\lambda}\right) \right] \sin \lambda t \, dt \right|$$

(4.12)
$$\le \frac{1}{2} \int_a^{b-\pi/\lambda} \left| g(t) - g\left(t + \frac{\pi}{\lambda}\right) \right| dt$$

$$< \frac{1}{2} \frac{\varepsilon}{b-a} \left(b - a - \frac{\pi}{\lambda} \right) < \frac{\varepsilon}{2}$$

Therefore, if we choose λ sufficiently large so that $\pi/\lambda < \delta$ and $M\pi/\lambda < \varepsilon/2$, then on taking absolute values in (4.9) and using the bounds in (4.10), (4.11), and (4.12), we get $|I| < \varepsilon$, which precisely implies (4.6).

In the general case, let $a = t_0 < t_1 < \cdots < t_n < t_{n+1} = b$ be the points where g is discontinuous. Then

(4.13)
$$\int_a^b g(t) \sin \lambda t \, dt = \sum_{i=0}^n \int_{t_i}^{t_{i+1}} g(t) \sin \lambda t \, dt$$

Since g is continuous on each of the subintervals $t_i \leq t \leq t_{i+1}$, $0 \leq i \leq n$, it follows from the preceding case that each of the integrals on the right in (4.13), and hence their sum, vanishes as $\lambda \to \infty$. This completes the proof of Riemann-Lebesgue's theorem.

With additional condition on the function f, the Riemann-Lebesgue theorem also holds when the integral in (4.6) is improper.

THEOREM 4.3. *If g is a piecewise continuous function on the interval $a \leq t < \infty$ such that the integral*

$$(4.14) \qquad \int_a^\infty |g(t)| \, dt$$

exists (i.e., g is absolutely integrable on $a \leq x < \infty$), then

$$(4.15) \qquad \lim_{\lambda \to \infty} \int_a^\infty g(t) \sin \lambda t \, dt = 0$$

We leave the proof of this theorem as an exercise (Problem 10).

Riemann-Lebesgue theorems (Theorems 4.2 and 4.3) will be essential in the convergence proof of Fourier series (Section 5) and of the Fourier integral formula (Section 7), respectively.

Exercises 5.3

1. From the Fourier series of the function $f(x) = x/2$, $-\pi < x < \pi$, show by Bessel's inequality that

$$\sum_{n=1}^\infty \frac{1}{n^2} \leq \frac{\pi^2}{6}$$

    (See Example 3.1.)

2. From the Fourier series of $f(x) = x^2$, $-\pi \leq x \leq \pi$, show that

$$\sum_{n=1}^\infty \frac{1}{n^4} \leq \frac{\pi^4}{90}$$

3. From the Fourier series of $f(x) = |x|$, $-\pi \leq x \leq \pi$, show that

$$\sum_{n=1}^\infty \frac{1}{(2n-1)^4} \leq \frac{\pi^4}{96}$$

    (See Example 2.2.)

4. From the Fourier series of the function $f(x) = e^x$, $-\pi < x < \pi$, show that

$$1 + 2 \sum_{n=1}^\infty \frac{1}{n^2 + 1} \leq \pi \coth \pi$$

    (See Problem 4, Exercise 5.1.)

5. Let f be piecewise continuous on $0 \le x \le \pi$ and let a_n $(n = 0, 1, \ldots)$ be the coefficients in the Fourier cosine series of f. Show that

$$\frac{a_0^2}{2} + \sum_{n=1}^{\infty} a_n^2 \le \frac{2}{\pi} \int_0^\pi f^2(x)\, dx$$

6. Let f be piecewise continuous on $0 \le x \le \pi$ and let b_n be the coefficients in the Fourier sine series of f. Show that

$$\sum_{n=1}^{\infty} b_n^2 \le \frac{2}{\pi} \int_0^\pi f^2(x)\, dx$$

7. Under the stronger condition that g is continuous and piecewise smooth on $a \le x \le b$, prove the Riemann-Lebesgue theorem by first performing an integration by parts.

8. If g is piecewise continuous on (a, b), show by the Riemann-Lebesgue theorem that

$$\lim_{m \to \infty} \int_a^b g(t) \sin\left(m + \frac{1}{2}\right) t\, dt = 0$$

9. Show that

$$\lim_{m \to \infty} \int_a^b g(t) \cos mt\, dt = 0$$

10. Prove Theorem 4.3. *Hint:* Absolute integrability of g on $a \le t < \infty$ implies that there is a constant B such that $\left| \int_b^\infty g(t)\, dt \right| < \varepsilon/2$, whenever $b > B$, corresponding to a given $\varepsilon > 0$. Let $b > B$ and write

$$\int_a^\infty g(t) \sin \lambda t\, dt = \int_a^b g(t) \sin \lambda t\, dt + \int_b^\infty g(t) \sin \lambda t\, dt$$

Take absolute values on both sides of the equation and use Theorem 4.2 in the first integral.

5. Convergence of Fourier Series

We shall now present conditions under which the Fourier series of a given function can converge to the function. Without loss of generality, we shall assume in our discussion that $L = \pi$. We do this mainly for the sake of convenience as the theorems that we shall prove hold for arbitrary value of L.

Thus, let f be a function defined on the interval $-\pi \le x \le \pi$ and let the function be extended outside $[-\pi, \pi]$ as periodic function with period 2π. Then the Fourier series of f is given by

(5.1) $$f(x) \sim \frac{a_0}{2} + \sum_{n=1}^{\infty} (a_n \cos nx + b_n \sin nx)$$

where

$$a_n = \frac{1}{\pi} \int_{-\pi}^{\pi} f(x) \cos nx \, dx \qquad (n = 0, 1, 2, \ldots)$$

(5.2)

$$b_n = \frac{1}{\pi} \int_{-\pi}^{\pi} f(x) \sin nx \, dx \qquad (n = 1, 2, \ldots)$$

Our goal is to establish conditions on f under which the symbol $\sim$ in (5.1) can be replaced by equality.

Consider the mth partial sum of the series in (5.1); that is,

(5.3) $$S_m(x) = \frac{a_0}{2} + \sum_{n=1}^{m} (a_n \cos nx + b_n \sin nx)$$

Substituting the formulas (5.2) for a_n and b_n in (5.3), we obtain

$$S_m(x) = \frac{1}{2\pi} \int_{-\pi}^{\pi} f(\xi) \, d\xi$$

$$+ \frac{1}{\pi} \sum_{n=1}^{m} \left[\left(\int_{-\pi}^{\pi} f(\xi) \cos n\xi \, d\xi \right) \cos nx \right.$$

(5.4)
$$\left. + \left(\int_{-\pi}^{\pi} f(\xi) \sin n\xi \, d\xi \right) \sin nx \right]$$

$$= \frac{1}{\pi} \int_{-\pi}^{\pi} f(\xi) \left[\frac{1}{2} + \sum_{n=1}^{m} (\cos n\xi \cos nx + \sin n\xi \sin nx) \right] d\xi$$

$$= \frac{1}{\pi} \int_{-\pi}^{\pi} f(\xi) \left[\frac{1}{2} + \sum_{n=1}^{m} \cos n(\xi - x) \right] d\xi$$

The sum inside the bracket in (5.4) can be expressed as

$$\frac{1}{2} + \sum_{n=1}^{m} \cos n(\xi - x) = \frac{\sin(m + \frac{1}{2})(\xi - x)}{2 \sin[(\xi - x)/2]}$$

This can be proved as follows: Let $\xi - x = u$ and set

(5.5) $$S = \frac{1}{2} + \sum_{n=1}^{m} \cos nu$$

Multiplying both sides of the above equation by $2 \sin(1/2)u$, we find

$$2S \sin \frac{1}{2} u = 2 \left(\sin \frac{1}{2} u \right) \left(\frac{1}{2} + \sum_{n=1}^{m} \cos nu \right)$$

$$= \sin \frac{1}{2} u + 2 \sum_{n=1}^{m} \sin \frac{1}{2} u \cos nu$$

Since

$$2 \sin \frac{1}{2} u \cos nu = \sin\left(n + \frac{1}{2}\right) u - \sin\left(n - \frac{1}{2}\right) u,$$

the last equation reduces to

$$2S \sin \frac{1}{2} u = \sin \frac{1}{2} u + \sum_{n=1}^{m} \left[\sin\left(n + \frac{1}{2}\right) u - \sin\left(n - \frac{1}{2}\right) u \right]$$

$$= \sin \frac{1}{2} u + \left[\sin \frac{3}{2} u - \sin \frac{1}{2} u \right] + \cdots$$

$$+ \left[\sin\left(m + \frac{1}{2}\right) u - \sin\left(m - \frac{1}{2}\right) u \right]$$

$$= \sin\left(m + \frac{1}{2}\right) u$$

or

$$S = \frac{\sin(m + 1/2)u}{2 \sin(u/2)}$$

Hence, we have

(5.6) $$\frac{1}{2} + \sum_{n=1}^{m} \cos nu = \frac{\sin(m + 1/2)u}{2 \sin(u/2)}$$

Therefore, (5.4) reduces to

(5.7) $$S_m(x) = \frac{1}{\pi} \int_{-\pi}^{\pi} f(\xi) \frac{\sin(m + 1/2)(\xi - x)}{2 \sin(\xi - x)/2} d\xi$$

If we set $\xi - x = t$, (5.7) becomes

(5.8) $$S_m(x) = \frac{1}{\pi} \int_{-\pi-x}^{\pi-x} f(x + t) \frac{\sin(m + 1/2)t}{2 \sin(t/2)} dt$$

where the interval $[-\pi - x, \pi - x]$ of integration remains of length 2π. Now, by assumption and from (5.6), the functions f and $[\sin(m + 1/2)t]/\sin(t/2)$, and hence their product, are periodic of period 2π. Since the integral of a periodic function is the same over any interval whose length is equal to a period, we finally have, from (5.8),

(5.9) $$S_m(x) = \frac{1}{\pi} \int_{-\pi}^{\pi} f(x + t) \frac{\sin(m + 1/2)t}{2 \sin(t/2)} dt$$

This is called Dirichlet's formula for the partial sum of a Fourier series. This formula will enable us to prove pointwise convergence of a Fourier series to its corresponding function.

In the particular case where $f(x) = 1$, so that the Fourier series of f consists only of the single term 1, (5.9) yields the special result

$$(5.10) \qquad 1 = \frac{1}{\pi} \int_{-\pi}^{\pi} \frac{\sin(m + 1/2)t}{2 \sin(t/2)} \, dt$$

for all m (see also Problem 2 in the exercises). Clearly, the integrand in formula (5.10) is even; hence, it follows that

$$(5.11) \qquad \frac{1}{\pi} \int_{-\pi}^{0} \frac{\sin(m + 1/2)t}{2 \sin(t/2)} \, dt = \frac{1}{\pi} \int_{0}^{\pi} \frac{\sin(m + 1/2)t}{2 \sin(t/2)} \, dt = \frac{1}{2}$$

With the preliminary results obtained above, we are now in position to state and prove our main theorem on convergence of Fourier series.

THEOREM 5.1. *Let f be a function that is piecewise smooth on the interval $-\pi \le x \le \pi$ and periodic with period 2π. Then f can be represented by its Fourier series; that is,*

$$(5.12) \qquad f(x) = \frac{a_0}{2} + \sum_{n=1}^{\infty} (a_n \cos nx + b_n \sin nx)$$

where the coefficients a_n and b_n are given by (5.2). The Fourier series converges to $f(x)$ at all points where f is continuous, and to the average $[f(x - 0) + f(x + 0)]/2$ at all points where f is discontinuous.

Proof: At a point x where f is continuous, we know that $f(x - 0) = f(x + 0) = f(x)$. Hence, it is enough to prove that the Fourier series converges to $[f(x - 0) + f(x + 0)]/2$ for all x. We do this by showing that

$$(5.13) \qquad \lim_{m \to \infty} S_m(x) = \frac{f(x - 0) + f(x + 0)}{2}$$

where S_m is the mth partial sum of the Fourier series.

From the integral formula (5.9), we have

$$S_m(x) = \frac{1}{\pi} \int_{-\pi}^{0} f(x + t) \frac{\sin(m + 1/2)t}{2 \sin(t/2)} \, dt$$

$$+ \frac{1}{\pi} \int_{0}^{\pi} f(x + t) \frac{\sin(m + 1/2)t}{2 \sin(t/2)} \, dt$$

Thus, (5.13) will be established if we can show that

$$(5.14) \qquad \lim_{m \to \infty} \frac{1}{\pi} \int_{-\pi}^{0} f(x + t) \frac{\sin(m + 1/2)t}{2 \sin(t/2)} \, dt = \frac{1}{2} f(x - 0)$$

and

$$(5.15) \qquad \lim_{m \to \infty} \frac{1}{\pi} \int_{0}^{\pi} f(x + t) \frac{\sin(m + 1/2)t}{2 \sin(t/2)} \, dt = \frac{1}{2} f(x + 0)$$

In view of the identities in (5.11), equations (5.14) and (5.15) are equivalent to

(5.16) $$\lim_{m \to \infty} \frac{1}{\pi} \int_{-\pi}^{0} [f(x + t) - f(x - 0)] \frac{\sin(m + 1/2)t}{2 \sin(t/2)} dt = 0$$

and

(5.17) $$\lim_{m \to \infty} \frac{1}{\pi} \int_{0}^{\pi} [f(x + t) - f(x + 0)] \frac{\sin(m + 1/2)t}{2 \sin(t/2)} dt = 0$$

respectively.

Let us consider (5.17) and set

(5.18) $$g(t) = \frac{f(x + t) - f(x + 0)}{2 \sin(t/2)} \qquad (0 < t \le \pi)$$

Since f is piecewise smooth on the interval $-\pi \le x \le \pi$ and is defined by periodicity outside this interval, g is piecewise smooth for $0 < t \le \pi$. At $t = 0$, we note that

$$g(0^+) = \lim_{\substack{t \to 0 \\ t > 0}} \frac{f(x + t) - f(x + 0)}{2 \sin(t/2)}$$

$$= \lim_{\substack{t \to 0 \\ t > 0}} \frac{f(x + t) - f(x + 0)}{t} \cdot \lim_{\substack{t \to 0 \\ t > 0}} \frac{t/2}{\sin(t/2)}$$

$$= \lim_{\substack{t \to 0 \\ t > 0}} \frac{f(x + t) - f(x + 0)}{t}$$

$$= f'_+(x)$$

which exists, since f is piecewise smooth. Hence, g is piecewise smooth, and consequently piecewise continuous, on the interval $0 \le t \le \pi$. By the Riemann-Lebesgue theorem (Theorem 4.2), it follows that

$$\lim_{m \to \infty} \int_{0}^{\pi} g(t) \sin(m + 1/2)t \, dt = 0$$

which proves (5.17). In exactly the same manner, we can show that (5.16) is also true. Thus, (5.13) is established and so the theorem is proved.

Returning to the examples of Section 2, we see that in Example 2.1 the function $f(x) = 0$ when $-\pi \le x \le 0$ and $f(x) = x$ when $0 \le x \le \pi$ is continuous and piecewise smooth on the interval $-\pi \le x \le \pi$. Hence, by the theorem just proved, it follows that

$$\frac{\pi}{4} - \sum_{n=1}^{\infty} \left[\frac{2}{(2n - 1)^2 \pi} \cos(2n - 1)x + \frac{(-1)^n}{n} \sin nx \right] = \begin{cases} 0 & (-\pi < x \le 0) \\ x & (0 \le x < \pi) \\ \pi/2 & (x = \pm\pi) \end{cases}$$

Further, the series converges for all x outside $-\pi \leq x \leq \pi$ to the periodic extension of f, except at $x = \pm n$, $n = 1, 2, \ldots$, where the series converges to the value $\pi/2$.

To illustrate the use of Fourier series in evaluating the sum of series of constants, let us set $x = \pi/2$ in the preceding series. We obtain

$$\frac{\pi}{4} = 1 - \frac{1}{3} + \frac{1}{5} - \frac{1}{7} + \cdots$$

Similarly, setting $x = \pi$, we find

$$\frac{\pi^2}{8} = 1 + \frac{1}{3^2} + \frac{1}{5^2} + \frac{1}{7^2} + \cdots$$

In Example 2.2, the function $f(x) = |x|$ is continuous and piecewise smooth, including its periodic extension outside $[-\pi, \pi]$ for all x. Hence,

$$|x| = \frac{\pi}{2} - \frac{4}{\pi} \sum_{n=1}^{\infty} \frac{\cos(2n-1)x}{(2n-1)^2} \qquad (-\pi \leq x \leq \pi)$$

By the comparison test and Weierstrass M-test (Chapter 1, Section 5), we see that this series converges absolutely and uniformly to $|x|$ on the interval indicated. This important result is actually true of every piecewise smooth continuous function that is periodic, and will be proved in Section 6.

The convergence of the Fourier cosine series or the Fourier sine series corresponding to a given function that is piecewise smooth on the interval $0 \leq x \leq \pi$ can be deduced from the main theorem. Indeed, we note that if f is piecewise smooth on the interval $0 \leq x \leq \pi$, its even or odd extension into the interval $-\pi \leq x \leq 0$ is likewise piecewise smooth so that the extended function is piecewise smooth on $[-\pi, \pi]$. According to Theorem 5.1, the Fourier series of either of these extended functions converges to f on the interval $0 \leq x \leq \pi$ in the manner stated in the theorem. But the Fourier series of an even function reduces to cosine series and that of an odd function to sine series. Thus, the following theorem follows from Theorem 5.1.

THEOREM 5.2. *Let f be a piecewise smooth function on the interval $0 \leq x \leq \pi$. Then f can be represented by a Fourier cosine series*

(5.19) $$f(x) = \frac{a_0}{2} + \sum_{n=1}^{\infty} a_n \cos nx$$

where

(5.20) $$a_n = \frac{2}{\pi} \int_0^{\pi} f(x) \cos nx \, dx \qquad (n = 0, 1, 2, \ldots)$$

or by a Fourier sine series

(5.21) $$f(x) = \sum_{n=1}^{\infty} b_n \sin nx$$

where

(5.22) $$b_n = \frac{2}{\pi} \int_0^\pi f(x) \sin nx \, dx \qquad (n = 1, 2, \ldots)$$

The cosine series and the sine series converge on the intervals $0 \le x \le \pi$ and $0 < x < \pi$, respectively, to $f(x)$ at points where f is continuous and to $[f(x - 0) + f(x + 0)]/2$ at points where f is discontinuous. Moreover, outside the interval $0 \le x \le \pi$, the cosine series converges to the even periodic extension of f, and the sine series to the odd periodic extension of f.

Notice that the even periodic extension of the function f is necessarily continuous at the points $x = \pm n\pi$, $n = 0, 1, 2, \ldots$. Hence, the Fourier cosine series in (5.19) converges at the points $x = 0$ and $x = \pi$ to $f(0^+)$ and $f(\pi^-)$, respectively. On the other hand, the odd periodic extension of f is continuous at $x = \pm n\pi$, $n = 0, 1, 2, \ldots$ if and only if $f(0^+) = f(\pi^-) = 0$. This is evident from the sine series in (5.21), which converges to zero at the points $x = \pm n\pi$.

Exercises 5.4

1. Consider the geometric series

    $$s = e^{iu} + e^{i2u} + \cdots + e^{imu}$$

    (a) Show that

    $$s = e^{iu} \frac{e^{imu} - 1}{e^{iu} - 1}$$

    (b) By multiplying the numerator and denominator by $e^{-iu/2}$, show that

    $$s = \frac{e^{i(m+1/2)u} - e^{iu/2}}{e^{iu/2} - e^{-iu/2}}$$

    (c) By using the formula $e^{iu} = \cos u + i \sin u$, take the real and imaginary parts on both sides of the result found in (b) and obtain the results

    $$\cos u + \cos 2u + \cdots + \cos mu = \frac{\sin(m + 1/2)u}{2 \sin(u/2)} - \frac{1}{2}$$

    $$\sin u + \sin 2u + \cdots + \sin mu = \frac{1}{2} \cot \frac{u}{2} - \frac{\cos(m + 1/2)u}{2 \sin(u/2)}$$

    This gives an alternate method of proving formula (5.6).

2. Obtain (5.10) by integrating the equation (5.6) with respect to u from $-\pi$ to π.

3. Establish the result (5.16).

4. Let $f(x) = x^2$ when $-\pi \le x \le \pi$ and $f(x + 2\pi) = f(x)$ for all x. Prove that

    $$f(x) = \frac{\pi^2}{3} + 4 \sum_{n=1}^\infty (-1)^n \frac{\cos nx}{n^2}$$

for all x, and deduce that

$$\sum_{n=1}^{\infty} \frac{(-1)^{n-1}}{n^2} = \frac{\pi^2}{12}, \qquad \sum_{n=1}^{\infty} \frac{1}{n^2} = \frac{\pi^2}{6}$$

5. Let $f(x + 2\pi) = f(x)$ for all x, where

$$f(x) = \begin{cases} 0 & (-\pi \le x \le 0) \\ \sin x & (0 \le x \le \pi) \end{cases}$$

Prove that for all x,

$$f(x) = \frac{1}{\pi} + \frac{1}{2} \sin x - \frac{2}{\pi} \sum_{n=1}^{\infty} \frac{\cos 2nx}{4n^2 - 1}$$

Deduce that

$$\sum_{n=1}^{\infty} \frac{1}{(4n^2 - 1)} = \frac{1}{2}$$

6. Let $f(x) = 0$ for $-1 < x < 0$, $f(0) = \frac{1}{2}$, and $f(x) = \cos \pi x$ for $0 < x < 1$. Prove that for $-1 < x < 1$,

$$f(x) = \frac{1}{2} \cos \pi x + \frac{4}{\pi} \sum_{n=1}^{\infty} \frac{n}{4n^2 - 1} \sin 2n\pi x$$

7. Let

$$f(x) = \begin{cases} x & (0 \le x \le \pi/2) \\ \pi - x & (\pi/2 \le x \le \pi) \end{cases}$$

(a) If $f(x) = f(x + \pi)$ for all x, show that

$$f(x) = \frac{\pi}{4} - \frac{2}{\pi} \sum_{n=1}^{\infty} \frac{\cos 2(2n - 1)x}{(2n - 1)^2}$$

(b) If $f(x) = -f(-x)$ for $-\pi \le x \le 0$, and $f(x + 2\pi) = f(x)$ for all x, show that

$$f(x) = \frac{4}{\pi} \sum_{n=1}^{\infty} (-1)^{n+1} \frac{\sin(2n - 1)x}{(2n - 1)^2}$$

8. Let the function

$$f(x) = \begin{cases} 1 - x/2h & (0 \le x \le 2h) \\ 0 & (2h \le x \le \pi) \end{cases}$$

be extended as an even periodic function with period 2π. Show that, for all x,

$$f(x) = \frac{2h}{\pi} \left[\frac{1}{2} + \sum_{n=1}^{\infty} \left(\frac{\sin nh}{nh} \right)^2 \cos nx \right]$$

9. Let $f(x - L) = f(x)$ for all x, where

$$f(x) = \begin{cases} \cos(\pi x/L) & (0 \le x \le L/2) \\ -\cos(\pi x/L) & (L/2 \le x \le L) \end{cases}$$

Show that, for all x,

$$f(x) = \frac{2}{\pi} + \frac{4}{\pi} \sum_{n=1}^{\infty} (-1)^{n+1} \frac{\cos(2n\pi x)/L}{4n^2 - 1}$$

(See Problem 13, Exercise 5.1.)

10. Let $f(x - \pi) = f(x)$ for all x, where $f(x) = \cos x$ when $0 < x < \pi$. Show that, for all x, $x \neq n$, $(n = 0, \pm 1, \pm 2, \ldots)$

$$f(x) = \frac{8}{\pi} \sum_{n=1}^{\infty} \frac{n \sin 2nx}{4n^2 - 1}$$

11. Let the function

$$f(x) = \begin{cases} (2/L)x & (0 \leq x \leq L/2) \\ \sin(\pi x/L) & (L/2 \leq x \leq L) \end{cases}$$

be extended as odd periodic function with period $2L$. Show that, for all x,

$$f(x) = \left(\frac{4}{\pi^2} + \frac{1}{2} \right) \sin \frac{\pi x}{L}$$

$$+ \frac{1}{\pi} \sum_{n=1}^{\infty} (-1)^n \left\{ \frac{\sin[(2n\pi x)/L]}{n(4n^2 - 1)} + \frac{4}{\pi} \frac{\sin[(2n + 1)\pi x/L]}{(2n + 1)^2} \right\}$$

Hence, deduce

$$\frac{\pi^2}{8} = \sum_{n=1}^{\infty} \frac{1}{(2n - 1)^2}$$

12. Prove that, for $-\pi \leq x \leq \pi$,

$$\cos ax = \frac{\sin \pi a}{\pi a} + \sum_{n=1}^{\infty} (-1)^n \frac{2a \sin \pi a}{\pi(a^2 - n^2)} \cos nx$$

where a is not an integer. Hence, deduce

$$\cot \pi a = \frac{1}{\pi} \left(\frac{1}{a} - \sum_{n=1}^{\infty} \frac{2a}{n^2 - a^2} \right)$$

6. Uniform Convergence of Fourier Series

In the preceding section we proved that the Fourier series of a piecewise smooth and periodic function converges at all points to the average value of the left-hand and right-hand limits of the function. If, in addition, the function is continuous, then the Fourier series converges to the function at all points. It turns out that in the latter case the series actually converges absolutely and uniformly to the function. We shall establish this fact in this section.

Let f be a continuous piecewise smooth function on the interval $-\pi \leq x \leq \pi$ such that $f(-\pi) = f(\pi)$. Since f is piecewise smooth, f' is piecewise continuous, and hence its Fourier coefficients

(6.1)

$$a'_n = \frac{1}{\pi} \int_{-\pi}^{\pi} f'(x) \cos nx \, dx \qquad (n = 0, 1, 2, \ldots)$$

$$b'_n = \frac{1}{\pi} \int_{-\pi}^{\pi} f'(x) \sin nx \, dx \qquad (n = 1, 2, \ldots)$$

exist. Since f is continuous and $f(-\pi) = f(\pi)$, we see by integration by parts that

$$a_0' = \frac{1}{\pi} \int_{-\pi}^{\pi} f'(x)\, dx = \frac{1}{\pi} [f(\pi) - f(-\pi)] = 0$$

$$a_n' = \frac{1}{\pi} [f(x) \cos nx]_{-\pi}^{\pi} + \frac{n}{\pi} \int_{-\pi}^{\pi} f(x) \sin nx\, dx$$

$$= \frac{\cos n\pi}{\pi} [f(\pi) - f(-\pi)] + nb_n$$

$$= nb_n \qquad\qquad (n = 1, 2, \ldots)$$

$$b_n' = \frac{1}{\pi} [f(x) \sin nx]_{-\pi}^{\pi} - \frac{n}{\pi} \int_{-\pi}^{\pi} f(x) \cos nx\, dx$$

$$= -na_n \qquad\qquad (n = 1, 2, \ldots)$$

where a_n and b_n are the Fourier coefficients of f. Thus,

$$(6.2) \qquad\qquad a_n = -\frac{b_n'}{n}, \qquad b_n = \frac{a_n'}{n} \qquad\qquad (n = 1, 2, \ldots)$$

From the obvious inequalities

$$\left(|a_n'| - \frac{1}{n}\right)^2 = a_n'^2 - \frac{2|a_n'|}{n} + \frac{1}{n^2} \geq 0$$

$$\left(|b_n'| - \frac{1}{n}\right)^2 = b_n'^2 - \frac{2|b_n'|}{n} + \frac{1}{n^2} \geq 0$$

it follows that

$$\frac{|a_n'|}{n} + \frac{|b_n'|}{n} \leq \frac{1}{2} (a_n'^2 + b_n'^2) + \frac{1}{n^2}$$

and, in view of (6.2),

$$|a_n| + |b_n| \leq \frac{1}{2} (a_n'^2 + b_n'^2) + \frac{1}{n^2}$$

Hence,

$$(6.3) \qquad\qquad \sum_{n=1}^{m} (|a_n| + |b_n|) \leq \frac{1}{2} \sum_{n=1}^{m} (a_n'^2 + b_n'^2) + \sum_{n=1}^{m} \frac{1}{n^2}$$

for arbitrary integer m. Since f' is piecewise continuous, it follows from Theorem 4.1 that the first sum on the right of (6.3) converges as $m \to \infty$. The second sum also converges since $\sum_{n=1}^{\infty} (1/n^2)$ is a p-series with $p = 2$. Therefore, the series

$$(6.4) \qquad\qquad \sum_{n=1}^{\infty} (|a_n| + |b_n|)$$

converges. Using this result, we now prove the following theorem on uniform convergence.

THEOREM 6.1. *Let f be a continuous piecewise smooth function on the interval* $-\pi \leq x \leq \pi$ *such that* $f(-\pi) = f(\pi)$. *Then the Fourier series of f*

(6.5)
$$\frac{a_0}{2} + \sum_{n=1}^{\infty} (a_n \cos nx + b_n \sin nx)$$

converges absolutely and uniformly to $f(x)$ *for all x on the interval* $-\pi \leq x \leq \pi$.

Proof: Since $f(-\pi) = f(\pi)$, the periodic extension of f is continuous and piecewise smooth for all x. Hence, by Theorem 5.1, the series (6.5) converges to $f(x)$ for all x on the interval $-\pi \leq x \leq \pi$. To show that the convergence is absolute and uniform, we observe that

$$|a_n \cos nx + b_n \sin nx| \leq |a_n \cos nx| + |b_n \sin nx|$$
$$\leq |a_n| + |b_n|$$

where, according to the previous result, the series $\sum_{n=1}^{\infty} (|a_n| + |b_n|)$ converges. The theorem then follows by the comparison test and Weierstrass M-test.

It should be pointed out that the conditions stated in the theorem actually ensure absolute and uniform convergence of the series (6.5) on any interval to the periodic extension of the function. In this connection, the condition $f(-\pi) = f(\pi)$, which guarantees continuity of the periodic extension of f, is essential because the sum of a uniformly convergent series of continuous functions must be continuous.

The next theorem on uniform convergence of Fourier cosine and sine series can be treated as special case of Theorem 6.1.

THEOREM 6.2. *Let f be a continuous piecewise smooth function on the interval* $0 \leq x \leq \pi$. *Then the Fourier cosine series of f*

$$\frac{a_0}{2} + \sum_{n=1}^{\infty} a_n \cos nx$$
$$(a_n = (2/\pi) \int_0^\pi f(x) \cos nx \, dx, \, n = 0, 1, \ldots)$$

converges absolutely and uniformly to $f(x)$ *for* $0 \leq x \leq \pi$ *and to the even periodic extension of f for all x.*

If, in addition, f satisfies the conditions $f(0) = f(\pi) = 0$, *then likewise the Fourier sine series of f,*

$$\sum_{n=1}^{\infty} b_n \sin nx$$
$$(b_n = (2/\pi) \int_0^\pi f(x) \sin nx \, dx, \, n \geq 1)$$

converges absolutely and uniformly to $f(x)$ *on the interval* $0 \leq x \leq \pi$, *and to the odd periodic extension of f for all x.*

Notice that here the condition $f(0) = f(\pi) = 0$ ensures continuity of the odd periodic extension of f, thus making it possible for the Fourier sine series to converge uniformly to $f(x)$ for all x.

Now suppose that f is a function that satisfies the conditions of Theorem 6.1. Then we have

(6.6) $$f(x) = \frac{a_0}{2} + \sum_{n=1}^{\infty} (a_n \cos nx + b_n \sin nx) \qquad (-\pi \leq x \leq \pi)$$

where the convergence of the series to f is absolute and uniform. Let us multiply both sides of (6.6) by f to obtain

(6.7) $$f^2(x) = \frac{a_0}{2} f(x) + \sum_{n=1}^{\infty} [a_n f(x) \cos nx + b_n f(x) \sin nx]$$

The series on the right of (6.7) converges uniformly to $f^2(x)$ on $-\pi \leq x \leq \pi$. To see this, let $\varepsilon > 0$ be an arbitrary small number, and let B denote the maximum value of $|f|$ on $-\pi \leq x \leq \pi$. By the definition of uniform convergence, there is an integer M such that

$$|S_m(x) - f(x)| < \frac{\varepsilon}{B} \qquad (\text{whenever } -\pi \leq x \leq \pi)$$

for all $m > M$. Here, S_m denotes the mth partial sum

$$S_m(x) = \frac{a_0}{2} + \sum_{n=1}^{m} (a_n \cos nx + b_n \sin nx)$$

Then, clearly,

(6.8) $$|S_m(x)f(x) - f^2(x)| = |f(x)|\,|S_m(x) - f(x)|$$

$$< B \cdot \frac{\varepsilon}{B} = \varepsilon$$

whenever $-\pi \leq x \leq \pi$ and for all $m > M$. This shows that the sequence $S_m(x)f(x)$, which is the mth partial sum of the series on the right of (6.7), converges uniformly to $f^2(x)$ on $[-\pi, \pi]$. Therefore, term-by-term integration of (6.7) is possible (Chapter 1, Section 5) and we obtain

$$\int_{-\pi}^{\pi} f^2(x)\, dx = \frac{a_0}{2} \int_{-\pi}^{\pi} f(x)\, dx$$

$$+ \sum_{n=1}^{\infty} \left[a_n \int_{-\pi}^{\pi} f(x) \cos nx\, dx + b_n \int_{-\pi}^{\pi} f(x) \sin nx\, dx \right]$$

$$= \pi \left[\frac{a_0^2}{2} + \sum_{n=1}^{\infty} (a_n^2 + b_n^2) \right]$$

or

(6.9) $$\frac{a_0^2}{2} + \sum_{n=1}^{\infty} (a_n^2 + b_n^2) = \frac{1}{\pi} \int_{-\pi}^{\pi} f^2(x)\, dx$$

which is Parseval's equation [see (6.16), Chapter 4].

Hence, from (6.10), (6.11), and (6.12) of Chapter 4, it follows that

$$\lim_{m \to \infty} \frac{1}{\pi} \int_{-\pi}^{\pi} [f(x) - S_m(x)]^2 \, dx$$

(6.10)
$$= \lim_{m \to \infty} \left\{ \frac{1}{\pi} \int_{-\pi}^{\pi} f^2(x) \, dx - \left[\frac{a_0^2}{2} + \sum_{n=1}^{m} (a_n^2 + b_n^2) \right] \right\}$$

$$= 0$$

which says that the Fourier series (6.6) converges to f in the mean. Thus, we see that uniform convergence of a Fourier series implies convergence in the mean. In terms of the idea of completeness that we introduced in Section 6 of Chapter 4, we can therefore conclude that the orthogonal system (4.1) of eigenfunctions is complete with respect to the class of functions that is continuous, piecewise smooth, and periodic of period 2π. Actually, the system (4.1) is complete with respect to the class of functions which is square integrable (e.g., piecewise continuous) on the interval $[-\pi, \pi]$. This means that the Fourier series of a function f converges in the mean whenever the integral $\int_{-\pi}^{\pi} f^2(x) \, dx$ exists. Then, for such a function, Parseval's equation (6.9) is satisfied.

Let f and g be two square integrable functions on $[-\pi, \pi]$, with Fourier coefficients denoted by a_n, b_n and a_n^*, b_n^*, respectively. From the obvious inequality

$$[f(x) + g(x)]^2 = 2[f^2(x) + g^2(x)] - [f(x) - g(x)]^2$$
$$\leq 2[f^2(x) + g^2(x)]$$

it follows that $f + g$ is also square integrable, with Fourier coefficients given by $a_n + a_n^*$ and $b_n + b_n^*$. Hence, according to Parseval's equation, we have

(6.11) $\quad \dfrac{1}{\pi} \displaystyle\int_{-\pi}^{\pi} [f(x) + g(x)]^2 \, dx$

$$= \frac{(a_0 + a_0^*)^2}{2} + \sum_{n=1}^{\infty} [(a_n + a_n^*)^2 + (b_n + b_n^*)^2]$$

Writing the corresponding Parseval's equation for $f - g$ and subtracting it from (6.11), we then obtain

(6.12) $\quad \dfrac{1}{\pi} \displaystyle\int_{-\pi}^{\pi} f(x)g(x) \, dx = \dfrac{a_0 a_0^*}{2} + \sum_{n=1}^{\infty} (a_n a_n^* + b_n b_n^*)$

This result is known as the generalized Parseval's equation.

If we define the function g in (6.12) by the equation

$$g(x) = \begin{cases} 1 & (-\pi < x < t) \\ 0 & (t < x < \pi) \end{cases}$$

where $-\pi \le t \le \pi$, then (6.12) becomes

(6.13) $$\int_{-\pi}^{t} f(x)\, dx = \tfrac{1}{2}a_0(t + \pi)$$

$$+ \sum_{n=1}^{\infty} \left[a_n \int_{-\pi}^{t} \cos nx\, dx + b_n \int_{-\pi}^{t} \sin nx\, dx \right]$$

This is precisely what we shall get if we formally integrate the series (6.6) term by term from $-\pi$ to t, where $-\pi \le t \le \pi$. In view of this result, we can therefore assert that if f is square integrable (say, piecewise continuous), then whether or not the Fourier series of f converges, the integrated series converges to the integral of f. (See also Problem 8.)

Exercises 5.5

1. Let a_n and b_n be real numbers and consider the quadratic equation

$$\sum_{n=1}^{m} (a_n + \lambda b_n)^2 = \sum_{n=1}^{m} a_n^2 + 2\lambda \sum_{n=1}^{m} a_n b_n + \lambda^2 \sum_{n=1}^{m} b_n^2 \ge 0$$

in the parameter λ. Prove that

$$\left(\sum_{n=1}^{m} a_n b_n \right)^2 \le \left(\sum_{n=1}^{m} a_n^2 \right) \left(\sum_{n=1}^{m} b_n^2 \right)$$

This is called the Cauchy-Schwarz inequality.

2. Consider the identity

$$\sum_{n=1}^{m} (a_n^2 + b_n^2)^{1/2} = \sum_{n=1}^{m} \frac{1}{n} (a_n'^2 + b_n'^2)^{1/2}$$

from equation (6.2). By using the Cauchy-Schwarz inequality and Theorem 4.1, prove that the series $\sum_{n=1}^{\infty} (a_n^2 + b_n^2)^{1/2}$ converges. Hence, deduce the convergence of the series (6.4).

3. Show that the Fourier series of the function $f(x) = x^2$, $-\pi \le x \le \pi$ (Problem 4, Exercises 5.4) can be integrated term by term from 0 to x when $-\pi \le x \le \pi$, and obtain the result

$$\sum_{n=1}^{\infty} (-1)^n \frac{\sin nx}{n^3} = \frac{1}{12} x(x^2 - \pi^2)$$

Deduce

$$\sum_{n=1}^{\infty} \frac{(-1)^{n+1}}{(2n-1)^3} = \frac{\pi^3}{32}$$

By Parseval's equation, show that

$$\sum_{n=1}^{\infty} \frac{1}{n^6} = \frac{\pi^6}{945}$$

4. Show that the Fourier series of the function given in Problem 5, Exercises 5.4, can be integrated term by term from 0 to x when $0 < x < \pi$, and obtain the result

$$\cos x = \frac{8}{\pi} \sum_{n=1}^{\infty} \frac{n \sin 2nx}{4n^2 - 1} \qquad (0 < x < \pi)$$

Hence, by Parseval's equation, show that

$$\sum_{n=1}^{\infty} \frac{n^2}{(4n^2 - 1)^2} = \frac{\pi^2}{64}$$

5. Justify the term-by-term integration of the Fourier series in Problem 7b, Exercises 5.4, and show that

$$\sum_{n=1}^{\infty} (-1)^{n+1} \frac{\cos(2n - 1)x}{(2n - 1)^2} = \begin{cases} \dfrac{\pi}{32} (\pi - 2x)(\pi + 2x) & (0 \le x \le \pi/2) \\[2mm] \dfrac{\pi}{32} (2x - \pi)(2x - 3\pi) & (\pi/2 \le x \le \pi) \end{cases}$$

6. Let $f(x) = 1 - x$, $0 \le x \le 2$. Show that the Fourier series of f converges uniformly to the function for $0 \le x \le 2$, and that

$$1 - x = \frac{8}{\pi^2} \sum_{n=1}^{\infty} \frac{1}{(2n - 1)^2} \cos \frac{(2n - 1)\pi x}{2}$$

Deduce

$$\sum_{n=1}^{\infty} \frac{1}{(2n - 1)^4} = \frac{\pi^4}{96}$$

7. Obtain from Problem 6 the series

$$x - \frac{x^2}{2} = \frac{16}{\pi^2} \sum_{n=1}^{\infty} \frac{1}{(2n - 1)^3} \sin \frac{(2n - 1)\pi x}{2} \qquad (0 \le x \le 2)$$

and deduce

$$\sum_{n=1}^{\infty} \frac{1}{(2n - 1)^6} = \frac{\pi^4}{960}$$

8. Let f be a piecewise continuous function on the interval $-\pi \le x \le \pi$ and consider its Fourier series

$$f(x) \sim \frac{a_0}{2} + \sum_{n=1}^{\infty} (a_n \cos nx + b_n \sin nx)$$

Set

$$F(x) = \int_a^x \left[f(t) - \frac{a_0}{2} \right] dt$$

where $-\pi \le x \le \pi$ and a is any constant.

(a) Show that for $-\pi \le x \le \pi$, $F(x)$ is continuous, piecewise smooth, and

$$F(\pi) - F(-\pi) = 0$$

Hint: Note that

$$F'(x) = f(x) - \frac{a_0}{2} \qquad \text{and} \qquad F(\pi) - F(-\pi) = \int_{-\pi}^{\pi} \left(f(t) - \frac{a_0}{2} \right) dt$$

Thus F satisfies the conditions of Theorem 6.1 and therefore can be represented by an absolutely and uniformly convergent Fourier series with Fourier coefficients given by

$$A_n = \frac{1}{\pi} \int_{-\pi}^{\pi} F(x) \cos nx \, dx \qquad (n = 0, 1, 2, \ldots)$$

$$B_n = \frac{1}{\pi} \int_{-\pi}^{\pi} F(x) \sin nx \, dx \qquad (n = 1, 2, \ldots)$$

(b) By integration by parts, show that

$$A = -\frac{b_n}{n}, \qquad B_n = \frac{a_n}{n} \qquad (n = 1, 2, \ldots)$$

Hence,

$$F(x) = \frac{A_0}{2} + \sum_{n=1}^{\infty} \left(-\frac{b_n}{n} \cos nx + \frac{a_n}{n} \sin nx \right)$$

and

$$0 = \frac{A_0}{2} + \sum_{n=1}^{\infty} \left(-\frac{b_n}{n} \cos na + \frac{a_n}{n} \sin na \right)$$

(c) Thus, obtain the result

$$\int_a^x f(t) \, dt = \frac{a_0}{2} (x - a)$$

$$+ \sum_{n=1}^{\infty} \left[a_n \frac{\sin nx - \sin na}{n} - b_n \frac{\cos nx - \cos na}{n} \right]$$

This proves that whether or not the Fourier series of a piecewise continuous function f converges to f, the series can be integrated term by term to yield a series that converges to the integral of f.

9. Integrate the series

$$\frac{x}{2} = \sum_{n=1}^{\infty} (-1)^{n+1} \frac{\sin nx}{n} \qquad (-\pi < x < \pi)$$

from 0 to x, term by term, to obtain successively

(a)
$$\frac{x^2}{4} = \frac{\pi^2}{12} + \sum_{n=1}^{\infty} (-1)^n \frac{\cos nx}{n^2} \qquad (-\pi \le x \le \pi)$$

(b)
$$\frac{x}{12} (x^2 - \pi^2) = \sum_{n=1}^{\infty} (-1)^n \frac{\sin nx}{n^2} \qquad (-\pi \le x \le \pi)$$

10. Integrate the series

$$\frac{\pi}{4} = \sum_{n=1}^{\infty} \frac{\sin(2n - 1)x}{(2n - 1)} \qquad (0 < x < \pi)$$

from 0 to x, term by term, to obtain successively

(a)
$$\frac{\pi}{8} (\pi - 2x) = \sum_{n=1}^{\infty} \frac{\cos(2n - 1)x}{(2n - 1)^2} \qquad (0 \le x \le \pi)$$

(b)
$$\frac{\pi}{8} (\pi x - x^2) = \sum_{n=1}^{\infty} \frac{\sin(2n - 1)x}{(2n - 1)^3} \qquad (0 \le x \le \pi)$$

7. Fourier Integral

So far, we have been concerned with the representation of a function by its Fourier series. We have seen that if the Fourier series converges to the function in some finite interval, then the series will represent the periodic extension of the function outside that interval. This means that in case a function is defined for all x, it cannot have a Fourier series representation that is valid for all x unless the function is periodic. In an attempt to find a representation analogous to Fourier series for a nonperiodic function that is defined for all x, we shall consider the Fourier series of the function on an arbitrary interval $[-L, L]$ and investigate its limit as L tends to infinity.

Let f be a piecewise smooth function on the interval $-\infty < x < \infty$. Then, on every subinterval $[-L, L]$, f has the Fourier series representation

$$(7.1) \qquad f(x) = \frac{a_0}{2} + \sum_{n=1}^{\infty} \left(a_n \cos \frac{n\pi x}{L} + b_n \sin \frac{n\pi x}{L} \right)$$

where

$$(7.2) \qquad \begin{aligned} a_n &= \frac{1}{L} \int_{-L}^{L} f(x) \cos \frac{n\pi x}{L} \, dx \qquad (n = 0, 1, 2, \ldots) \\[2mm] b_n &= \frac{1}{L} \int_{-L}^{L} f(x) \sin \frac{n\pi x}{L} \, dx \qquad (n = 1, 2, \ldots) \end{aligned}$$

We understand that at a point x where f is discontinuous, $f(x)$ is to be replaced by $[f(x - 0) + f(x + 0)]/2$. Substituting (7.2) for a_n and b_n in (7.1) and simplifying, we obtain

$$(7.3) \qquad f(x) = \frac{1}{2L} \int_{-L}^{L} f(\xi) \, d\xi + \sum_{n=1}^{\infty} \frac{1}{L} \int_{-L}^{L} f(\xi) \cos \frac{n\pi}{L} (\xi - x) \, d\xi$$

As we let $L \to \infty$, the first term on the right of (7.3) will vanish, provided the integral $\int_{-\infty}^{\infty} f(\xi) \, d\xi$ exists; which it certainly does if we assume that f is absolutely integrable on the interval $-\infty < x < \infty$. We assume that this is the case. Then, on letting $L \to \infty$, from (7.3) we obtain

$$(7.4) \qquad f(x) = \lim_{L \to \infty} \sum_{n=1}^{\infty} \frac{1}{L} \int_{-L}^{L} f(\xi) \cos \frac{n\pi}{L} (\xi - x) \, d\xi$$

In order to investigate the limit on the right of (7.4), let us set

$$s_n = \frac{n\pi}{L}, \qquad \Delta s_n = s_{n+1} - s_n = \frac{\pi}{L} \qquad (n = 1, 2, \ldots)$$

Then (7.4) can be written as

$$(7.5) \qquad f(x) = \lim_{L \to \infty} \frac{1}{\pi} \sum_{n=1}^{\infty} \left[\int_{-L}^{L} f(\xi) \cos s_n(\xi - x) \, d\xi \right] \Delta s_n$$

The sum in equation (7.5) reminds us of the sum defining the definite integral of the function

$$F(x, s) = \frac{1}{\pi} \int_{-L}^{L} f(\xi) \cos s(\xi - x) \, d\xi$$

over the interval $0 \le s < \infty$. Thus, it seems natural to expect that as $L \to \infty$, (7.5) leads to

(7.6) $$f(x) = \frac{1}{\pi} \int_{0}^{\infty} ds \int_{-\infty}^{\infty} f(\xi) \cos s(\xi - x) \, d\xi$$

It should be emphasized that the argument used above in arriving at the formula (7.6) was purely heuristic and did not constitute a proof. In the theorem to follow, we shall show that under the assumptions made on f, the function can indeed be represented by (7.6). This is the representation we seek for a non-periodic function that is defined for all x. The formula (7.6) is called the Fourier integral formula for the function f.

THEOREM 7.1. *Let f be a function that is piecewise smooth and absolutely integrable on the interval $-\infty < x < \infty$. Then, at every point x in $(-\infty, \infty)$,*

(7.7) $$\frac{f(x - 0) + f(x + 0)}{2} = \frac{1}{\pi} \int_{0}^{\infty} ds \int_{-\infty}^{\infty} f(\xi) \cos s(\xi - x) \, d\xi$$

Proof: By the definition of improper integrals, we have

(7.8) $$\frac{1}{\pi} \int_{0}^{\infty} ds \int_{-\infty}^{\infty} f(\xi) \cos s(\xi - x) \, d\xi$$

$$= \lim_{\lambda \to \infty} \frac{1}{\pi} \int_{0}^{\lambda} ds \int_{-\infty}^{\infty} f(\xi) \cos s(\xi - x) \, d\xi$$

The inner integral on the right side of equation (7.8) is uniformly convergent with respect to s for $0 \le s \le \lambda$, since

$$|f(\xi) \cos s (\xi - x)| \le |f(\xi)|$$

and f is absolutely integrable on $(-\infty, \infty)$. Hence, the order of integration with respect to ξ and s can be interchanged (Chapter 1, Theorem 5.3), and we obtain

$$\frac{1}{\pi} \int_{0}^{\infty} ds \int_{-\infty}^{\infty} f(\xi) \cos s(\xi - x) \, d\xi = \lim_{\lambda \to \infty} \frac{1}{\pi} \int_{-\infty}^{\infty} f(\xi) \int_{0}^{\lambda} \cos s(\xi - x) \, ds \, d\xi$$

$$= \lim_{\lambda \to \infty} \frac{1}{\pi} \int_{-\infty}^{\infty} f(\xi) \frac{\sin \lambda(\xi - x)}{(\xi - x)} \, d\xi$$

If we set $t = \xi - x$, then this becomes

(7.9) $$\frac{1}{\pi} \int_{0}^{\infty} ds \int_{-\infty}^{\infty} f(\xi) \cos s(\xi - x) \, d\xi = \lim_{\lambda \to \infty} \frac{1}{\pi} \int_{-\infty}^{\infty} f(x + t) \frac{\sin \lambda t}{t} \, dt$$

In Chapter 1, Example 6.3, we found that $\int_0^\infty (\sin t)/t \, dt = \pi/2$. From this it is easily shown that

(7.10)
$$\int_{-\infty}^0 \frac{\sin \lambda t}{t} \, dt = \int_0^\infty \frac{\sin \lambda t}{t} \, dt = \frac{\pi}{2} \qquad (\lambda > 0)$$

Hence, the Fourier integral formula (7.7) will be established if we can show that

(7.11)
$$\lim_{\lambda \to \infty} \frac{1}{\pi} \int_{-\infty}^0 [f(x + t) - f(x - 0)] \frac{\sin \lambda t}{t} \, dt = 0$$

and

(7.12)
$$\lim_{\lambda \to \infty} \frac{1}{\pi} \int_0^\infty [f(x + t) - f(x + 0)] \frac{\sin \lambda t}{t} \, dt = 0$$

in view of (7.9) and (7.10).

Consider the integral in (7.12) and let us write

$$I = \frac{1}{\pi} \int_0^\infty \frac{f(x + t) - f(x + 0)}{t} \sin \lambda t \, dt$$

$$= I_1 + I_2 - I_3$$

where

$$I_1 = \frac{1}{\pi} \int_0^b \frac{f(x + t) - f(x + 0)}{t} \sin \lambda t \, dt$$

$$I_2 = \frac{1}{\pi} \int_b^\infty \frac{f(x + t)}{t} \sin \lambda t \, dt$$

$$I_3 = \frac{f(x + 0)}{\pi} \int_b^\infty \frac{\sin \lambda t}{t} \, dt$$

with b being an arbitrary positive number. Since $[f(x + t) - f(x + 0)]/t$ is piecewise continuous for $0 \le t \le b$ and $f(x + t)/t$ is piecewise continuous and absolutely integrable on $b \le t < \infty$, it follows from Riemann-Lebesgue Theorems 4.2 and 4.3 that I_1 and I_2 tend to zero as $\lambda \to \infty$, respectively. The change of variable $\lambda t = z$ transforms I_3 into

$$I_3 = \frac{f(x + 0)}{\pi} \int_{\lambda b}^\infty \frac{\sin z}{z} \, dz$$

which clearly goes to zero as $\lambda \to \infty$. Thus,

$$\lim_{\lambda \to \infty} I = \lim_{\lambda \to \infty} (I_1 + I_2 - I_3) = 0$$

and so (7.12) is proved. By the same method we can also show that the limit in (7.11) is zero. This completes the proof of the theorem.

Example 7.1. Find the Fourier integral formula of the function

$$f(x) = \begin{cases} 1 & (|x| \leq 1) \\ 0 & (|x| > 1) \end{cases}$$

Solution: It is clear that the function here satisfies the conditions of Theorem 7.1. Thus, for $-\infty < x < \infty$, we have

$$\frac{f(x - 0) + f(x + 0)}{2} = \frac{1}{\pi} \int_0^\infty ds \int_{-1}^1 \cos s(\xi - x) \, d\xi$$

$$= \frac{1}{\pi} \int_0^\infty \left[\frac{\sin s(\xi - x)}{s} \right]_{-1}^1 ds$$

$$= \frac{1}{\pi} \int_0^\infty \frac{\sin s(1 - x) + \sin s(1 + x)}{s} \, ds$$

$$= \frac{2}{\pi} \int_0^\infty \frac{\cos sx \sin s}{s} \, ds$$

It follows that

$$\frac{2}{\pi} \int_0^\infty \frac{\cos sx \sin s}{s} \, ds = \begin{cases} 1 & (|x| < 1) \\ \frac{1}{2} & (|x| = 1) \\ 0 & (|x| > 1) \end{cases}$$

In particular, at $x = 0$, we have

$$\int_0^\infty \frac{\sin s}{s} \, ds = \frac{\pi}{2}$$

a result we also obtained in Example 6.3, Chapter 1. The result at $x = 1$ can be verified directly. Indeed, at $x = 1$ we see that

$$\frac{2}{\pi} \int_0^\infty \frac{\cos s \sin s}{s} \, ds = \frac{1}{\pi} \int_0^\infty \frac{\sin 2s}{s} \, ds = \frac{1}{2}$$

by (7.10).

By expanding the function $\cos s(\xi - x)$ in (7.6), we see that Fourier integral formula can be written as

(7.13) $$f(x) = \int_0^\infty [A(s) \cos sx + B(s) \sin sx] \, ds$$

where

(7.14)
$$A(s) = \frac{1}{\pi} \int_{-\infty}^\infty f(\xi) \cos s\xi \, d\xi$$

$$B(s) = \frac{1}{\pi} \int_{-\infty}^\infty f(\xi) \sin s\xi \, d\xi$$

In this form, (7.13) is analogous to a Fourier series representation and (7.14) to the formulas for the Fourier coefficients. It is significant in this connection to note that the functions cos sx and sin sx are linearly independent eigenfunctions, corresponding to the same eigenvalue $\lambda = s^2$, of the singular eigenvalue problem

$$u'' + \lambda u = 0 \qquad\qquad (-\infty < x < \infty)$$

$$u \text{ bounded as } |x| \to \infty$$

The eigenvalues $\lambda = s^2$ in this case are no longer discrete but continuous, and consist of all real nonnegative numbers. Thus, the representation (7.13) is a generalization of eigenfunction expansion where summation with respect to the eigenvalues is now achieved by integration.

Now suppose that f is an even function that satisfies the conditions of Theorem 7.1. Since $f(\xi) \cos s\xi$ and $f(\xi) \sin s\xi$ are respectively even and odd functions of ξ, the formulas (7.14) yield

$$A(s) = \frac{1}{\pi} \int_{-\infty}^{\infty} f(\xi) \cos s\xi \, d\xi = \frac{2}{\pi} \int_{0}^{\infty} f(\xi) \cos s\xi \, d\xi$$

$$B(s) = \frac{1}{\pi} \int_{-\infty}^{\infty} f(\xi) \sin s\xi \, d\xi = 0$$

so that (7.13) reduces to

$$(7.15) \qquad f(x) = \frac{2}{\pi} \int_{0}^{\infty} \cos sx \left(\int_{0}^{\infty} f(\xi) \cos s\xi \, d\xi \right) ds$$

This is called the Fourier cosine integral formula. In case f is defined only on the interval $0 \le x < \infty$, (7.15) extends f for all x as an even function.

Similarly, if f is an odd function, then from (7.14) we have

$$A(s) = 0, \qquad B(s) = \frac{2}{\pi} \int_{0}^{\infty} f(\xi) \sin s\xi \, d\xi$$

so that (7.13) reduces to the Fourier sine integral formula

$$(7.16) \qquad f(x) = \frac{2}{\pi} \int_{0}^{\infty} \sin sx \left(\int_{0}^{\infty} f(\xi) \sin s\xi \, d\xi \right) ds$$

This extends f for all x as an odd function when f is defined only for $x \ge 0$.

Let us state these results in the following theorem.

THEOREM 7.2. *Let f be a function that is piecewise smooth and absolutely integrable on $0 \le x < \infty$. Then f can be represented by the Fourier cosine integral formula (7.15) on $0 \le x < \infty$, or by the Fourier sine integral formula (7.16) on $0 < x < \infty$. Each of the integrals converges to $f(x)$ at all points where f is continuous and to $[f(x - 0) + f(x + 0)]/2$ at all points where f is discontinuous.*

Notice that the Fourier cosine integral necessarily converges to $f(0^+)$ at $x = 0$ and the sine integral converges to zero at $x = 0$.

As in the case of (7.13), it is worth noting that (7.15) is a generalized eigen-function expansion in terms of the eigenfunctions $\cos sx$ of the singular eigen-value problem

$$u'' + \lambda u = 0 \qquad\qquad (0 \le x < \infty)$$
$$u'(0) = 0, \qquad u \text{ bounded as } x \to \infty$$

whose eigenvalues $\lambda = s^2$ consist of all nonnegative real numbers. Similarly, (7.16) is a generalized eigenfunction expansion involving the eigenfunctions $\sin sx$ of the singular problem

$$u'' + \lambda u = 0 \qquad\qquad (0 \le x < \infty)$$
$$u(0) = 0, \qquad u \text{ bounded as } x \to \infty$$

with eigenvalues $\lambda = s^2 > 0$.

Example 7.2. Find the Fourier cosine integral formula for the function

$$f(x) = \begin{cases} \sin x & (0 \le x \le \pi) \\ 0 & (x > 0) \end{cases}$$

Solutions: Note that the function here is continuous for all $x \ge 0$. By (7.15) we have

$$f(x) = \frac{2}{\pi} \int_0^\infty \cos sx \left(\int_0^\pi \sin \xi \cos s\xi \, d\xi \right) ds$$

The inner integral with respect to ξ yields

$$\int_0^\pi \sin \xi \cos s\xi \, d\xi = \frac{1}{2} \int_0^\pi [\sin(1 + s)\xi + \sin(1 - s)\xi] \, d\xi$$

$$= -\frac{1}{2} \left[\frac{\cos(1 + s)\xi}{1 + s} + \frac{\cos(1 - s)\xi}{1 - s} \right]_0^\pi$$

$$= \frac{1}{2} \left[\frac{1 - \cos(1 + s)\pi}{1 + s} + \frac{1 - \cos(1 - s)\pi}{1 - s} \right]$$

$$= \frac{1}{2} \left[\frac{1 + \cos s\pi}{1 + s} + \frac{1 + \cos s\pi}{1 - s} \right]$$

$$= \frac{1 + \cos s\pi}{1 - s^2}$$

Hence, the Fourier cosine integral formula is

$$f(x) = \frac{2}{\pi} \int_0^\infty \frac{1 + \cos s\pi}{1 - s^2} \cos sx \, dx$$

$$= \begin{cases} \sin x & (0 \le x \le \pi) \\ 0 & (x > \pi) \end{cases}$$

The integral converges for all x to the even extension of the function (Fig. 5.6).

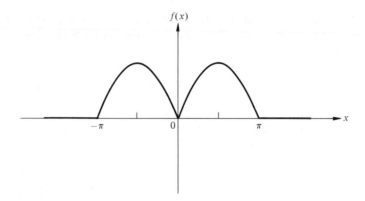

FIG. 5–6 *Even extension of $f(x)$.*

Example 7.3. Find the Fourier sine integral formula for the function given in Example 7.2.

Solution: By (7.16) we have

$$f(x) = \frac{2}{\pi} \int_0^\infty \sin sx \left(\int_0^\infty \sin \xi \sin s\xi \, d\xi \right) ds$$

Since

$$\int_0^\pi \sin \xi \sin s\xi \, d\xi = \frac{1}{2} \int_0^\pi [\cos(1 - s)\xi - \cos(1 + s)\xi] \, d\xi$$

$$= \frac{1}{2} \left[\frac{\sin(1 - s)\xi}{1 - s} - \frac{\sin(1 + s)\xi}{1 + s} \right]_0^\pi$$

$$= \frac{1}{2} \left[\frac{\sin(1 - s)\pi}{1 - s} - \frac{\sin(1 + s)\pi}{1 + s} \right]$$

$$= \frac{1}{2} \left[\frac{\sin s\pi}{1 - s} + \frac{\sin s\pi}{1 + s} \right]$$

$$= \frac{\sin s\pi}{1 - s^2}$$

the Fourier sine integral formula is

$$f(x) = \frac{2}{\pi} \int_0^\infty \frac{\sin s\pi \sin sx}{1 - s^2} \, ds$$

$$= \begin{cases} \sin x & (0 \le x \le \pi) \\ 0 & (x > \pi) \end{cases}$$

Here, the integral converges to the function for all x ($-\infty < x < \infty$), since the function is odd for all x (Fig. 5.7).

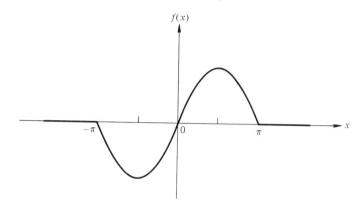

FIG. 5–7 *Odd extension of f(x).*

Exercises 5.6

1. Let

$$f(x) = \begin{cases} 1 & (0 < x < k) \\ 0 & (\text{otherwise}) \end{cases}$$

Show that the Fourier integral formula applies to f and evaluate

$$\int_0^\infty \frac{\sin s(k - x) + \sin sx}{s} \, ds$$

for all x.

2. Let

$$f(x) = \begin{cases} 0 & (x \le 0, x > 1) \\ x & (0 \le x < 1) \end{cases}$$

Show that the Fourier integral formula applies to f and evaluate

$$\int_0^\infty \frac{s \sin s(1 - x) + \cos s(1 - x) - \cos sx}{s^2} \, ds$$

for all x.

3. Represent the function

$$f(x) = \begin{cases} \sin x & (0 \le x \le \pi) \\ 0 & (\text{otherwise}) \end{cases}$$

by Fourier integral formula and verify that

$$\sin x = \frac{1}{\pi} \int_0^\infty \frac{\cos s(x - \pi) + \cos sx}{1 - s^2} \, ds$$

when $0 \le x \le \pi$.

4. Represent the function

$$f(x) = \begin{cases} \cos x & (|x| < \pi) \\ 0 & (|x| > \pi) \end{cases}$$

by Fourier integral formula and verify that

$$\cos x = \frac{2}{\pi} \int_0^\infty \frac{s \cos sx \sin s\pi}{1 - s^2} \, ds$$

when $-\pi < x < \pi$. What is the value of the integral at the points $x = \pm\pi$?

5. Represent the function

$$f(x) = \begin{cases} 0 & (x < 0) \\ e^{-x} & (x > 0) \end{cases}$$

by Fourier integral formula and evaluate

$$\int_0^\infty \frac{s \sin sx + \cos sx}{1 + s^2} \, ds$$

for all x.

6. Show that the Fourier cosine integral formula applies to the function

$$f(x) = e^{-x} \qquad (x \geq 0)$$

to give the representation

$$e^{-x} = \frac{2}{\pi} \int_0^\infty \frac{\cos sx}{1 + s^2} \, ds \qquad (x \geq 0)$$

7. Show that the function

$$f(x) = \begin{cases} 1 - x & (0 \leq x \leq 1) \\ 0 & (x > 1) \end{cases}$$

can be represented by Fourier cosine integral formula and thus evaluate

$$\int_0^\infty \frac{(1 - \cos s)}{s^2} \cos sx \, ds$$

for all $x \geq 0$.

8. Express the function $f(x) = e^{-x} \cos x$, $x \geq 0$, by Fourier cosine integral formula and show that

$$e^{-x} \cos x = \frac{2}{\pi} \int_0^\infty \frac{s^2 + 2}{s^4 + 4} \cos sx \, ds \qquad (x \geq 0)$$

9. Express the function $f(x) = xe^{-x}$, $x \geq 0$, by Fourier cosine integral formula and show that

$$xe^{-x} = \frac{2}{\pi} \int_0^\infty \frac{1 - s^2}{(1 + s^2)^2} \cos sx \, ds \qquad (x \geq 0)$$

10. Show that the Fourier sine integral formula applies to the function

$$f(x) = \begin{cases} 1 & (0 < x < 1) \\ 0 & (x > 1) \end{cases}$$

and evaluate

$$\int_0^\infty \frac{1 - \cos s}{s} \sin sx \, ds$$

for all $x \geq 0$.

11. Establish the result

$$e^{-x} \sin x = \frac{4}{\pi} \int_0^\infty \frac{s \sin sx}{s^2 + 4} \, ds \qquad (x \geq 0)$$

12. Show that the function

$$f(x) = \begin{cases} \cos x & (0 < x < \pi) \\ 0 & (x > \pi) \end{cases}$$

can be represented by Fourier sine integral formula, and thus evaluate

$$\int_0^\infty \frac{s(\cos s\pi + 1)}{s^2 - 1} \sin sx \, ds$$

for all x.

13. Establish the result

$$e^{-x} = \frac{2}{\pi} \int_0^\infty \frac{s \sin sx}{1 + s^2} \, ds \qquad (x > 0)$$

14. Express the function $f(x) = xe^{-x}$, $x \geq 0$, by Fourier sine integral formula and show that

$$xe^{-x} = \frac{4}{\pi} \int_0^\infty \frac{s \sin sx \, ds}{(1 + s^2)^2} \qquad (x \geq 0)$$

8. Fourier Transform

The Fourier integral formula (7.6) can be written in a complex form if we replace the function $\cos s(\xi - x)$ by the expression

$$\frac{e^{is(\xi-x)} + e^{-is(\xi-x)}}{2}$$

In fact, upon making this substitution for $\cos s(\xi - x)$ in (7.6), we find

$$f(x) = \frac{1}{\pi} \int_0^\infty \int_{-\infty}^\infty f(\xi) \frac{e^{is(\xi-x)} + e^{-is(\xi-x)}}{2} \, d\xi \, ds$$

(8.1)
$$= \frac{1}{2\pi} \int_0^\infty \int_{-\infty}^\infty f(\xi) e^{is(\xi-x)} \, d\xi \, ds$$

$$+ \frac{1}{2\pi} \int_0^\infty \int_{-\infty}^\infty f(\xi) e^{-is(\xi-x)} \, d\xi \, ds$$

If in the first integral on the right we make the change of variable from s to $-s$ and then combine the result with the second integral, we obtain

(8.2)
$$f(x) = \frac{1}{2\pi} \int_{-\infty}^\infty \int_{-\infty}^\infty f(\xi) e^{-is(\xi-x)} \, d\xi \, ds$$

This is the complex form of the Fourier integral formula.

Let us set

$$F(s) = \frac{1}{\sqrt{2\pi}} \int_{-\infty}^{\infty} f(\xi)e^{-is\xi} \, d\xi$$

Then (8.2) can be written as

$$f(x) = \frac{1}{\sqrt{2\pi}} \int_{-\infty}^{\infty} F(s)e^{isx} \, ds$$

which is now analogous to the complex form (2.6) of the Fourier series. Using these symmetric formulas, we can restate Theorem 7.1 as follows:

THEOREM 8.1.   *Let f be piecewise smooth and absolutely integrable on* $(-\infty, \infty)$, *and let*

$$(8.3) \qquad\qquad F(s) = \frac{1}{\sqrt{2\pi}} \int_{-\infty}^{\infty} f(\xi)e^{-is\xi} \, d\xi$$

Then

$$(8.4) \qquad\qquad f(x) = \frac{1}{\sqrt{2\pi}} \int_{-\infty}^{\infty} F(s)e^{isx} \, ds$$

(where $f(x)$ *is to be replaced by the average of* $f(x - 0)$ *and* $f(x + 0)$ *at points where f is discontinuous).*

The function F defined by (8.3) is called the Fourier transform of f, and f defined by (8.4) is the inverse Fourier transform of F. Along with other integral transforms (e.g., Laplace transform), the Fourier transform is an invaluable tool in applied mathematics.

Example 8.1.   Find the Fourier transform of the function

$$f(x) = \begin{cases} 1 & (|x| \le a) \\ 0 & (|x| > a) \end{cases}$$

Solution: By (8.3) the Fourier transform is

$$F(s) = \frac{1}{\sqrt{2\pi}} \int_{-a}^{a} e^{-is\xi} \, d\xi = \frac{1}{\sqrt{2\pi}} \left[\frac{-e^{-is\xi}}{is} \right]_{-a}^{a}$$

$$= \frac{1}{\sqrt{2\pi}} \frac{e^{isa} - e^{-isa}}{is} = \frac{2}{\sqrt{2\pi} \, s} \frac{e^{isa} - e^{-isa}}{2i}$$

$$= \left(\frac{2}{\pi}\right)^{1/2} \frac{\sin as}{s}$$

Thus, by Theorem 8.1, we have

$$\frac{1}{\pi} \int_{-\infty}^{\infty} \frac{\sin as}{s} e^{isx} \, ds = \begin{cases} 1 & (|x| < a) \\ \frac{1}{2} & (|x| = a) \\ 0 & (|x| > a) \end{cases}$$

Next, we define the Fourier transform of a function that is defined only for $x \geq 0$. In the Fourier cosine integral formula (7.15), let us set

(8.5) $$F_c(s) = \left(\frac{2}{\pi}\right)^{1/2} \int_0^\infty f(\xi) \cos s\xi \, d\xi$$

Then (7.15) can be written as

(8.6) $$f(x) = \left(\frac{2}{\pi}\right)^{1/2} \int_0^\infty F_c(s) \cos sx \, ds$$

The function $F_c(s)$ is called the Fourier cosine transform of f. In view of the symmetry between (8.5) and (8.6), we see that f is in turn the Fourier cosine transform of $F_s(s)$; thus, f and F_c are cosine transforms of each other.

Similarly, from the Fourier sine integral formula (7.16), we define the Fourier sine transform of f as the function

(8.7) $$F_s(s) = \left(\frac{2}{\pi}\right)^{1/2} \int_0^\infty f(\xi) \sin s\xi \, d\xi$$

This, in turn, has the Fourier sine transform

(8.8) $$f(x) = \left(\frac{2}{\pi}\right)^{1/2} \int_0^\infty F_s(s) \sin sx \, ds$$

When f is a given function, the formulas (8.5) and (8.7) can be regarded as the solutions of the integral equations (8.6) and (8.8), respectively. Applications of these various transforms will be illustrated in the chapters to follow.

Example 8.2. Find the Fourier cosine and sine transforms of the function

$$f(x) = e^{-ax} \qquad\qquad [x \geq 0; (a > 0)]$$

Solution: It is clear that the function is smooth and absolutely integrable on $0 \leq x < \infty$. By (8.5), its Fourier cosine transform is

$$F_c(s) = \left(\frac{2}{\pi}\right)^{1/2} \int_0^\infty e^{-a\xi} \cos s\xi \, d\xi$$

$$= \left(\frac{2}{\pi}\right)^{1/2} \left[\frac{e^{-a\xi}}{a^2 + s^2} (s \sin s\xi - a \cos s\xi)\right]_0^\infty$$

$$= \left(\frac{2}{\pi}\right)^{1/2} \frac{a}{a^2 + s^2}$$

and, by (8.7), its Fourier sine transform is

$$F_s(s) = \left(\frac{2}{\pi}\right)^{1/2} \int_0^\infty e^{-a\xi} \sin s\xi \, d\xi$$

$$= \left(\frac{2}{\pi}\right)^{1/2} \left[\frac{-e^{-a\xi}}{a^2 + s^2} (s \cos s\xi + a \sin s\xi)\right]_0^\infty$$

$$= \left(\frac{2}{\pi}\right)^{1/2} \frac{s}{a^2 + s^2}$$

By (8.6) and (8.8), it then follows that

$$\int_0^\infty \frac{\cos sx}{a^2 + s^2}\, ds = \frac{\pi e^{-ax}}{2a} \qquad (x \geq 0)$$

and

$$\int_0^\infty \frac{s \sin sx}{a^2 + s^2} = \frac{\pi e^{-ax}}{2} \qquad (x > 0)$$

respectively.

Exercises 5.7

1. Find the Fourier transform of the function

$$f(x) = \begin{cases} 1 - |x| & (|x| \leq 1) \\ 0 & (|x| > 1) \end{cases}$$

2. Find the Fourier transform of the function $f(x) = e^{-a|x|}$, where $a > 0$.

3. Find the Fourier transform of the function $f(x) = 1/(1 + x^2)$. (Use the result of Problem 6, Exercises 5.6.)

4. Show that the Fourier transform of the function $f(x) = e^{-x^2/2}$ is $F(s) = e^{-s^2/2}$; that is, $e^{-x^2/2}$ is its own Fourier transform. (Use the result of Problem 10, Exercises 1.6.)

5. Let $F(s)$ be the Fourier transform of $f(x)$. Show that—
    (a) the Fourier transform of $f(x)e^{iax}$ is $F(s - a)$.
    (b) the Fourier transform of $f(ax)$ is $(1/a)F(s/a)$.
    (c) the Fourier transform of $g(x)$, where

$$g(x) = \begin{cases} f(x - a) & (x > a > 0) \\ 0 & (0 < x < a) \end{cases}$$

    is $e^{-isa}F(s)$.

6. If the Fourier transform of f and f' exist and $f(x) \to \infty$ as $|x| \to \infty$, show that the Fourier transform of $f'(x)$ is $F(s)$.

7. Find the Fourier cosine transform of each of the following functions:

    (a) $$f(x) = \begin{cases} \cos x & (0 \leq x \leq \pi/2) \\ 0 & (x > \pi/2) \end{cases}$$

    (b) $$f(x) = xe^{-x} \qquad (x \geq 0)$$

8. Find the Fourier sine transform of each of the functions given in Problem 7.

9. Solve the following integral equations for the function f:
    (a) $\int_0^\infty f(s) \sin sx\, ds = e^{-x} \cos x,\ x > 0$.
    (b) $\int_0^\infty f(s) \cos sx\, ds = e^{-x} \sin x,\ x \geq 0$.

10. Let f and g satisfy the conditions of Theorem 8.1 and let F and G denote their respective Fourier transforms. Define

$$h(x) = \int_{-\infty}^{\infty} f(x - y)g(y)\, dy$$

$$= f(x) * g(x)$$

This is called the convolution of f and g.

(a) Show that $f(x) * g(x) = g(x) * f(x)$; that is,

$$\int_{-\infty}^{\infty} f(x - y)g(y)\, dy = \int_{-\infty}^{\infty} f(x)g(x - y)\, dy$$

(b) Show formally that $H(s) = (2\pi)^{1/2}F(s)G(s)$, where H is the Fourier transform of h. (Take the Fourier transform of h and interchange the order of integration.)

11. Solve the integral equation

$$h(x) = \int_{0}^{x} f(x - y)e^{-y}\, dy = \begin{cases} 0 & (x < 0) \\ x^2 e^{-x} & (x \geq 0) \end{cases}$$

for the function f, and then verify part (b) of the preceding problem.

Chapter 6

The Heat Equation

In this chapter we shall be concerned with some problems dealing with the
typical linear parabolic partial differential equation

$$\frac{\partial u}{\partial t} - k\,\frac{\partial^2 u}{\partial x^2} = F(x,\,t)$$

in two independent variables x and t. This equation, known as the one-dimensional heat equation, arises in the analysis of conduction of heat in solids as
well as in a variety of diffusion phenomena. We shall formulate and study
various types of problems for this equation by reference to the conduction of
heat in a thin rod.

1. Derivation of the Heat Equation

Consider a heat-conducting homogeneous rod, extending from $x = 0$ to
$x = L$ along the x-axis (Fig. 6.1). Let us assume that the rod has uniform cross
section A and constant density ρ. Further, let us assume that the rod is insulated
laterally so that heat flows only in the x-direction, and that the rod is sufficiently
thin so that the temperature at all points of a cross section is constant. Let
$u(x,\,t)$ denote the temperature of the cross section at the point x at an instant of
time t, and let c denote the specific heat of the rod (that is, the amount of heat
required to raise the temperature of a unit mass of the rod by 1 degree). Consider a segment of the rod between the cross section at x and the cross section

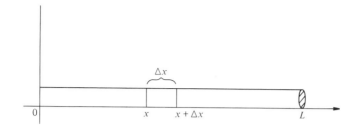

FIG. 6-1 *Heat conduction in a thin rod.*

at $x + \Delta x$. According to the theory of heat flow, the amount of heat in this segment is

$$
(1.1) \qquad Q(t) = \int_x^{x+\Delta x} c\rho A u(s, t)\, ds
$$

On the other hand, the rate at which heat flows into the segment across the cross section at x is known to be proportional to the product of the cross section and the gradient of the temperature of the cross section; that is, it is equal to

$$
(1.2) \qquad -KA \frac{\partial u}{\partial x}(x, t)
$$

where K denotes the thermal conductivity of the rod. The negative sign in (1.2) is used to indicate the fact that heat flows in the direction of decreasing temperature. Similarly, the rate at which heat flows out of the segment through the cross section at $x + \Delta x$ is given by

$$
(1.3) \qquad -KA \frac{\partial u}{\partial x}(x + \Delta x, t)
$$

The difference between the amount of heat that flows in through the cross section at x and the amount of heat that flows out through the cross section at $x + \Delta x$ must be equal to the change in the heat content of the segment $x \leq s \leq x + \Delta x$. Hence, by subtracting (1.3) from (1.2) and equating the result to the time derivative of (1.1), we obtain

$$
(1.4) \qquad
\begin{aligned}
\frac{\partial Q}{\partial t} &= \int_x^{x+\Delta x} c\rho A \frac{\partial u}{\partial t}(s, t)\, ds \\[2mm]
&= KA \left[\frac{\partial u}{\partial x}(x + \Delta x, t) - \frac{\partial u}{\partial x}(x, t) \right]
\end{aligned}
$$

We assume that the integrand in (1.4) is a continuous function of s. Then, by the mean value theorem for integrals (Chapter 1, Theorem 1.3), we have

$$
\int_x^{x+\Delta x} \frac{\partial u}{\partial t}(s, t)\, ds = \frac{\partial u}{\partial t}(\xi, t)\, \Delta x \qquad (x < \xi < x + \Delta x)
$$

so that (1.4) becomes

$$c\rho \frac{\partial u}{\partial t}(\xi, t)\, \Delta x = K\left[\frac{\partial u}{\partial x}(x + \Delta x, t) - \frac{\partial u}{\partial x}(x, t)\right]$$

Dividing both sides of this equation by $c\rho\,\Delta x$ and taking the limit as $\Delta x \to 0$, we finally obtain

$$\frac{\partial u}{\partial t}(x, t) = k\frac{\partial^2 u}{\partial x^2}(x, t)$$

or

(1.5) $$\frac{\partial u}{\partial t}(x, t) - k\frac{\partial^2 u}{\partial x^2}(x, t) = 0 \qquad \left(k = \frac{K}{c\rho}\right)$$

by recalling the definition of partial derivative. Equation (1.5) is called the one-dimensional heat equation. It is an important example of a partial differential equation of the parabolic type. The constant k is usually called the diffusivity.

If heat is supplied to the rod from an external source at a rate, say, $f(x, t)$ per unit volume per unit time, then the term $\int_x^{x+\Delta x} f(s, t)\, ds$ must be added to the right-hand side of (1.4). Thus, in passing to the limit as $\Delta x \to 0$, we get

(1.6) $$\frac{\partial u}{\partial t}(x, t) - k\frac{\partial^2 u}{\partial x^2}(x, t) = F(x, t)$$

where $F(x, t) = f(x, t)/c\rho$ is the source density. This equation is called the nonhomogeneous heat equation.

On the other hand, if heat is being radiated from the rod into the surrounding medium at a rate proportional to the temperature of the rod, then we shall have the so-called radiation equation

(1.7) $$\frac{\partial u}{\partial t}(x, t) - k\frac{\partial^2 u}{\partial x^2}(x, t) + hu(x, t) = 0$$

where h is a positive constant. A combination of (1.6) and (1.7) will, of course, lead to the nonhomogeneous radiation equation

(1.8) $$\frac{\partial u}{\partial t}(x, t) - k\frac{\partial^2 u}{\partial x^2}(x, t) + hu(x, t) = F(x, t)$$

2.   Initial and Boundary Conditions

In each of the cases of heat conduction in a thin rod discussed above, we saw that the temperature function u satisfies a partial differential equation of parabolic type. From physical considerations, we know that the differential equation alone cannot determine the temperature distribution in the rod at any subsequent time. We need to have additional information regarding the initial temperature of the rod and the conditions imposed at its two ends. This means that we must specify $u(x, t)$ at some initial time (say, at time $t = 0$) and describe how the two ends of the rod exchange heat energy with the surrounding medium. Thus, with reference to the case in which there is no heat source, if the temperature of the rod at $t = 0$ is described by the function $f(x)$, $0 \leq x \leq L$, and the two ends are maintained at zero temperature at all time, then the temperature distribution u in the rod at any later time $t > 0$ is found by solving the differential equation

(2.1) $$u_t - ku_{xx} = 0 \qquad\qquad (0 < x < L, t > 0)$$

subject to the conditions

(2.2) $$u(x, 0) = f(x) \qquad\qquad (0 \leq x \leq L)$$

and

(2.3) $$u(0, t) = 0, \qquad u(L, t) = 0 \qquad\qquad (t \geq 0)$$

This problem is called an initial-boundary value problem for the heat equation. The auxiliary conditions (2.2) and (2.3) are called initial condition and boundary conditions, respectively.

We notice in the problem (2.1), (2.2), (2.3) that only the value of u is prescribed initially and not both u and u_t, as in the case of the wave equation. This is, of course, dictated by the physical problem being considered. But even from a mathematical standpoint, u_t cannot be prescribed arbitrarily, since it is related to u_{xx} initially through the differential equation. As a matter of fact, we shall see in the next section that the set of auxiliary conditions (2.2) and (2.3) is appropriate for the heat equation or for any of the other related differential equations given in the preceding section, in the sense that the problem is well posed.

The conditions (2.3) correspond to the fixed boundary conditions for a vibrating string, which we considered in Chapter 3 for the wave equation. Other forms of appropriate boundary conditions corresponding to the free and the elastic boundary conditions for a vibrating string can also arise in our heat conducting problem. Indeed, if both ends of the rod are insulated so that there is no heat flow across the ends, then according to (1.2) the boundary conditions assume the form

(2.4) $$\frac{\partial u}{\partial x}(0, t) = 0, \qquad \frac{\partial u}{\partial x}(L, t) = 0 \qquad\qquad (t \geq 0)$$

On the other hand, if there is radiation of heat at the ends of the rod into the surrounding medium, which is kept, say, at zero temperature, then the boundary conditions will be of the form

(2.5)
$$\frac{\partial u}{\partial x}(0, t) + hu(0, t) = 0$$

$$\frac{\partial u}{\partial x}(L, t) + hu(L, t) = 0$$

for $t \geq 0$, where h is a constant. Notice that all these boundary conditions are linear. As in Chapter 3, we shall refer to these conditions, (2.3), (2.4), and (2.5), as boundary conditions of the first, second, and third kind, respectively.

It is also possible to consider the problem of finding a solution of the heat equation or any of its related equations in the infinite domain $-\infty < x < \infty$, $t > 0$, which satisfies only the initial condition (2.2) prescribed for $-\infty < x < \infty$. Such a problem physically represents conduction of heat along an infinite thin rod; accordingly, the problem is called an initial value problem. It will be seen in later sections and exercises that an initial value problem for the heat equation and its related differential equations is well posed.

Exercises 6.1

1. Verify that each of the given functions satisfies the heat equation (1.5) for $0 < x < \pi$ and the accompanying initial and boundary conditions.
   (a) $u(x, t) = e^{-kt} \sin x$; $u(x, 0) = \sin x$, $u(0, t) = u(\pi, t) = 0$.
   (b) $u(x, t) = e^{-kt} \cos x$; $u(x, 0) = \cos x$, $u_x(0, t) = u_x(\pi, t) = 0$.
   (c) $u(x, t) = \frac{1}{2} + \frac{1}{2}e^{-4kt} \cos 2x$; $u(x, 0) = \cos^2 x$, $u_x(0, t) = u_x(\pi, t) = 0$.

2. Verify that the function

$$u(x, t) = \frac{1}{\sqrt{t}} e^{-x^2/4t}$$

   satisfies the heat equation (1.5) for $k = 1$, $t > 0$ and that

$$\lim_{t \to 0^+} u(x, t) = 0 \qquad \qquad \text{(provided } x \neq 0\text{)}$$

3. Consider the initial-boundary value problem

$$u_t - ku_{xx} = F(x, t) \qquad \qquad (0 < x < L, t > 0)$$
$$u(x, 0) = f(x) \qquad \qquad (0 \leq x \leq L)$$
$$u(0, t) = a(t), \qquad u(L, t) = b(t) \qquad \qquad (t \geq 0)$$

   (a) Determine a function ϕ of the form $\phi(x, t) = A(t) + xB(t)$ such that $\phi(0, t) = a(t)$ and $\phi(L, t) = b(t)$.
   (b) By introducing a new function v, defined by $v = u - \phi$, reduce problem (a) to one in which the boundary conditions are homogeneous.

4. Consider the initial-boundary value problem in Problem 3, with the boundary conditions $u_x(0, t) = a(t)$, $u_x(L, t) = b(t)$. Determine a function ϕ such that $\phi_x(0, t) = a(t)$ and $\phi_x(L, t) = b(t)$ and thus reduce the problem to one with homogeneous boundary conditions.

5. Reduce the problem

$$u_t - ku_{xx} = 0 \qquad \qquad (0 < x < \pi, t > 0)$$
$$u(x, 0) = \sin x \qquad \qquad (0 \leq x \leq \pi)$$
$$u(0, t) = t^2, \qquad u(\pi, t) = e^t \qquad \qquad (t > 0)$$

   to one with homogeneous boundary conditions.

6. Reduce the problem

$$u_t - ku_{xx} = xt \qquad\qquad (0 < x < 1, t > 0)$$
$$u(x, 0) = x \qquad\qquad (0 < x < 1)$$
$$u_x(0, t) = \sin t, \qquad u(1, t) = \ln(1 + t) \qquad\qquad (t > 0)$$

to a problem in which the boundary conditions are homogeneous.

7. Consider the problem

$$u_t - ku_{xx} = Ae^{-ax} \qquad (a > 0, 0 < x < L, t > 0)$$
$$u(x, 0) = f(x) \qquad\qquad (0 \le x \le L)$$
$$u(0, t) = 0, \qquad u(L, t) = 0 \qquad\qquad (t \ge 0)$$

where A is a constant. Introduce a new function v, defined by $u(x, t) = v(x, t) + \phi(x)$, where ϕ is a function of only the variable x. (a) Determine ϕ so that v satisfies $v_t - kv_{xx} = 0$; (b) determine ϕ so that v also satisfies $v(0, t) = 0$ and $v(L, t) = 0$, and thus reduce the given problem to one with homogeneous differential equation and boundary conditions.

8. Reduce the problem

$$u_t - ku_{xx} = 0 \qquad\qquad (x > 0, t > 0)$$
$$u(x, 0) = 0 \qquad\qquad (x > 0)$$
$$u(0, t) = h(t) \qquad\qquad (t > 0)$$

to one in which the boundary condition is homogeneous.

9. Reduce the problem

$$u_t - ku_{xx} + bu = 0 \qquad\qquad (x > 0, t > 0)$$
$$u(x, 0) = 0 \qquad\qquad (x > 0)$$
$$u_x(0, t) = h(t) \qquad\qquad (t > 0)$$

to one in which the boundary condition is homogeneous.

10. Let u denote the solution of the initial-boundary value problem

$$u_t - ku_{xx} = 0 \qquad\qquad (x > 0, t > 0)$$
$$u(x, 0) = f(x) \qquad\qquad (x \ge 0)$$
$$u_x(0, t) + hu(0, t) = 0 \qquad [t \ge 0; (h = \text{constant})]$$

where u is sufficiently differentiable. Set $v(x, t) = u_x(x, t) + hu(x, t)$. Show that v satisfies the heat equation, the initial condition $v(x, 0) = f'(x) + hf(x)$, and the boundary condition $v(0, t) = 0$. Assuming that v has been found, what will be a solution u of the original problem?

3. The Maximum Principle and Uniqueness Theorem

Before we proceed to the consideration of an initial-boundary value problem for the heat equation, we shall first establish an important property that is possessed by every continuous solution of the heat equation in a rectangular region. This property, known as the maximum principle, enables us to prove that an initial-boundary value problem is indeed well posed for the heat equation.

THEOREM 3.1 (Maximum Principle) *Let u be a solution of the heat equation (1.5), which is continuous in the rectangular region $0 \le x \le L, 0 \le t \le T$. Then u assumes its maximum value either at the base $t = 0$ or at the sides $x = 0$ and $x = L$ (Fig. 6.2).*

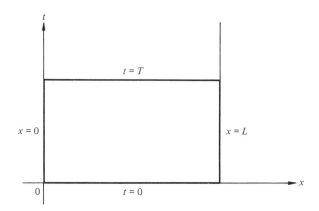

FIG. 6–2   *The maximum principle.*

Proof: We first prove that the maximum principle holds for a continuous function v that satisfies the differential inequality

(3.1)
$$\frac{\partial v}{\partial t} - k \frac{\partial^2 v}{\partial x^2} < 0$$

for $0 \le x \le L, 0 \le t \le T$. Indeed, suppose v assumed its maximum value at (x_0, t_0), where $0 < x_0 < L$ and $0 < t_0 \le T$. Then, from elementary calculus, we know that

$$v_t(x_0, t_0) \ge 0 \qquad \text{and} \qquad v_{xx}(x_0, t_0) \le 0$$

Since $k > 0$, these lead to the inequality

$$\frac{\partial v}{\partial t}(x_0, t_0) - k \frac{\partial^2 v}{\partial x^2}(x_0, t_0) \ge 0$$

which is contrary to the fact that v satisfies (3.1) at (x_0, t_0). Hence, v cannot assume a maximum at (x_0, t_0). Since v is continuous in the closed region $0 \le x \le L, 0 \le t \le T$, v has a maximum value. It must therefore occur either at $t = 0$ or $x = 0$ or $x = L$.

Now consider a continuous solution u of the heat equation (1.5) in the region $0 \le x \le L, 0 \le t \le T$. Let $u \le M$ at $t = 0$ for $0 \le x \le L$, and at $x = 0$ and $x = L$ for $0 \le t \le T$. We shall show that $u \le M$ at all points in the rectangular region. Define the function v by the equation

$$v(x, t) = u(x, t) + \varepsilon x^2$$

where ε is an arbitrary positive number. Then

$$v_t - kv_{xx} = u_t - ku_{xx} - 2\varepsilon = -2\varepsilon < 0$$

so that v satisfies (3.1). Hence, by the previous result, v must assume its maximum value at $t = 0$ or $x = 0$ or $x = L$. On all these, we see that

$$v = u + \varepsilon x^2 \leq M + \varepsilon L^2$$

Therefore, at all points in the region $0 \leq x \leq L, 0 \leq t \leq T$, it is true that

$$u = v - \varepsilon x^2 \leq v \leq M + \varepsilon L^2$$

for any $\varepsilon > 0$. Letting $\varepsilon \to 0$, we find that $u \leq M$ for $0 \leq x \leq L$ and $0 \leq t \leq T$, as we wanted to show. This establishes our theorem.

We remark that the maximum principle stated in Theorem 3.1 is often referred to as the weak maximum principle, since it permits the maximum of the solution to occur both on the boundary and at interior points. A stronger version of this principle, which contains Theorem 3.1 as a special case, asserts that if the maximum occurs at an interior point, then the solution must be constant in a certain region. The proof of this assertion is so involved that we shall not bother ourselves with it.

By applying the maximum principle to the negative of the function u, we obtain a similar result for the minimum value of u. That is, the minimum value of a continuous solution of the heat equation is also taken either at $t = 0$ or $x = 0$ or $x = L$. Physically, the maximum-minimum principle says that the temperature in the rod at any instant of time cannot get higher (or lower) than the highest (or lowest) temperature that occurs initially or which is yet to be observed at the ends of the rod.

As a consequence of the maximum principle, we can prove a uniqueness theorem for the following initial-boundary value problem for the heat equation:

$$
\begin{aligned}
&u_t - ku_{xx} = F(x, t) && (0 < x < L, t > 0) \\
\text{(3.2)} \quad &u(x, 0) = f(x) && (0 \leq x \leq L) \\
&u(0, t) = a(t), \quad u(L, t) = b(t) && (t \geq 0)
\end{aligned}
$$

THEOREM 3.2   *A solution of the initial-boundary value problem (3.2) which is continuous for $0 \leq x \leq L$ and $t \geq 0$ is uniquely determined.*

Proof: Suppose that v and w are two solutions of the problem (3.2). Then $u = v - w$ satisfies the homogeneous heat equation and vanishes at $t = 0$, $x = 0$, and $x = L$; that is, $u(x, 0) = 0$, $u(0, t) = 0$, and $u(L, t) = 0$. Hence, by the maximum principle, the value of u inside the region $0 \leq x \leq L, t \geq 0$, cannot be greater than zero; likewise, the minimum value of u cannot be less than zero. Therefore, u must be identically zero throughout the region and so v and w are identical solutions.

Another consequence of the maximum principle is the following theorem on the continuous dependence of the solution of (3.2) on the initial and boundary conditions.

THEOREM 3.3   *Let* u_i *be the solution of the problem* (3.2) *corresponding to initial-boundary conditions* $u(x, 0) = f_i(x)$, $u(0, t) = a_i(t)$, $u(L, t) = b_i(t)$ ($i = 1, 2$). *If* $|f_1(x) - f_2(x)| \leq \varepsilon$, $|a_1(t) - a_2(t)| \leq \varepsilon$, *and* $|b_1(t) - b_2(t)| \leq \varepsilon$, *then*

$$|u_1(x, t) - u_2(x, t)| \leq \varepsilon$$

for all (x, t) *where* $0 \leq x \leq L$ *and* $t \geq 0$.

Proof: Set $u = u_1 - u_2$; then u satisfies the homogeneous heat equation (1.5).   The hypothesis of the theorem implies $|u| \leq \varepsilon$ at $t = 0$, $x = 0$, and $x = L$; that is,

$$(3.3) \qquad\qquad -\varepsilon \leq u_1(x, t) - u_2(x, t) \leq \varepsilon$$

on the base and on the sides of the region $0 \leq x \leq L$, $t \geq 0$.   By the maximum principle, the inequality (3.3) holds throughout this region.   Thus, the theorem is proved.

In a later section we shall see how a solution of the problem (3.2) can be constructed.   Then, in view of Theorems 3.2 and 3.3, we can conclude that the problem (3.2) is well posed; that is, the problem has a unique solution that depends continuously on the initial and boundary data.

We conclude this section by establishing a corresponding uniqueness theorem for the initial value problem

$$(3.4) \qquad\qquad \begin{aligned} u_t - k u_{xx} &= F(x, t) & (-\infty < x < \infty, t > 0) \\ u(x, 0) &= f(x) & (-\infty < x < \infty) \end{aligned}$$

We shall require that our solution of this problem be bounded in the infinite region $-\infty < x < \infty$, $t \geq 0$.   Then we have—

THEOREM 3.4   *A solution of the initial value problem* (3.4) *which is continuous and bounded for* $-\infty < x < \infty$, $t \geq 0$, *is uniquely determined.*

Proof: Suppose v and w are two continuous solutions of the problem (3.4) such that

$$|v| \leq M, \qquad |w| \leq M$$

for $-\infty < x < \infty$, $t \geq 0$, where M is a constant.   Set $u = v - w$; then, clearly, u satisfies the homogeneous heat equation (1.5), the initial condition $u(x, 0) = 0$, and the inequality

$$|u| \leq |v - w| \leq |v| + |w| \leq 2M$$

Let us consider the finite region $-L \le x \le L, 0 \le t \le T$, where L and T are arbitrary numbers, and define

$$V(x, t) = \frac{4M}{L^2} \left(\frac{1}{2} x^2 + kt \right)$$

It is easily verified that, in this region, V satisfies equation (1.5) and that, at $t = 0$,

$$V(x, 0) = \frac{2Mx^2}{L^2} \ge u(x, 0) = 0$$

and, at $x = \pm L$,

$$V(\pm L, t) = 2M + \frac{4Mkt}{L^2} \ge 2M \ge u(\pm L, t)$$

Hence, by the maximum principle, it follows that

$$V(x, t) \ge u(x, t) \qquad (-L \le x \le L, 0 \le t \le T)$$

Similarly, by considering the function $-V(x, t)$, we obtain

$$u(x, t) \ge -V(x, t) \qquad (-L \le x \le L, 0 \le t \le T)$$

Consequently, for each point (x, t) in the region $-L \le x \le L, 0 \le t \le T$, we have

(3.5) $$|u(x, t)| \le V(x, t) = \frac{4M}{L^2} \left(\frac{1}{2} x^2 + kt \right)$$

for arbitrary numbers L and T, no matter how large. Letting $L \to \infty$, we then find $|u| = 0$, which means that $v(x, t) = w(x, t)$ for $-\infty < x < \infty, t \ge 0$.

Exercises 6.2

1. Show that if u and v are two solutions of the heat equation (1.5) for $0 < x < L$ such that $u(x, 0) \le v(x, 0)$, $u(0, t) \le v(0, t)$, and $u(L, t) \le v(L, t)$, then $u(x, t) \le v(x, t)$ for $0 \le x \le L, t \ge 0$.

2. Let u be a solution of the heat equation (1.5) which is sufficiently differentiable for $0 \le x \le L, t \ge 0$, and set $v(x, t) = u_x(x, t)$. Show that v satisfies the maximum principle.

3. Let u be a solution of the nonhomogeneous heat equation (1.6), with $0 < x < L$, $t > 0$, which is continuous for $0 \le x \le L, t \ge 0$. Prove that if $F(x, t) < 0$, then the maximum of u is attained at $t = 0$, or $x = 0$, or $x = L$.

4. Show that if u is a continuous solution of the heat equation (1.5) for $0 \le x \le L$, $t \ge 0$, such that $u_x(0, t) = 0$, then the maximum of u is attained either at $t = 0$ or at $x = L$. *Hint:* Apply the maximum principle to the function v over $-L \le x \le L, 0 \le t \le T$, where $v(x, t) = u(x, t)$ for $0 \le x \le L$ and $v(x, t) = u(-x, t)$ for $-L \le x \le 0$.

5. Let u be a solution of the heat equation for $0 < x < L$, $t > 0$, such that $u(0, t) = u(L, t) = 0$. Consider the identity

$$0 = \int_0^L u(u_t - ku_{xx})\, dx = \frac{1}{2}\frac{\partial}{\partial t}\int_0^L u^2\, dx - k\int_0^L uu_{xx}\, dx$$

(a) By integrating by parts the second integral on the right, deduce that

$$\frac{\partial}{\partial t}\int_0^L u^2\, dx \le 0 \qquad\qquad (t \ge 0)$$

This means that the function $v(t) = \int_0^L u^2(x, t)\, dx$ is nonincreasing for $t \ge 0$.
(b) If $u(x, 0) = 0$, $0 \le x \le L$, obtain the result $u(x, t) = 0$ for $0 \le x \le L$, $t \ge 0$, and thus give an alternate proof of Theorem 3.2.

6. Let u be a solution of the initial value problem

$$u_t - ku_{xx} = 0 \qquad\qquad (-\infty < x < \infty, t > 0)$$
$$u(x, 0) = f(x) \qquad\qquad (-\infty < x < \infty)$$

where f is continuous on every finite interval. If u tends to zero uniformly in t as $|x|$ tends to ∞, show that $|u(x, t)| \le \max|f(x)|$. *Hint:* Apply Theorem 3.1 to the strip $-L \le x \le L$, $t \ge 0$, and let $L \to \infty$.

7. Formulate and prove the corresponding maximum principle for the two-dimensional heat equation $u_t - k(u_{xx} + u_{yy}) = 0$ in the cylindrical region $\Omega = \{(x, y, t) \mid (x, y) \in D + C, 0 \le t \le T\}$, where D is a domain in the xy-plane bounded by a continuous curve C.

8. Prove that the following initial-boundary value problem

$$u_t - k(u_{xx} + u_{yy}) = 0 \qquad\qquad [(x, y) \text{ in } D, 0 < t < T]$$
$$u(x, y, 0) = f(x, y) \qquad\qquad [(x, y) \text{ in } D]$$
$$u = g(x, y, t) \qquad\qquad [\text{on } C, 0 \le t \le T]$$

has at most one solution. Here, D is a domain in the xy-plane bounded by the continuous closed curve C.

9. Let u be a solution of the two-dimensional heat equation of Problem 8 such that $u = 0$ on C for $0 \le t \le T$. By considering the identity

$$0 = \iint u[u_t - k(u_{xx} + u_{yy})]\, dx\, dy = 0$$

over the domain D for $0 \le t \le T$ and using Green's identity [(8.6), Chapter 1], show that

$$\frac{\partial}{\partial t}\iint u^2\, dx\, dy \le 0$$

Hence, deduce that $u(x, y, t) \equiv 0$ in D for $0 \le t \le T$ if $u(x, y, 0) = 0$. This provides an alternative proof of the uniqueness of solution for Problem 8.

4. Initial-Boundary Value Problems

Let us now consider the problem of finding a solution of the homogeneous heat equation

(4.1) $u_t - ku_{xx} = 0$ $(0 < x < L, t > 0)$

which satisfies the initial condition

(4.2) $u(x, 0) = f(x)$ $(0 \leq x \leq L)$

and the boundary conditions

(4.3) $u(0, t) = 0, \quad u(L, t) = 0$ $(t \geq 0)$

We shall solve this problem by the method of separation of variables presented in Section 9 of Chapter 3. Accordingly, we seek particular solutions of (4.1) in the form

(4.4) $u(x, t) = X(x)T(t)$

which satisfy the boundary conditions (4.3). Substituting (4.4) in (4.1) and separating the variables, we obtain

$$\frac{T'}{kT} = \frac{X''}{X} = -\lambda$$

This leads to the two ordinary differential equations $X'' + \lambda X = 0$ and

(4.5) $T' + \lambda kT = 0$

for the functions X and T, respectively.

In order for (4.4) to satisfy the boundary conditions (4.3), we must have $X(0) = 0$ and $X(L) = 0$. Thus, the function X is determined by solving the Sturm-Liouville problem

(4.6)
$$X'' + \lambda X = 0 \qquad (0 \leq x \leq L)$$
$$X(0) = 0, \qquad X(L) = 0$$

This is the same problem we encountered in Section 9 of Chapter 3, for which we found the eigenvalues

(4.7) $\lambda_n = \dfrac{n^2\pi^2}{L^2}$ $(n = 1, 2, \ldots)$

and the corresponding eigenfunctions

(4.8) $X_n(x) = \sin \dfrac{n\pi x}{L}$ $(n = 1, 2, \ldots)$

Now, for each $\lambda_n = n^2\pi^2/L^2$, $n \geq 1$, a solution of the equation (4.5) is given by

(4.9) $T_n(t) = e^{-k\lambda_n t}$

Thus, the functions

(4.10)
$$u_n(x, t) = e^{-k\lambda_n t} \sin \frac{n\pi x}{L} \qquad (n = 1, 2, \ldots)$$

with λ_n given by (4.7), are all particular solutions of (4.1) satisfying the homogeneous boundary conditions (4.3).

To obtain a solution of our problem, we consider a series of the functions (4.10) in the form

(4.11)
$$u(x, t) = \sum_{n=1}^{\infty} b_n e^{-k\lambda_n t} \sin \frac{n\pi x}{L}$$

and determine the coefficients b_n so as to satisfy the initial condition (4.2). Thus, setting $t = 0$ in (4.11), we see from (4.2) that the coefficients b_n must satisfy the relation

(4.12)
$$f(x) = \sum_{n=1}^{\infty} b_n \sin \frac{n\pi x}{L} \qquad (0 \leq x \leq L)$$

This is precisely the Fourier sine series representation of f on the interval $[0, L]$. Therefore, the coefficients b_n are given by the formula

(4.13)
$$b_n = \frac{2}{L} \int_0^L f(x) \sin \frac{n\pi x}{L} \, dx \qquad (n = 1, 2, \ldots)$$

The function u represented by the series (4.11), with b_n given by (4.13), is the solution of our problem. In order to verify this, we now assume that the function f in (4.2) is continuous and piecewise smooth on $[0, L]$ and that $f(0) = f(L) = 0$. Then, according to Theorem 6.2 of Chapter 5, the Fourier sine series (4.12) of f converges absolutely and uniformly to the function on $[0, L]$. Now, for $t \geq 0$,

$$\sum_{n=1}^{\infty} \left| b_n e^{-k\lambda_n t} \sin \frac{n\pi x}{L} \right| \leq \sum_{n=1}^{\infty} |b_n|$$

where the series on the right converges. Therefore, the series (4.11) converges absolutely and uniformly to $u(x, t)$ for $0 \leq x \leq L$ and $t \geq 0$. Since each term of the series is continuous and satisfies (4.3), it follows that u, too, is continuous and satisfies (4.3). Moreover, on setting $t = 0$, we see from (4.12) that u satisfies the initial condition (4.2) as well.

There remains to be verified only the fact that u satisfies the heat equation. To this end, we need to show that the series (4.11) can be differentiated term by term, once with respect to t and twice with respect to x. Let us consider the series

(4.14)
$$-\sum_{n=1}^{\infty} k\lambda_n b_n e^{-k\lambda_n t} \sin \frac{n\pi x}{L}$$

which is the formal derivative of (4.11) with respect to t. Since f is continuous on $[0, L]$, it is bounded there and so there is a constant M such that $|b_n| \leq M$ for all $n \geq 1$. Then, clearly, for any $t_0 > 0$,

$$\left| k\lambda_n b_n e^{-k\lambda_n t} \sin \frac{n\pi x}{L} \right| \leq k\lambda_n M e^{-k\lambda_n t_0}$$

whenever $t \geq t_0$. Since the series with the general term $k\lambda_n M \exp(-k\lambda_n t_0)$ converges, it follows by the Weierstrass M-test that the series (4.14) converges uniformly for $0 \leq x \leq L$ and $0 < t_0 \leq t$. This shows that (4.11) has continuous derivative with respect to t for $0 \leq x \leq L$, $t > 0$, which can be obtained by differentiating the series term by term.

In the same way we can establish that (4.11) has continuous second-order derivative with respect to x for $0 \leq x \leq L$, $t > 0$, which is obtainable by termwise differentiation. Thus, substituting (4.11) in equation (4.1), we see that

$$u_t - ku_{xx} = \sum_{n=1}^{\infty} b_n e^{-k\lambda_n t} \sin \frac{n\pi x}{L} [-k\lambda_n + k\lambda_n] = 0$$

This completes the verification that (4.11) with (4.13) is a solution of the problem (4.1), (4.2), (4.3) under the conditions that f is continuous and piecewise smooth on $[0, L]$ and vanishes at the end points. That this solution is uniquely determined follows by Theorem 3.2.

It is noteworthy that by applying repeatedly the procedure we have described above, the series solution (4.11) can be shown to have continuous derivatives of all orders with respect to x and t for $0 \leq x \leq L$ and $t > 0$. This result is quite in contrast with the result we obtained in an example problem in Chapter 3, Section 9, involving the wave equation. Although there the function f satisfies the same conditions as given above, yet the series solution cannot be differentiated twice, term by term; we have had to resort to the concept of generalized solution. This is a basic difference between solutions of hyperbolic and parabolic differential equations.

If we substitute (4.13) for b_n in (4.11) and interchange the order of summation and integration, we can write (4.11) in the integral form

(4.15) $$u(x, t) = \int_0^L G(x, t; \xi)f(\xi) \, d\xi$$

where

(4.16) $$G(x, t; \xi) = \frac{2}{L} \sum_{n=1}^{\infty} e^{-k\lambda_n t} \sin \frac{n\pi\xi}{L} \sin \frac{n\pi x}{L} \qquad (t > 0)$$

with $\lambda_n = n^2\pi^2/L^2$, $n \geq 1$. Notice that for $t > 0$, the series (4.16) is uniformly convergent in ξ so that the interchange of summation and integration in (4.15) is perfectly valid. The function G defined by (4.16) is known as the Green's function for the heat equation corresponding to the boundary conditions (4.3), and the series is called its bilinear expansion [Chapter 4, Section 7]. Physically,

$G(x, t; \xi)$ represents the temperature distribution in the rod for $0 \leq x \leq L$, $t > 0$, due to a concentrated heat source at the point $x = \xi$ at time $t = 0$, with the temperature at the end points maintained at zero degree.

It is easy to verify from (4.16) that: (i) G satisfies the heat equation with respect to x and t for $t > 0$, provided $x \neq \xi$; (ii) G is continuous at $x = \xi$; (iii) G satisfies the boundary conditions (4.3) with respect to the variable x; and (iv) G is symmetric with respect to x and ξ. These properties are analogous to the properties possessed by a Green's function for an ordinary differential equation [see (2.15), Chapter 4].

Example 4.1.   Find the solution of the initial-boundary value problem

$$u_t - u_{xx} = 0 \qquad\qquad (0 < x < \pi, t > 0)$$
$$u(x, 0) = \sin x \qquad\qquad (0 \leq x \leq \pi)$$
$$u(0, t) = u(\pi, t) = 0 \qquad\qquad (t \geq 0)$$

Solution: By (4.13) we have

$$b_n = \frac{2}{\pi} \int_0^\pi \sin x \sin nx \, dx$$

$$= \begin{cases} 1 & (n = 1) \\ 0 & (n > 1) \end{cases}$$

Hence, the solution is $u(x, t) = e^{-t} \sin x$.

Example 4.2.   Find the solution of the problem

$$u_t - u_{xx} = 0 \qquad\qquad (0 < x < \pi, t > 0)$$
$$u(x, 0) = x(\pi - x) \qquad\qquad (0 \leq x \leq \pi)$$
$$u(0, t) = 0, \qquad u(\pi, t) = 0 \qquad\qquad (t \geq 0)$$

Solution: According to (4.11), the solution is given by

$$u(x, t) = \sum_{n=1}^\infty b_n e^{-n^2 t} \sin nx$$

where, by (4.13),

$$b_n = \frac{2}{\pi} \int_0^\pi x(\pi - x) \sin nx \, dx$$

$$= 2 \int_0^\pi x \sin nx \, dx - \frac{2}{\pi} \int_0^\pi x^2 \sin nx \, dx$$

$$= 4 \frac{1 - (-1)^n}{\pi n^3}$$

Hence, we have

$$u(x, t) = \frac{8}{\pi} \sum_{n=1}^\infty \frac{e^{-(2n-1)^2 t}}{(2n - 1)^3} \sin(2n - 1)x$$

In case both ends of the rod are insulated so that the initial-boundary value problem consists of (4.1), (4.2) and the boundary conditions

$$(4.17) \qquad u_x(0, t) = 0, \qquad u_x(L, t) = 0 \qquad (t \geq 0)$$

the method of separation of variables leads to the Sturm-Liouville problem

$$(4.18) \qquad X'' + \lambda X = 0, \qquad X'(0) = 0, \qquad X'(L) = 0$$

for the function X together with equation (4.5) for the function T. We recall that the eigenvalues of the problem (4.18) are $\lambda_n = n^2 \pi^2 / L^2$, $n = 0, 1, 2, \ldots$, with the corresponding eigenfunctions $X_n(x) = \cos(n\pi x/L)$, $n = 0, 1, 2, \ldots$. Thus, the functions

$$(4.19) \qquad u_n(x, t) = e^{-k\lambda_n t} \cos \frac{n\pi x}{L} \qquad (n = 0, 1, 2, \ldots)$$

are all particular solutions of (4.1) satisfying the boundary conditions (4.17).

Now, to obtain a solution of the problem (4.1), (4.2), (4.17), we consider a series consisting of the functions (4.19) in the form

$$(4.20) \qquad u(x, t) = \frac{a_0}{2} + \sum_{n=1}^{\infty} a_n e^{-k\lambda_n t} \cos \frac{n\pi x}{L}$$

The initial condition (4.2) then requires that the coefficients a_n satisfy the relation

$$f(x) = \frac{a_0}{2} + \sum_{n=1}^{\infty} a_n \cos \frac{n\pi x}{L}$$

which is the Fourier cosine series representation of the function f on the interval $0 \leq x \leq L$. Hence, the coefficients are given by the formula

$$(4.21) \qquad a_n = \frac{2}{L} \int_0^L f(x) \cos \frac{n\pi x}{L} \, dx \qquad (n = 0, 1, 2, \ldots)$$

Thus, a solution of the problem (4.1), (4.2), (4.17) is given by (4.20), with a_n ($n \geq 0$) given by (4.21).

The verification that (4.20) with (4.21) satisfies (4.1), (4.2), and (4.17) under the conditions that f is continuous and piecewise smooth on the interval $0 \leq x \leq L$ is done in the same manner as in the previous case. That the solution is uniquely determined follows from a modified maximum principle corresponding to the boundary conditions (4.17) (Problem 2, Exercises 6.2).

If we substitute (4.21) for the coefficients a_n in (4.20), the solution can be written in the integral form

$$(4.22) \qquad u(x, t) = \int_0^L G(x, t; \xi) f(\xi) \, d\xi$$

where, as in the previous case,

$$(4.23) \qquad G(x, t; \xi) = \frac{1}{L} + \frac{2}{L} \sum_{n=1}^{\infty} e^{-k\lambda_n t} \cos \frac{n\pi \xi}{L} \cos \frac{n\pi x}{L}$$

is called the Green's function corresponding to the boundary conditions (4.17). Here, G is again represented by its bilinear expansion.

Example 4.3. Find the solution of the problem

$$u_t - u_{xx} = 0 \qquad\qquad (0 < x < \pi,\, t > 0)$$
$$u(x, 0) = x \qquad\qquad (0 \le x \le \pi)$$
$$u_x(0, t) = 0, \qquad u_x(\pi, t) = 0 \qquad\qquad (t \ge 0)$$

Solution: By the formula (4.21) we find

$$a_0 = \frac{2}{\pi} \int_0^\pi x \, dx = \pi$$

$$a_n = \frac{2}{\pi} \int_0^\pi x \cos nx \, dx = \frac{2}{\pi} \left[\frac{x \sin nx}{n} + \frac{\cos nx}{n^2} \right] \Big|_0^\pi$$

$$= \frac{2}{\pi} \left[\frac{\cos n\pi - 1}{n^2} \right] = \frac{2}{\pi} \frac{(-1)^n - 1}{n^2} \qquad (n \ge 1)$$

Thus, $a_n = 0$ when n is even and $a_n = -(4/\pi n^2)$ when n is odd; therefore

$$a_{2k-1} = \frac{-4}{\pi(2k - 1)^2} \qquad\qquad (k \ge 1)$$

Hence, by (4.20), the solution is

$$u(x, t) = \frac{\pi}{2} - \frac{4}{\pi} \sum_{k=1}^{\infty} \frac{e^{-(2k-1)^2 t}}{(2k - 1)^2} \cos(2k - 1)x$$

Exercises 6.3

In Problems 1 through 6, find the solution of the initial-boundary value problem for the heat equation (4.1), $0 < x < \pi$, $t > 0$, satisfying the given initial and boundary conditions.

1. $u(x, 0) = A$, A a constant; $u(0, t) = 0$, $u(\pi, t) = 0$, $t > 0$.
2. $u(x, 0) = \sin^3 x$; $u(0, t) = 0$, $u(\pi, t) = 0$, $t \ge 0$.
3. $u(x, 0) = \cos^2 x$; $u_x(0, t) = 0$, $u_x(\pi, t) = 0$, $t \ge 0$.
4. $u(x, 0) = x(\pi - x)$; $u(0, t) = 0$, $u(\pi, t) = 0$, $t \ge 0$.
5. $u(0, t) = 0$, $u(\pi, t) = 0$, $t \ge 0$,

$$u(x, 0) = \begin{cases} x & (0 \le x \le \pi/2) \\ \pi - x & (\pi/2 \le x \le \pi) \end{cases}$$

6. $u(x, 0) = x^2 - \pi^2$; $u_x(0, t) = 0$, $u(\pi, t) = 0$, $t \ge 0$.
7. Solve the initial-boundary value problem

$$u_t - ku_{xx} - u = 0 \qquad\qquad (0 < x < 1,\, t > 0)$$
$$u(x, 0) = x(1 - x) \qquad\qquad (0 \le x \le 1)$$
$$u(0, t) = 0, \qquad u_x(1, t) = 0 \qquad\qquad (t \ge 0)$$

8. Solve the initial-boundary value problem

$$u_t - ku_{xx} + u = 0 \qquad\qquad (0 < x < \pi/2,\ t > 0)$$
$$u(x, 0) = \cos x \qquad\qquad (0 \le x \le \pi/2)$$
$$u_x(0, t) = 0, \qquad u(\pi/2, t) = 0 \qquad\qquad (t \ge 0)$$

9. Solve the initial-boundary value problem

$$u_t - u_{xx} - u = 0 \qquad\qquad (0 < x < \pi,\ t > 0)$$
$$u(x, 0) = \sin^3 x \qquad\qquad (0 \le x \le \pi)$$
$$u(0, t) = 0, \qquad u(\pi, t) = 0 \qquad\qquad (t \ge 0)$$

10. Find the solution of the initial-boundary value problem

$$v_t - kv_{xx} + hv = 0 \qquad\qquad (0 < x < L,\ t > 0)$$
$$v(x, 0) = f(x) \qquad\qquad (0 \le x \le L)$$
$$v_x(0, t) = 0, \qquad v_x(L, t) = 0 \qquad\qquad (t \ge 0)$$

where h is a positive constant, and show that $v(x, t) = u(x, t)e^{-ht}$, with u given by (4.20).

11. Find the solution of the initial-boundary value problem

$$u_t - u_{xx} + u = 0 \qquad\qquad (0 < x < 1,\ t > 0)$$
$$u(x, 0) = x^2 - 1 \qquad\qquad (0 \le x \le 1)$$
$$u_x(0, t) = 0, \qquad u(1, t) = 0 \qquad\qquad (t \ge 0)$$

12. Find the solution of the problem

$$u_t - ku_{xx} = 0 \qquad\qquad (0 < x < L,\ t > 0)$$
$$u(x, 0) = f(x) \qquad\qquad (0 \le x \le L)$$
$$u(0, t) = 0, \qquad u_x(L, t) + hu(L, t) = 0$$
$$(t \ge 0;\ h \text{ a positive constant})$$

13. Find the solution of the problem

$$u_t - ku_{xx} = 0 \qquad\qquad (0 < x < L,\ t > 0)$$
$$u(x, 0) = f(x) \qquad\qquad (0 \le x \le L)$$
$$u_x(0, t) + hu(0, t) = 0, \qquad u(L, t) = 0$$
$$(t \ge 0;\ h = \text{const} > 0)$$

5. Nonhomogeneous Initial-Boundary Value Problems

The problems we have considered so far all involved homogeneous differential equation and homogeneous boundary conditions. In this section we shall consider problems in which either the differential equation or the boundary conditions, or both, are nonhomogeneous. Such problems will be called nonhomogeneous problems. The method that we shall describe here for solving these types of problems is a variation of that described in Section 7 of Chapter 4 for ordinary differential equations.

We first consider the problem consisting of the nonhomogeneous heat equation

(5.1) $u_t - ku_{xx} = F(x, t)$ $(0 < x < L, t > 0)$

together with the initial condition (4.2) and boundary conditions (4.3). We assume a series solution of this problem in the form

(5.2) $u(x, t) = \sum\limits_{n=1}^{\infty} u_n(t) \sin \dfrac{n\pi x}{L}$

where the coefficients u_n are functions of t. This is actually the eigenfunction expansion of the yet unknown function u, in terms of the eigenfunctions (4.8) of the associated Sturm-Liouville problem (4.6). Thus, the coefficients u_n must be related to the function u by the formula

(5.3) $u_n(t) = \dfrac{2}{L} \displaystyle\int_0^L u(x, t) \sin \dfrac{n\pi x}{L} dx$ $(n = 1, 2, \ldots)$

Now let us assume that u is twice continuously differentiable for $0 \le x \le L$, $t \ge 0$, and that the function F in (5.1) can be represented in Fourier sine series

(5.4) $F(x, t) = \sum\limits_{n=1}^{\infty} F_n(t) \sin \dfrac{n\pi x}{L}$

so that

(5.5) $F_n(t) = \dfrac{2}{L} \displaystyle\int_0^L F(x, t) \sin \dfrac{n\pi x}{L} dx$ $(n = 1, 2, \ldots)$

Then, by differentiating (5.3) with respect to t and using (5.1), we obtain

(5.6) $u_n'(t) = \dfrac{2}{L} \displaystyle\int_0^L u_t \sin \dfrac{n\pi x}{L} dx$

$= \dfrac{2k}{L} \displaystyle\int_0^L u_{xx} \sin \dfrac{n\pi x}{L} dx + F_n(t)$

where $F_n(t)$ is given in (5.5). By using the boundary conditions (4.3), the first term on the right of equation (5.6) can be integrated by parts twice, to give

$\dfrac{2k}{L} \displaystyle\int_0^L u_{xx} \sin \dfrac{n\pi x}{L} dx = -k\lambda_n u_n(t)$

where λ_n is as given in (4.7). Thus, (5.6) leads to the ordinary differential equation

(5.7) $u_n'(t) + k\lambda_n u_n(t) = F_n(t)$

for the functions u_n, $n = 1, 2, \ldots$. The initial condition (4.2) implies that

$$(5.8) \qquad u_n(0) = \frac{2}{L} \int_0^L f(x) \sin \frac{n\pi x}{L} \, dx = b_n \qquad (n = 1, 2, \ldots)$$

Hence, by solving the initial value problem (5.7), (5.8), we find

$$(5.9) \qquad u_n(t) = \int_0^t e^{-k\lambda_n(t-\tau)} F_n(\tau) \, d\tau + b_n e^{-k\lambda_n t}$$

Fourier Expansion

for $n = 1, 2, \ldots$. Substituting this in (5.2), we thus obtain

$$(5.10) \qquad u(x, t) = \sum_{n=1}^{\infty} \left\{ \int_0^t e^{-k\lambda_n(t-\tau)} F_n(\tau) \, d\tau \right\} \sin \frac{n\pi x}{L} + \sum_{n=1}^{\infty} b_n e^{-k\lambda_n t} \sin \frac{n\pi x}{L}$$

for a solution of the problem (5.1), (4.2), (4.3).

To verify that (5.10) satisfies (5.1), (4.2), and (4.3), we need show only that the first term on the right of (5.10) satisfies (5.1), (4.3), and vanishes at $t = 0$ because the second term is just the solution (4.11) of the homogeneous initial-boundary value problem (4.1), (4.2), (4.3). Thus, set

$$(5.11) \qquad v(x, t) = \sum_{n=1}^{\infty} v_n(t) \sin \frac{n\pi x}{L}$$

with

$$(5.12) \qquad v_n(t) = \int_0^t e^{-k\lambda_n(t-\tau)} F_n(\tau) \, d\tau \qquad (n \geq 1)$$

If we assume that F is continuous for $0 \leq x \leq L$, $t \geq 0$, then for any fixed T we see from (5.5) that

$$|F_n(t)| \leq \frac{2}{L} \int_0^L |F(x, t)| \, dx \leq 2M$$

where M denotes the maximum value of $|F|$ in the region $0 \leq x \leq L$, $0 \leq t \leq T$. Hence, from (5.12), we have

$$|v_n(t)| \leq e^{-k\lambda_n t} \int_0^t e^{k\lambda_n \tau} |F_n(\tau)| \, d\tau$$

$$\leq 2M e^{-k\lambda_n t} \frac{e^{k\lambda_n t} - 1}{k\lambda_n} < \frac{2M}{k\lambda_n}$$

Since the series of constants $2M/k\lambda_n$ converges, it follows by Weierstrass M-test that the series (5.11) converges uniformly in the region $0 \leq x \leq L$, $0 \leq t \leq T$ for arbitrary T. This implies that v is a continuous function for $0 \leq x \leq L$, $t \geq 0$, and thus satisfies (4.3) and vanishes at $t = 0$ because each of the terms of the series does. Under more stringent conditions on F [say, F, F_x, and F_{xx} are continuous for $0 \leq x \leq L$, $t \geq 0$, and $F(0, t) = F(L, t) = 0$], we can verify that the series (5.11) can be differentiated term by term. Then, by (5.7) and (5.4), it follows that

$$v_t - kv_{xx} = \sum_{n=1}^{\infty} [v_n'(t) + k_n v(t)] \sin \frac{n\pi x}{L}$$

$$= \sum_{n=1}^{\infty} F_n(t) \sin \frac{n\pi x}{L}$$

$$= F(x, t)$$

so that v satisfies (5.1).

If we substitute (5.5) for F_n in (5.11) and formally interchange the order of summation and integration, we can write (5.11) in the integral form

$$(5.13) \qquad v(x, t) = \int_0^t \int_0^L G(x, t - \tau; \xi) F(\xi, \tau) \, d\xi \, d\tau$$

where $G(x, t; \xi)$ is the Green's function given in (4.16). In this form, it can be verified that (5.13) gives a solution of the problem (5.1), (4.3) with homogeneous initial conditions under the less restrictive conditions that F and F_x are continuous and $F(0, t) = F(L, t) = 0$. Indeed, from the discussion in Section 4, we see that the inner integral in (5.13) is a solution of the problem

$$(5.14) \qquad \begin{aligned} u_t - ku_{xx} &= 0 & (0 < x < L, 0 < \tau < t) \\ u(x, 0; \tau) &= F(x, \tau) & (\tau > 0) \\ u(0, t; \tau) &= u(L, t; \tau) = 0 & (0 < \tau \le t) \end{aligned}$$

Our assertion then follows by the Duhamel's principle (Problem 10, Exercises 6.4). The uniqueness of our solution follows by Theorem 3.2.

Example 5.1. Find the solution of the problem

$$\begin{aligned} u_t - u_{xx} &= t \sin x & (0 < x < \pi, t > 0) \\ u(x, 0) &= 0 & (0 \le x \le \pi) \\ u(0, t) &= u(\pi, t) = 0 & (t \ge 0) \end{aligned}$$

Solution: By (5.5) we find

$$F_n(t) = \frac{2t}{\pi} \int_0^\pi \sin x \sin nx \, dx = \begin{cases} t & (n = 1) \\ 0 & (n > 1) \end{cases}$$

Hence, by (5.11), the solution is

$$u(x, t) = \left(\int_0^t e^{-(t-\tau)} \tau \, d\tau \right) \sin x$$

$$= (e^{-t} + t - 1) \sin x$$

Example 5.2.   Find the solution of the problem

$$u_t - u_{xx} = F(x, t) \qquad\qquad (0 < x < \pi, t > 0)$$
$$u(x, 0) = 0 \qquad\qquad (0 \le x \le \pi)$$
$$u(0, t) = u(\pi, t) = 0 \qquad\qquad (t \ge 0)$$

where $F(x, t) = x$ when $0 \le x \le \pi/2$, and $F(x, t) = \pi - x$ when $\pi/2 \le x \le \pi$.

Solution: The coefficients in the Fourier sine series expansion of F are given by

$$F_n(t) = \frac{2}{\pi} \int_0^{\pi/2} x \sin nx \, dx + \frac{2}{\pi} \int_{\pi/2}^{\pi} (\pi - x) \sin nx \, dx$$

$$= \frac{4}{\pi n^2} \sin \frac{n\pi}{2} \qquad\qquad (n = 1, 2, \dots)$$

or

$$F_{2n-1}(t) = \frac{4(-1)^{n-1}}{\pi(2n-1)^2} \qquad\qquad (n = 1, 2, \dots)$$

(See Example 9.1, Chapter 3.) Hence, by (5.12),

$$v_{2n-1}(t) = \frac{4(-1)^{n-1}}{\pi(2n-1)^2} \int_0^t \exp[-(2n-1)^2(t - \tau)] \, d\tau$$

$$= \frac{4(-1)^{n-1}}{\pi(2n-1)^4} [1 - e^{-(2n-1)^2 t}]$$

and therefore, by (5.11), the solution is

$$u(x, t) = \frac{4}{\pi} \sum_{n=1}^{\infty} \frac{(-1)^{n-1}}{(2n-1)^4} [1 - e^{-(2n-1)^2 t}] \sin(2n-1)x$$

Next we consider the initial-boundary value problem

(5.15)
$$u_t - ku_{xx} = 0 \qquad\qquad (0 < x < L, t > 0)$$
$$u(x, 0) = 0 \qquad\qquad (0 < x < L)$$
$$u(0, t) = a(t), \qquad u_x(L, t) = b(t) \qquad\qquad (t > 0)$$

which involves nonhomogeneous boundary conditions. This problem can, of course, be reduced to a problem of the kind considered above, in which the differential equation is nonhomogeneous and the boundary conditions are homogeneous. In fact, if we introduce the new dependent variable w, defined by $w = u - v$, where $v(x, t) = a(t) + xb(t)$, then the problem (5.15) becomes

(5.16)
$$w_t - kw_{xx} = -[a'(t) + xb'(t)]$$
$$w(x, 0) = -a(0) - xb(0)$$
$$w(0, t) = 0, \qquad w_x(L, t) = 0$$

which can be treated by the method described above.

It is possible, however, to apply the method directly to the problem (5.15) without reducing it to (5.16). That is, we assume a solution of (5.15) in the form of a series involving the eigenfunctions of the Sturm-Liouville problem

$$X'' + \lambda X = 0, \qquad X(0) = 0, \qquad X'(L) = 0$$

which arises if the method of separation of variables is applied to the problem when the boundary conditions are homogeneous. This problem has the eigenvalues

$$\lambda_n = \left(\frac{2n - 1}{2} \frac{\pi}{L} \right)^2$$

with the corresponding eigenfunctions

$$X_n(x) = \sin\left(\frac{2n - 1}{2} \right) \frac{\pi x}{L} \qquad (n = 0, 1, 2, \ldots)$$

Therefore, we assume a solution u in the form

(5.17) $$u(x, t) = \sum_{n=1}^{\infty} u_n(t) \sin\left(\frac{2n - 1}{2} \right) \frac{\pi x}{L}$$

with

(5.18) $$u_n(t) = \frac{2}{L} \int_0^L u(x, t) \sin\left(\frac{2n - 1}{2} \right) \frac{\pi x}{L} \, dx \qquad (n = 1, 2, \ldots)$$

Assuming that u is twice continuously differentiable for $0 \le x \le L, t \ge 0$, we obtain, by differentiating (5.18) with respect to t and using the differential equation,

$$u_n'(t) = \frac{2}{L} \int_0^L u_t(x, t) \sin\left(\frac{2n - 1}{2} \right) \frac{\pi x}{L} \, dx$$

$$= \frac{2k}{L} \int_0^L u_{xx}(x, t) \sin\left(\frac{2n - 1}{2} \right) \frac{\pi x}{L} \, dx$$

Using the boundary conditions in (5.15), this can be integrated by parts twice to give

(5.19) $$u_n'(t) + k\lambda_n u_n(t) = g_n(t)$$

where $\lambda_n = [(2n - 1)\pi]^2/4L^2$ and

$$g_n(t) = \frac{2k}{L} [\sqrt{\lambda_n} \, a(t) + (-1)^{n-1} b(t)] \qquad (n = 1, 2, \ldots)$$

From the initial condition in (5.15) we see that $u_n(0) = 0$. Hence, by solving the differential equation (5.19) with the initial condition $u_n(0) = 0$, we find

(5.20) $$u_n(t) = \int_0^t \exp(-k\lambda_n(t - \tau)) g_n(\tau) \, d\tau \qquad (n = 1, 2, \ldots)$$

Substituting this in (5.17), we thus obtain

$$(5.21) \qquad u(x, t) = \sum_{n=1}^{\infty} \left\{ \int_0^t \exp(-k\lambda_n(t - \tau))g_n(\tau)\, d\tau \right\} \sin\left(\frac{2n - 1}{2}\right) \frac{\pi x}{L}$$

The verification that this gives a solution of the problem (5.15) is not so straight-forward as in problems we encountered before. We shall illustrate the situation in this case by means of the following example.

Example 5.3. Find and verify the solution of the problem

$$\begin{aligned} u_t - u_{xx} &= 0 && (0 < x < \pi, t > 0) \\ u(x, 0) &= 0 && (0 < x < \pi) \\ u(0, t) &= 0, \quad u_x(\pi, t) = 1 && (t > 0) \end{aligned}$$

Solution: Here we have $g_n(t) = (2/\pi)(-1)^{n-1}$ so that by the formula (5.21) our solution is

$$\begin{aligned} u(x, t) &= \frac{2}{\pi} \sum_{n=1}^{\infty} (-1)^{n-1} \left\{ \int_0^t \exp\left(\frac{-(2n - 1)^2(t - \tau)}{4}\right) d\tau \right\} \sin\left(\frac{2n - 1}{2}\right) x \\ &= \frac{8}{\pi} \sum_{n=1}^{\infty} (-1)^{n-1} \frac{1 - e^{-(2n-1)^2 t/4}}{(2n - 1)^2} \sin\left(\frac{2n - 1}{2}\right) x \end{aligned}$$

To verify that this gives a solution of the problem, we observe that the function $f(x) = x$ has the Fourier series representation

$$x = \frac{8}{\pi} \sum_{n=1}^{\infty} \frac{(-1)^{n-1}}{(2n - 1)^2} \sin\left(\frac{2n - 1}{2}\right) x \qquad (0 < x < \pi)$$

in terms of the eigenfunctions $X_n(x) = \sin[(2n - 1)/2]x, n = 1, 2, \ldots$. Hence, we can write our solution above in the form

$$u(x, t) = x - \frac{8}{\pi} \sum_{n=1}^{\infty} \frac{(-1)^{n-1}}{(2n - 1)^2} \exp\left(\frac{-(2n - 1)^2 t}{4}\right) \sin\left(\frac{2n - 1}{2}\right) x$$

The series on the right converges uniformly in the region $0 \le x \le \pi, t \ge 0$, so that u is a continuous function there. Further, for $0 < x < u$ and $t > 0$, the function u has continuous derivatives of all orders with respect to x and t, which can be obtained by termwise differentiation. Moreover, it is clear that $u(x, 0) = 0$, $u(0, t) = 0$, and $u_x(\pi, t) = 1$. By a straightforward calculation it is readily seen that u satisfies the differential equation for $0 \le x \le \pi, t > 0$. This completes the verification that u is a solution of the given problem.

Exercises 6.4

In Problems 1 through 5, reduce the problem to one involving homogeneous boundary conditions and then find the solution.

1. $u_t - ku_{xx} = 0, 0 < x < L, t > 0; u(x, 0) = 0, u(0, t) = u(L, t) = A, A$ a constant.

2. $u_t - ku_{xx} = 0, 0 < x < L, t > 0; u(x, 0) = 0, u_x(0, t) = A, u(L, t) = 0, A$ a constant.

3. $u_t - k u_{xx} = 0, 0 < x < L, t > 0; u(x, 0) = 0, u(0, t) = \sin \omega t, u(L, t) = 0, \omega$ a constant.

4. $u_t - k u_{xx} = 0, 0 < x < L, t > 0; u(x, 0) = 0, u(0, t) = 0, u_x(L, t) = \cos \omega t.$

5. $u_t - u_{xx} + hu = 0, h$ a positive constant, $0 < x < \pi, t > 0; u(x, 0) = 0, u(0, t) = 0, u(\pi, t) = 1.$

6. Solve the problem

$$u_t - k u_{xx} = e^{-x} \qquad\qquad (0 < x < \pi, t > 0)$$
$$u(x, 0) = f(x) \qquad\qquad (0 \le x \le \pi)$$
$$u(0, t) = 0, \qquad u_x(\pi, t) = 0$$

(See Problem 7, Exercises 6.1.)

7. Solve the problem

$$u_t - k u_{xx} = A \cos \omega t \qquad\qquad (0 < x < \pi, t > 0)$$
$$u(x, 0) = f(x) \qquad\qquad (0 \le x \le \pi)$$
$$u_x(0, t) = 0, \qquad u_x(\pi, t) = 0 \qquad\qquad (A \text{ a constant})$$

(Observe that any function of t satisfies the boundary conditions.)

8. Find the solution of the problem

$$u_t - k u_{xx} = g(x, t) \qquad\qquad (0 < x < L, t > 0)$$
$$u(x, 0) = 0 \qquad\qquad (0 < x < L)$$
$$u(0, t) = 0, \qquad u(L, t) = h(t) \qquad\qquad (t > 0)$$

9. Find the solution of the problem

$$u_t - k u_{xx} = g(x, t) \qquad\qquad (0 < x < L, t > 0)$$
$$u_x(0, t) = h(t), \qquad u_x(L, t) = 0 \qquad\qquad (t > 0)$$
$$u(x, 0) = 0 \qquad\qquad (0 < x < L)$$

10. (Duhamel's Principle) Let $u(x, t, \tau)$ be the solution of problem (5.14) and set $v(x, t) = \int_0^t u(x, t - \tau, \tau) \, d\tau$. Show that v agrees with (5.13) and that it satisfies (5.1), (4.3), and the initial condition $v(x, 0) = 0$.

6. The Initial Value Problem

We now consider the problem of heat flow in an infinite rod without heat source, whose lateral surface is thermally insulated. This problem leads to the initial value problem

$$(6.1) \qquad\qquad u_t - k u_{xx} = 0 \qquad\qquad (-\infty < x < \infty, t > 0)$$

$$(6.2) \qquad\qquad u(x, 0) = f(x) \qquad\qquad (-\infty < x < \infty)$$

for the heat equation. We shall solve this problem by means of the Fourier transform presented in Chapter 5.

We suppose that the problem (6.1), (6.2) has a solution u, which has the property that u, u_t, u_x, and u_{xx} are all piecewise smooth in x and t, and absolutely integrable in x for $-\infty < x < \infty$. Then, according to Theorem 8.1 of Chapter 5, the Fourier transforms of all these functions exist; in particular, we have

(6.3)
$$U(s, t) = \frac{1}{\sqrt{2\pi}} \int_{-\infty}^{\infty} u(x, t) e^{-isx}\, dx$$

and

(6.4)
$$u(x, t) = \frac{1}{\sqrt{2\pi}} \int_{-\infty}^{\infty} U(s, t) e^{isx}\, ds$$

Thus, if we can find the transform (6.3), then the solution of the problem will be given by the formula (6.4).

To determine the function U, let us differentiate (6.3) with respect to t and use the differential equation (6.1) to obtain

(6.5)
$$\frac{\partial U}{\partial t}(s, t) = \frac{1}{\sqrt{2\pi}} \int_{-\infty}^{\infty} u_t(x, t) e^{-isx}\, dx$$
$$= \frac{k}{\sqrt{2\pi}} \int_{-\infty}^{\infty} u_{xx}(x, t) e^{-isx}\, dx$$

Note that because u_t and u_{xx} are absolutely integrable on $-\infty < x < \infty$ for all s and $t > 0$, differentiation with respect to t under the integral sign is valid. Integrating by parts twice the last integral above, we have

$$\frac{\partial U}{\partial t}(s, t) = \frac{k}{\sqrt{2\pi}} (u_x e^{-isx} + isue^{-isx}) \Big|_{-\infty}^{\infty}$$
$$- \frac{ks^2}{\sqrt{2\pi}} \int_{-\infty}^{\infty} u(x, t) e^{-isx}\, dx$$

If we further assume that u and u_x vanish as $|x| \to \infty$, then equation (6.5) reduces to

(6.6)
$$\frac{\partial U}{\partial t}(s, t) = -ks^2 U(s, t)$$

where we have used (6.3).

We now require for this discussion that the function f in (6.2) be piecewise smooth and absolutely integrable on $(-\infty, \infty)$ so that its Fourier transform $F(s)$ exists. Then, from (6.3) and (6.2), we have

(6.7)
$$U(s, 0) = \frac{1}{\sqrt{2\pi}} \int_{-\infty}^{\infty} u(x, 0) e^{-isx}\, dx$$
$$= \frac{1}{\sqrt{2\pi}} \int_{-\infty}^{\infty} f(x) e^{-isx}$$
$$= F(s)$$

Thus, as a function of the variable t, the Fourier transform of the solution u satisfies the first-order differential equation (6.6) and the initial condition (6.7). In this way we have therefore transformed the problem (6.1), (6.2) for the function u into the simpler problem (6.6), (6.7) for the Fourier transform U of u. The solution of the differential equation (6.6), which satisfies the initial condition (6.7), is given by

(6.8) $$U(s, t) = F(s)e^{-ks^2t}$$

Consequently, by (6.4) and (6.7), we have

(6.9)
$$u(x, t) = \frac{1}{\sqrt{2\pi}} \int_{-\infty}^{\infty} F(s) \exp(-ks^2t + isx)\, ds$$
$$= \frac{1}{2\pi} \int_{-\infty}^{\infty} \int_{-\infty}^{\infty} \exp(is(x - \xi) - ks^2t)f(\xi)\, d\xi\, ds$$

Now the double integral corresponding to the iterated integral in (6.9) is absolutely convergent because both $f(x)$ and e^{-ks^2t} are absolutely integrable. Therefore, we can interchange the order of integration in (6.9) and write

(6.10) $$u(x, t) = \int_{-\infty}^{\infty} G(x - \xi, t)f(\xi)\, d\xi$$

where

(6.11) $$G(x, t) = \frac{1}{2\pi} \int_{-\infty}^{\infty} \exp(isx - ks^2t)\, ds$$

The integral on the right of (6.11) can be evaluated as follows: By using the Euler formula

$$e^{ix} = \cos x + i \sin x$$

(6.11) can be written as

(6.12) $$G(x, t) = \frac{1}{2\pi} \int_{-\infty}^{\infty} e^{-ks^2t}(\cos sx + i \sin sx)\, ds$$

where the functions $e^{-ks^2t} \cos x$ and $e^{-ks^2t} \sin sx$ are both absolutely integrable on $-\infty < s < \infty$, uniformly in x and t for $t > 0$. Since $e^{-ks^2t} \cos sx$ is even in s and $e^{-ks^2t} \sin sx$ is odd, it follows that

$$\int_{-\infty}^{\infty} e^{-ks^2t} \sin sx\, ds = 0$$

so that (6.12) becomes

$$G(x, t) = \frac{1}{2\pi} \int_{-\infty}^{\infty} e^{-ks^2t} \cos sx\, ds$$
$$= \frac{1}{\pi} \int_{0}^{\infty} e^{-ks^2t} \cos sx\, ds$$

Introducing the new variable $z = s\sqrt{kt}$, we obtain

$$G(x, t) = \frac{1}{\sqrt{kt}\,\pi} \int_0^\infty e^{-z^2} \cos\left(\frac{xz}{\sqrt{kt}}\right) dz$$

By Problem 10, Exercises 1.6, we find

$$\int_0^\infty e^{-z^2} \cos\left(\frac{xz}{\sqrt{kt}}\right) dz = \frac{\sqrt{\pi}}{2} e^{-x^2/4kt}$$

so that

$$G(x, t) = \frac{1}{\pi} \int_0^\infty e^{-ks^2t} \cos sx \, ds$$

(6.13)

$$= \frac{1}{2\sqrt{\pi kt}} e^{-x^2/4kt}$$

Substituting this in (6.10), we finally obtain

(6.14) $$u(x, t) = \frac{1}{2\sqrt{\pi kt}} \int_{-\infty}^\infty \exp\left(\frac{-(x - \xi)^2}{4kt}\right) f(\xi) \, d\xi$$

for a solution of the initial value problem (6.1), (6.2).

The function

(6.15) $$G(x - \xi, t) = \frac{1}{2\sqrt{\pi kt}} \exp\left(\frac{-(x - \xi)^2}{4kt}\right) \qquad (t > 0)$$

is called the fundamental solution or the Green's function for the heat equation in the infinite domain $-\infty < x < \infty$, $t > 0$. Physically, the Green's function (6.15) represents the temperature at a point x at time t due to a concentrated heat source at a point ξ at time zero.

It is easily verified from (6.15) that (i) G has continuous partial derivatives of all orders with respect to x and t for $-\infty < x < \infty$, $t > 0$, and satisfies the heat equation for all x and $t > 0$, provided $x \neq \xi$ (see Problem 2, Exercises 6.1); (ii) G is continuous at $x = \xi$; (iii) G vanishes as $|x| \to \infty$ for $t > 0$; (iv) G has the property

$$\int_{-\infty}^\infty G(x - \xi, t) \, d\xi = 1$$

and, finally, (v) G is symmetric with respect to x and ξ. These properties are analogous to those of a Green's function for an ordinary differential equation.

Now, to verify that (6.14) actually gives a solution of the problem (6.1), (6.2), it is enough to require that f be continuous and bounded on $(-\infty, \infty)$. Then, for arbitrary constants $L > 0$ and $t_0 > 0$, the integral (6.14) together with its partial derivatives of any order obtained by differentiating under the integral sign with respect to x and t converges uniformly in x and t for $-L \leq x \leq L$, $t_0 \leq t$. Therefore, the function u and its derivatives of all orders exist for $-\infty < x < \infty$, $t > 0$, and these derivatives can be found by differentiating under the integral sign. Since $G(x - \xi, t)$ satisfies equation (6.1) whenever $x \neq \xi$, it follows that u does also.

Finally, set $z = (\xi - x)/(4kt)^{1/2}$ in (6.14) to obtain

$$u(x, t) = \frac{1}{\sqrt{\pi}} \int_{-\infty}^{\infty} f(x + \sqrt{4kt}\, z)e^{-z^2}\, dz$$

Since f is bounded for all values of its argument, the preceding integral converges uniformly with respect to x and t for $-\infty < x < \infty$, $t \geq 0$. Hence,

$$\lim_{t \to 0^+} u(x, t) = \frac{1}{\sqrt{\pi}} \int_{-\infty}^{\infty} f(x)e^{-z^2}\, dz$$

$$= f(x)$$

which verifies (6.2). From the boundedness of f it follows that u is also bounded. If we define $u(x, 0) = f(x)$, then u is bounded and continuous for $-\infty < x < \infty$, $t \geq 0$, so that by Theorem 3.4, u is uniquely determined.

Example 6.1.   Find the solution of the problem (6.1), (6.2) if the function f is given by

$$f(x) = \begin{cases} 0 & (x < 0) \\ 1 & (x > 0) \end{cases}$$

Solution: According to the formula (6.14), the solution is

$$u(x, t) = \frac{1}{2\sqrt{\pi kt}} \int_0^\infty \exp\left(\frac{-(x - \xi)^2}{4kt}\right) d\xi$$

In terms of the error function,

$$\text{erf}(r) = \frac{2}{\sqrt{\pi}} \int_0^r e^{-z^2}\, dz$$

which has the property that $\text{erf}(\infty) = 1$, this solution can be written as

$$u(x, t) = \frac{1}{2} + \frac{1}{2}\,\text{erf}\left(\frac{x}{\sqrt{4kt}}\right)$$

Then, by the Leibnitz rule, it is easily verified that this satisfies the heat equation (6.1). Also, as $t \to 0^+$, $u(x, t) \to 1$ if $x > 0$, and $u(x, t) \to 0$ if $x < 0$. At $x = 0$, we have $u(0, t) = 1/2$, which is in accordance with the theory of Fourier integral transform, since f has a jump discontinuity at that point.

In the case of the initial value problem

(6.16)
$$u_t - ku_{xx} = h(x, t) \qquad (-\infty < x < \infty, t > 0)$$

$$u(x, 0) = 0 \qquad (-\infty < x < \infty)$$

which involves the nonhomogeneous heat equation, the method described above leads to the differential equation

(6.17) $$U_t + ks^2U = H(s, t)$$

for the Fourier transform (6.3) of the solution u. Here, H is the Fourier transform of the function h; that is,

(6.18) $$H(s, t) = \frac{1}{\sqrt{2\pi}} \int_{-\infty}^{\infty} h(x, t)e^{-isx} dx$$

From (6.3) and the initial condition in (6.16), we see that $U(s, 0) = 0$. By solving the differential equation (6.17) with the initial condition $U(s, 0) = 0$, we thus find

(6.19) $$U(s, t) = \int_0^t e^{-ks^2(t-\tau)}H(s, \tau)\, d\tau$$

Therefore, according to (6.4), the solution of the problem (6.16) is given by

(6.20) $$u(x, t) = \frac{1}{\sqrt{2\pi}} \int_{-\infty}^{\infty} e^{isx} \int_0^t e^{-ks^2(t-\tau)}H(s, \tau)\, d\tau\, ds$$

By substituting (6.18) for H and formally interchanging the order of integrations, this solution can be written as

(6.21) $$u(x, t) = \int_0^t \int_{-\infty}^{\infty} G(x - \xi, t - \tau)h(\xi, \tau)\, d\xi\, d\tau$$

where, by (6.13),

$$G(x - \xi, t - \tau) = \frac{1}{2\pi} \int_{-\infty}^{\infty} \exp(is(x - \xi) - ks^2(t - \tau))\, ds$$

$$= \frac{\exp(-(x - \xi)^2/4k(t - \tau))}{2\sqrt{\pi k(t - \tau)}}$$

is the Green's function for the problem.

To verify that (6.21) gives the solution of (6.16), we assume that h is continuous and bounded for all x and $t \geq 0$. Then, for $0 < \tau < t$, we know from the previous case that the function

$$w(x, t; \tau) = \int_{-\infty}^{\infty} G(x - \xi, t - \tau)h(\xi, \tau)\, d\xi$$

is the solution of the initial value problem

$$w_t - kw_{xx} = 0 \qquad\qquad (-\infty < x < \infty, t > \tau)$$

$$w(x, \tau; \tau) = h(x, \tau)$$

Hence, by Duhamel's principle (Problem 8, Exercises 6.5), it follows that (6.21) is the solution of the problem (6.16).

Exercises 6.5

1. Write the solution of the problem

$$u_t - u_{xx} = 0 \qquad\qquad (-\infty < x < \infty, t > 0)$$
$$u(x, 0) = e^{-|x|} \qquad\qquad (-\infty < x < \infty)$$

2. Solve the problem

$$u_t - k u_{xx} = 0 \qquad\qquad (-\infty < x < \infty, t > 0)$$
$$u(x, 0) = \begin{cases} 1 & (|x| \le L) \\ 0 & (|x| > L) \end{cases}$$

and express the solution in terms of the error function

$$\operatorname{erf} x = \frac{2}{\sqrt{\pi}} \int_0^x e^{-s^2} \, ds$$

3. As in Problem 2, find the solution of the problem

$$u_t - k u_{xx} = 0 \qquad\qquad (-\infty < x < \infty, t > 0)$$
$$u(x, 0) = \begin{cases} A & (x < 0) \\ B & (x > 0) \end{cases}$$

4. Show that if the function f in (6.2) is odd (or even), then the solution (6.14) is also odd (or even) with respect to the variable x. Thus, deduce that $u(0, t) = 0$ (or $u_x(0, t) = 0$).

5. Verify the result in Problem 4 without resorting to the formula (6.14) and using only the fact that a solution of the problem (6.1), (6.2) is uniquely determined.

6. Find the solution of the problem

$$u_t - k u_{xx} = t \qquad\qquad (-\infty < x < \infty, t > 0)$$
$$u(x, 0) = 0 \qquad\qquad (-\infty < x < \infty)$$

and show that (6.21) yields $u(x, t) = t^2/2$.

7. Find the solution of the problem

$$u_t - k u_{xx} = e^{-t} \qquad\qquad (-\infty < x < \infty, t > 0)$$
$$u(x, 0) = 0 \qquad\qquad (-\infty < x < \infty)$$

and show that (6.21) yields $u(x, t) = 1 - e^{-t}$.

8. (Duhamel's Principle) Let $u(x, t, \tau)$ be the solution of the initial value problem

$$u_t - k u_{xx} = 0 \qquad\qquad (-\infty < x < \infty, t > 0)$$
$$u(x, 0, \tau) = f(x, \tau) \qquad\qquad (-\infty < x < \infty, \tau > 0)$$

and set

$$v(x, t) = \int_0^t u(x, t - \tau, \tau) \, d\tau$$

Prove that v is the solution of the problem

$$v_t - k v_{xx} = f(x, t) \qquad\qquad (-\infty < x < \infty, t > 0)$$
$$v(x, 0) = 0 \qquad\qquad (-\infty < x < \infty)$$

9. Find the solution of the problem

$$v_t - kv_{xx} + hv = 0 \qquad\qquad (h = \text{const}; t > 0)$$

$$v(x, 0) = f(x) \qquad\qquad (-\infty < x < \infty)$$

and show that $v(x, t) = u(x, t)e^{-ht}$, where u is given by (6.14).

10. By the substitution $u(x, t) = v(x, t)e^{ht}$, show that Problem 9 can be reduced to the problem (6.1), (6.2).

11. By using the result of Problem 9 and the corresponding Duhamel's principle for the differential equation, obtain the solution of the initial value problem

$$u_t - ku_{xx} + hu = f(x, t) \quad (-\infty < x < \infty, t > 0)$$

$$u(x, 0) = 0$$

$$(-\infty < x < \infty; h = \text{const} > 0)$$

7. Initial-Boundary Value Problems in Infinite Domain

In this last section of the chapter we shall consider initial-boundary value problems for the heat equation in the domain $0 < x < \infty, t > 0$. The solutions of our problems will be obtained by means of Fourier sine or cosine transform, as this becomes appropriate for this type of problem. We first consider the problem

(7.1) $$\qquad\qquad u_t - ku_{xx} = 0 \qquad\qquad (x > 0, t > 0)$$

(7.2) $$\qquad\qquad u(x, 0) = f(x) \qquad\qquad (x \geq 0)$$

(7.3) $$\qquad\qquad u(0, t) = 0 \qquad\qquad (t \geq 0)$$

which corresponds to the problem of heat flow in a semi-infinite rod $x > 0$, with initial temperature distribution described by the function $f(x)$ for $x \geq 0$, and whose end point $x = 0$ is maintained at zero temperature. To solve this problem, we shall use the Fourier sine transform. This choice is based on the fact that the singular eigenvalue problem that is related to the problem at hand is

$$X'' + \lambda X = 0, \qquad X(0) = 0 \quad (X \text{ bounded as } x \to \infty)$$

which has the eigenfunctions $X_s(x) = \sin sx$ corresponding to the eigenvalues $\lambda = s^2, s > 0$. Accordingly, we assume that the problem (7.1), (7.2), (7.3) has a solution u, which has the property that u and its partial derivatives up to the second order are all piecewise smooth and absolutely integrable on $0 < x < \infty$ for $t > 0$. Then the Fourier sine transform of u,

(7.4) $$\qquad\qquad U_s(s, t) = \left(\frac{2}{\pi}\right)^{1/2} \int_0^\infty u(x, t) \sin sx \, dx$$

exists and

(7.5) $$\qquad\qquad u(x, t) = \left(\frac{2}{\pi}\right)^{1/2} \int_0^\infty U_s(s, t) \sin sx \, ds$$

Here, U_s does not mean the partial derivative of U with respect to s. Following the procedure described in the preceding section, we proceed to find the transform U_s of our solution. Once this function is found, then our solution is given by (7.5).

By differentiating (7.4) with respect to t under the integral sign and using the differential equation (7.1), we have

$$\frac{\partial U_s}{\partial t}(s, t) = \left(\frac{2}{\pi}\right)^{1/2} \int_0^\infty u_t(x, t) \sin sx \, dx$$

$$= k \left(\frac{2}{\pi}\right)^{1/2} \int_0^\infty u_{xx}(x, t) \sin sx \, dx$$

After integration by parts twice, this gives

$$\frac{\partial U_s}{\partial t}(s, t) = k \left(\frac{2}{\pi}\right)^{1/2} (u_x \sin sx - su \cos sx) \Big|_0^\infty$$

(7.6)

$$- ks^2 \left(\frac{2}{\pi}\right)^{1/2} \int_0^\infty u(x, t) \sin sx \, dx$$

If we assume as before that u and u_x vanish as $x \to \infty$, then because of the boundary condition (7.3), the boundary terms on the right of (7.6) vanish, and by (7.4) we are led to the differential equation

(7.7)
$$\frac{\partial U_s}{\partial t}(s, t) + ks^2 U_s(s, t) = 0$$

for the function U_s. Let us assume that the function f in (7.2) is piecewise smooth and absolutely integrable on $(0, \infty)$. Then, from the initial condition (7.2) and (7.4), we find

$$U_s(s, 0) = \left(\frac{2}{\pi}\right)^{1/2} \int_0^\infty u(x, 0) \sin sx \, dx$$

(7.8)

$$= \left(\frac{2}{\pi}\right)^{1/2} \int_0^\infty f(x) \sin sx \, dx$$

$$= F_s(s)$$

which is the Fourier sine transform of the function f. The solution of equation (7.7) that satisfies the initial condition (7.8) is

(7.9)
$$U_s(s, t) = F_s(s)e^{-ks^2 t}$$

Hence, by (7.5) and (7.8), we obtain

$$u(x, t) = \left(\frac{2}{\pi}\right)^{1/2} \int_0^\infty F_s(s)e^{-ks^2 t} \sin sx \, ds$$

(7.10)

$$= \frac{2}{\pi} \int_0^\infty \int_0^\infty f(\xi)e^{-ks^2 t} \sin s\xi \sin sx \, d\xi \, ds$$

This gives the solution of the problem (7.1), (7.2), (7.3).

If we replace the function $\sin s\xi \sin sx$ in the integrand of the integral in (7.10) by

$$\tfrac{1}{2}[\cos s(x - \xi) - \cos s(x + \xi)]$$

and formally interchange the order of integration, we can write (7.10) in the form

(7.11) $u(x, t) = \dfrac{1}{2\sqrt{\pi kt}} \displaystyle\int_0^\infty \left[\exp\left(\dfrac{-(x - \xi)^2}{4kt}\right) - \exp\left(\dfrac{-(x + \xi)^2}{4kt}\right)\right] f(\xi)\, d\xi$

in which we have used the result (6.13). In this form, it can be verified that u is the solution of our problem under the weaker condition that f is continuous and bounded for $x \geq 0$ with $f(0) = 0$.

We remark that the solution (7.11) of our problem (7.1), (7.2), (7.3) can also be obtained by extending the initial datum f in (7.2) as an odd function for $-\infty < x < \infty$ and then solving the resulting initial value problem by the formula (6.14). [See Problem 4, Exercises 6.5.] Using the fact that $f(-x) = -f(x)$, the solution as given by (6.14) then reduces to (7.11). Observe that this is precisely the method we employed in Section 6 of Chapter 3 for finding the solution of an initial-boundary value problem for the wave equation. The method works because both the wave and the heat equations remain unchanged in form when the variable x is replaced by $-x$.

In the same manner, we can find the solution of the problem (7.1), (7.2) with the boundary condition

(7.12) $u_x(0, t) = 0$ $(t \geq 0)$

by extending the function f as an even function for $-\infty < x < \infty$. In this case, the solution is given by

(7.13) $u(x, t) = \dfrac{1}{2\sqrt{\pi kt}} \displaystyle\int_0^\infty \left[\exp\left(\dfrac{-(x - \xi)^2}{4kt}\right) + \exp\left(\dfrac{-(x + \xi)^2}{4kt}\right)\right] f(\xi)\, d\xi$

We note here that to solve the problem (7.1), (7.2), (7.12) by the method of Fourier transform, it will be necessary to employ the Fourier cosine transform of the solution u. This is also the case even in the more difficult problem where the boundary condition (7.12) is nonhomogeneous. We illustrate the procedure in connection with the problem

$$u_t - ku_{xx} = 0 \qquad\qquad (x > 0, t > 0)$$
(7.14)
$$u(x, 0) = 0 \qquad\qquad (x \geq 0)$$
$$u_x(0, t) = h(t) \qquad\qquad (t \geq 0)$$

As usual, we suppose this problem has a solution that is piecewise smooth and absolutely integrable on $(0, \infty)$ including its first- and second-order derivatives. We consider the Fourier cosine transform of u,

(7.15) $U_c(s, t) = \left(\dfrac{2}{\pi}\right)^{1/2} \displaystyle\int_0^\infty u(x, t) \cos sx\, dx$

Differentiating this with respect to t and proceeding as in previous cases, we have

$$\frac{\partial U_c}{\partial t}(s, t) = \left(\frac{2}{\pi}\right)^{1/2} \int_0^\infty u_t(x, t) \cos sx \, dx$$

$$= k \left(\frac{2}{\pi}\right)^{1/2} \int_0^\infty u_{xx}(x, t) \cos sx \, dx$$

$$= k \left(\frac{2}{\pi}\right)^{1/2} (u_x \cos sx + su \sin sx) \Big|_0^\infty$$

$$- ks^2 \left(\frac{2}{\pi}\right)^{1/2} \int_0^\infty u(x, t) \cos sx \, dx$$

Under the assumption that u and u_x vanish as $x \to \infty$, and taking note of the boundary condition in (7.14), this leads to the nonhomogeneous differential equation

(7.16) $$\frac{\partial U_c}{\partial t}(s, t) + ks^2 U_c(s, t) = -k \left(\frac{2}{\pi}\right)^{1/2} h(t)$$

The solution of this equation that, by the initial condition in (7.14), satisfies the condition $U_c(s, 0) = 0$ is given by

(7.17) $$U_c(s, t) = -k \left(\frac{2}{\pi}\right)^{1/2} \int_0^t e^{-ks^2(t-\tau)} h(\tau) \, d\tau$$

Hence, by taking the inverse transform, we obtain

$$u(x, t) = \left(\frac{2}{\pi}\right)^{1/2} \int_0^\infty U_c(s, t) \cos sx \, ds$$

(7.18)

$$= -\frac{2k}{\pi} \int_0^\infty \int_0^t e^{-ks^2(t-\tau)} h(\tau) \cos sx \, d\tau \, ds$$

If we formally interchange the order of integration and use the result in (6.13), this formula simplifies to the form

(7.19) $$u(x, t) = -\left(\frac{k}{\pi}\right)^{1/2} \int_0^t \frac{\exp(-x^2/4k(t-\tau))h(\tau) \, d\tau}{\sqrt{t-\tau}}$$

This can be shown to provide the solution of the problem (7.14) under the assumption that h is differentiable for $t \geq 0$.

We remark that we cannot verify that (7.19) satisfies the boundary condition of (7.14) by simply differentiating (7.19) under the integral sign and setting $x = 0$. In fact, such a formal manipulation would lead to the false result $u_x(0, t) = 0$. We illustrate the situation in this case by means of the following example.

Example 7.1.   Find the solution of the problem

$$u_t - u_{xx} = 0 \qquad\qquad (x > 0, t > 0)$$
$$u(x, 0) = 0 \qquad\qquad (x \geq 0)$$
$$u_x(0, t) = 1 \qquad\qquad (t \geq 0)$$

Solution: By the formula (7.19) we have

$$u(x, t) = -\frac{1}{\sqrt{\pi}} \int_0^t \frac{\exp(-x^2/4(t - \tau))}{\sqrt{t - \tau}} \, d\tau$$

On setting $z = x/\sqrt{4(t - \tau)}$, this becomes

$$u(x, t) = -\frac{x}{\sqrt{\pi}} \int_{x/\sqrt{4t}}^{\infty} \frac{e^{-z^2}}{z^2} \, dz$$

for which it is readily seen that

$$u_x(x, t) = -\frac{1}{\sqrt{\pi}} \int_{x/\sqrt{4t}}^{\infty} \frac{e^{-z^2}}{z^2} \, dz + \frac{4t}{\pi} \frac{e^{-x^2/4t}}{x}$$

$$u_{xx}(x, t) = \frac{4t}{\pi} \frac{e^{-x^2/4t}}{x^2} - \frac{4t}{\pi} \frac{e^{-x^2/4t}}{x^2} - \frac{e^{-x^2/4t}}{\sqrt{\pi t}}$$

$$u_t(x, t) = -\frac{e^{-x^2/4t}}{\sqrt{\pi t}}$$

for $x > 0$ and $t > 0$. Thus, $u_t - u_{xx} = 0$, showing that u satisfies the heat equation for $x > 0$, $t > 0$. As $t \to 0^+$, it is clear that $u(x, t) \to 0$. Now, to verify the boundary condition $u_x(0, t) = 1$, we perform an integration by parts to put u in the form

$$u(x, t) = -\frac{x}{\sqrt{\pi}} \left(-\frac{1}{z} e^{-z^2} \right) \Big|_{x/\sqrt{4t}}^{\infty} + \frac{2x}{\sqrt{\pi}} \int_{x/\sqrt{4t}}^{\infty} e^{-z^2} \, dz$$

$$= -\left(\frac{4t}{\pi} \right)^{1/2} e^{-x^2/4t} + \frac{2x}{\sqrt{\pi}} \int_{x/\sqrt{4t}}^{\infty} e^{-z^2} \, dz$$

Then

$$u_x(x, t) = \frac{2}{\sqrt{\pi}} \int_{x/\sqrt{4t}}^{\infty} e^{-z^2} \, dz$$

which immediately yields $u_x(0, t) = 1$, since $\int_0^{\infty} e^{-z^2} \, dz = \sqrt{\pi}/2$.

Exercises 6.6

1. (a) Obtain the solution formula (7.11) from (6.14) by extending the function f in (7.2) as an odd function for $-\infty < x < \infty$.
   (b) Obtain the solution formula (7.13) of the problem (7.1), (7.2), (7.12) by extending the function f as an even function for $-\infty < x < \infty$.

2. Obtain the solution (7.13) by using the Fourier cosine transform.

3. Find the solution of the problem

$$u_t - ku_{xx} = 0 \qquad\qquad (x > 0, t > 0)$$
$$u(x, 0) = xe^{-x} \qquad\qquad (x \geq 0)$$
$$u(0, t) = 0 \qquad\qquad (t \geq 0)$$

4. Find the solution of the problem

$$u_t - ku_{xx} = 0 \qquad\qquad (x > 0, t > 0)$$
$$u(x, 0) = e^{-ax} \qquad\qquad (a > 0, x \geq 0)$$
$$u_x(0, t) = 0 \qquad\qquad (t \geq 0)$$

5. Solve the problem

$$u_t - ku_{xx} = 0 \qquad\qquad (x > 0, t > 0)$$
$$u(x, 0) = 0 \qquad\qquad (x > 0)$$
$$u(0, t) = A \qquad\qquad (A \text{ a constant}; t > 0)$$

and express the solution in terms of the error function. Verify that it gives the solution of the problem.

6. Find the solution of the problem

$$u_t - ku_{xx} = 0 \qquad\qquad (x > 0, t > 0)$$
$$u(x, 0) = 0 \qquad\qquad (x \geq 0)$$
$$u(0, t) = h(t) \qquad\qquad (t \geq 0)$$

7. Find the solution of the problem

$$u_t - ku_{xx} = f(x, t) \qquad\qquad (x > 0, t > 0)$$
$$u(x, 0) = 0 \qquad\qquad (x \geq 0)$$
$$u_x(0, t) = h(t) \qquad\qquad (t \geq 0)$$

8. Find the solution of the problem

$$u_t - ku_{xx} + hu = 0 \qquad\qquad (h = \text{const} > 0)$$
$$u(x, 0) = f(x) \qquad\qquad (x \geq 0)$$
$$u_x(0, t) = 0 \qquad\qquad (t \geq 0)$$

9. Obtain the solution of Problem 8 from the result of Problem 9, Exercises 6.5, by extending the function f as an even function for $-\infty < x < \infty$.

10. Find the solution of the problem

$$u_t - ku_{xx} + bu = 0$$
$$(b = \text{const} > 0; x > 0; t > 0)$$
$$u(x, 0) = 0 \qquad\qquad (x \geq 0)$$
$$u(0, t) = h(t) \qquad\qquad (t \geq 0)$$

11. Find the solution of the problem

$$u_t - ku_{xx} + bu = f(x, t) \qquad (b = \text{const} > 0)$$
$$u(x, 0) = 0 \qquad (x \geq 0)$$
$$u_x(0, t) = h(t) \qquad (t \geq 0)$$

12. By using the Fourier cosine transform, obtain the solution of the problem

$$u_t - ku_{xx} + tu = 0 \qquad (x > 0, t > 0)$$
$$u(x, 0) = e^{-x} \qquad (x \geq 0)$$
$$u_x(0, t) = 0 \qquad (t \geq 0)$$

13. Solve the problem

$$u_t - ku_{xx} = 0 \qquad (x > 0, t > 0)$$
$$u(x, 0) = f(x) \qquad (x \geq 0)$$
$$u_x(0, t) - hu(0, t) = 0 \qquad (h = \text{const} > 0; t \geq 0)$$

Hint: Let $v(x, t) = u_x(x, t) - hu(x, t)$. See Problem 10, Exercises 6.1.

14. Solve the problem

$$u_t - ku_{xx} = 0 \qquad (x > 0, t > 0)$$
$$u(x, 0) = 0 \qquad (x \geq 0)$$
$$u_x(0, t) - hu(0, t) = g(t) \qquad (t \geq 0)$$

15. Solve the problem

$$u_t - ku_{xx} + bu = 0 \qquad (x > 0, t > 0)$$
$$u(x, 0) = f(x) \qquad (x \geq 0)$$
$$u_x(0, t) - hu(0, t) = 0 \qquad (t \geq 0)$$

16. Solve the problem

$$u_t - u_{xx} - \frac{2}{x} u_x = 0 \qquad (0 < a < x, t > 0)$$
$$u(x, 0) = 0 \qquad (x \geq a)$$
$$u(a, t) = A \qquad (A \text{ constant}; t \geq 0)$$

Hint: Set $xu = v$, $z = x - a$ and use the result in Problem 5.

Chapter 7

Laplace's Equation

In the previous chapters we studied initial value and initial-boundary value problems for the wave and the heat equations. We saw that these problems are well posed for the wave and heat equations in the sense that the problems have unique solutions that depend continuously on the initial or boundary data. In this last chapter we shall be concerned with certain problems that are well posed for Laplace's equation in two independent variables

$$\frac{\partial^2 u}{\partial x^2} + \frac{\partial^2 u}{\partial y^2} = 0$$

This equation serves as the prototype for elliptic differential equations in much the same way as the wave and the heat equations do for hyperbolic and parabolic differential equations, respectively.

1. Boundary Value Problems

In order to see how Laplace's equation may arise in a physical problem, let us consider the temperature distribution u in a uniform thin plate occupying a domain D in the xy-plane (Fig. 7.1). We assume that D has a continuous boundary C. By making assumptions similar to those made in deriving the one-dimensional heat flow equation, it can be shown that the temperature distribution u on the plate satisfies the homogeneous equation

$$(1.1) \qquad \frac{\partial u}{\partial t} - k \left(\frac{\partial^2 u}{\partial x^2} + \frac{\partial^2 u}{\partial y^2} \right) = 0$$

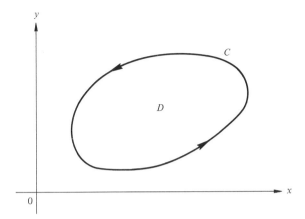

FIG. 7–1   *Plane domain and boundary curve.*

in D. This equation is called the two-dimensional heat equation. Suppose now that the heat flow in D is steady; then the temperature distribution u is independent of time (that is, $\partial u/\partial t = 0$) and hence equation (1.1) becomes

$$(1.2) \qquad \frac{\partial^2 u}{\partial x^2} + \frac{\partial^2 u}{\partial y^2} = 0$$

which is the two-dimensional Laplace's equation.

If there is a heat source in D, the temperature function u will satisfy the non-homogeneous heat equation

$$(1.3) \qquad \frac{\partial u}{\partial t} - k \left(\frac{\partial^2 u}{\partial x^2} + \frac{\partial^2 u}{\partial x^2} \right) = f(x, y, t)$$

Consequently, when the heat flow is steady so that f does not depend on t, (1.3) reduces to the nonhomogeneous Laplace's equation

$$(1.4) \qquad \frac{\partial^2 u}{\partial x^2} + \frac{\partial^2 u}{\partial x^2} = q, \qquad q(x, y) = -\frac{f(x, y)}{k}$$

Equation (1.4) is known as Poisson's equation. Both equations, (1.2) and (1.4), are prominent examples of elliptic differential equations that are of great importance in mathematical physics. We shall often write these equations in the compact form $\Delta u = 0$ and $\Delta u = q$, where Δ denotes the Laplace's operator

$$\Delta = \frac{\partial^2}{\partial x^2} + \frac{\partial^2}{\partial y^2}$$

From the preceding discussion, it appears that in a steady state, the temperature distribution in a uniform heat-conducting body satisfies Laplace's equation. Correspondingly, when there is a known heat source, the temperature function satisfies Poisson's equation. From this physical consideration it seems natural to consider boundary value problems for the Laplace's operator rather than initial value or initial-boundary value problems. As a matter of fact, boundary value problems are typical for elliptic differential equations because initial value or initial-boundary value problems are in general not well posed for this type of equation. In this connection, let us examine an example devised by Hadamard for the Laplace's equation. Consider the following initial value problem:

(1.5)
$$u_{xx} + u_{yy} = 0 \qquad (-\infty < x < \infty, y > 0)$$
$$u(x, 0) = 0 \qquad (-\infty < x < \infty)$$
$$u_y(x, 0) = e^{-\sqrt{n}} \sin nx \qquad (-\infty < x < \infty)$$

By the method of separation of variables, we readily obtain the explicit solution

(1.6)
$$u(x, y) = \frac{e^{-\sqrt{n}}}{n} \sin nx \sinh ny$$

of this problem. Now we observe that as the parameter n becomes infinite, the initial data of the problem tend to zero uniformly, whereas for $x \neq 0$, the solution (1.6) becomes arbitrarily large. This shows that the solution of the problem does not depend continuously on the initial data, and hence the problem is not well posed.

A typical boundary value problem for a given elliptic differential equation consists in finding a solution of the differential equation in a given domain D that satisfies certain conditions on the boundary C of D. In this chapter we shall be concerned with boundary value problems for the Laplace's equation with boundary conditions that are typical for elliptic differential operators. Our discussion will be confined to the two-dimensional xy-plane, although many of the results that will be obtained and the procedures used can be immediately extended to the case of three-space dimensions.

The first type of boundary value problem for the Laplace's equation consists in finding a solution of the equation in a given domain D, which assumes prescribed values on the boundary C of D. That is,

(1.7)
$$\Delta u = 0 \qquad \text{in } D$$
$$u = f \qquad \text{on } C$$

where f is a known function on C. This type of problem is called a Dirichlet problem, and the boundary condition is often called Dirichlet condition or boundary condition of the first kind. Physically, the problem can be interpreted as finding the equilibrium temperature distribution in D when a fixed temperature distribution is given on the boundary of D.

The second type of problem for equation (1.2) consists in finding a solution of the equation in the domain D satisfying the boundary condition

(1.8)
$$\frac{\partial u}{\partial n} = f$$

on the boundary C of D.   Here $\partial u/\partial n$ denotes the outward normal derivative of u on C.   This problem is called the Neumann problem, and the condition (1.8) is called Neumann condition or boundary condition of the second kind. Such a problem arises, for example, when we determine the equilibrium temperature in a uniform body D for which a given amount of heat is supplied to the boundary C of D.

The third type of boundary value problem involves the condition

(1.9)
$$\frac{\partial u}{\partial n} + hu = g$$

on the boundary C where h and g are known functions.   Such a problem is called the Robin problem or a mixed boundary value problem.   The boundary condition (1.9) arises when, for instance, we allow for radiation of heat from the boundary of the body into the surrounding medium.

It is of interest to observe that the boundary conditions (1.7), (1.8), and (1.9) correspond to the three types of boundary conditions we encountered in connection with our discussion of the vibrating string and the conduction of heat in a thin rod.

Analogous problems can, of course, be considered for Poisson's equation (1.4).   Oftentimes, however, it may be possible to reduce a problem involving Poisson's equation to one that involves Laplace's equation.   The procedure consists in first looking for a particular solution v of Poisson's equation $\Delta u = q$ and setting $w = u - v$.   Then w satisfies Laplace's equation and a corresponding boundary condition that will involve v.   The function v must, of course, be such that it is defined and differentiable on the boundary of the domain under consideration.   In the general case, the problem is best approached by using certain kernel functions, which are discussed in Section 9 of this chapter.

Each of the various problems mentioned above is called an interior-boundary value problem inasmuch as the solution is required to satisfy the differential equation inside the domain D.   If, instead, we seek a solution of the differential equation outside the domain D with boundary condition on C, then the problem is called an exterior-boundary value problem.   In this work we shall be concerned primarily with interior problems, although some exterior problems will be presented in the exercises.

2.   Green's Theorem and Uniqueness of Solutions

In this section we shall settle the question of uniqueness of the solutions of the Dirichlet problem, the Neumann problem, and the Robin problem for the Laplace equation, with the help of Green's identity.   Let us consider first the Dirichlet problem (1.7).   Suppose that u_1 and u_2 are two solutions of this problem and set $w = u_1 - u_2$.   It is clear that

(2.1)
$$\Delta w = \Delta u_1 - \Delta u_2 = 0 \qquad \text{in } D$$

and

(2.2)
$$w = f - f = 0 \qquad \text{on } C$$

Let us consider Green's first identity over the domain D:

(2.3)
$$\int_C u \frac{\partial v}{\partial n} ds = \iint_D (u \Delta v + u_x v_x + u_y v_y) dx\, dy$$

Setting $u = v$ in (2.3), we have

(2.4)
$$\int_C u \frac{\partial u}{\partial n} ds = \iint_D (u \Delta u + u_x^2 + u_y^2) dx\, dy$$

If we substitute the function $w = u_1 - u_2$ for u in (2.4) and use (2.1) and (2.2), we then obtain

(2.5)
$$\iint_D (w_x^2 + w_y^2) dx\, dy = 0$$

Since the integrand in (2.5) is continuous and nonnegative, we conclude that $w_x^2 + w_y^2 = 0$ identically in D. This implies that w must be constant in $D + C$. But $w = 0$ on C. Hence, it follows that $w = 0$ identically in $D + C$; that is, $u_1 = u_2$. Thus, we have proved our first theorem in this section.

THEOREM 2.1   *A solution of the Dirichlet problem* (1.7) *is uniquely determined.*

In the case of the Neumann problem

(2.6)
$$\Delta u = 0 \quad \text{in } D, \quad \frac{\partial u}{\partial n} = f \quad \text{on } C$$

if u_1 and u_2 are two solutions, then their difference $w = u_1 - u_2$ will be a solution of the homogeneous problem

(2.7)
$$\Delta w = 0 \quad \text{in } D, \quad \frac{\partial w}{\partial n} = 0 \quad \text{on } C$$

Applying the identity (2.4) to the function w and using (2.7), we are again led to the conclusion that w must be constant in $D + C$; that is, $w(x, t) = K$. In this case, however, it cannot be established that $K = 0$, since w does not necessarily vanish on C. Therefore, we can have only

$$u_1 = u_2 + K$$

which says that any two solutions of the problem (2.6) differ by a constant. We state this result as our second theorem.

THEOREM 2.2   *A solution of the Neumann problem* (2.6) *is unique up to an additive constant.*

Finally, for the Robin problem

(2.8)
$$\Delta u = 0 \quad \text{in } D, \quad \frac{\partial u}{\partial n} + hu = g \quad \text{on } C$$

uniqueness of the solution can be established if we assume that $h \geq 0$ and h is not identically zero on C. Indeed, suppose u_1 and u_2 are two solutions of the problem (2.8). Then $w = u_1 - u_2$ satisfies the condition

$$\frac{\partial w}{\partial n} + hw = 0$$

or

(2.9) $$\frac{\partial w}{\partial n} = -hw \qquad \text{on } C$$

Hence, by the identity (2.4), we have

(2.10) $$-\int_C hw^2 \, ds = \iint_D (w_x^2 + w_y^2) \, dx \, dy$$

Since $h \geq 0$ on C, the term on the left of (2.10) is not positive and the term on the right is nonnegative. Therefore, both terms must be equal to zero, and so

$$\iint_D (w_x^2 + w_y^2) \, dx \, dy = 0$$

which implies that $w = \text{const}$ in $D + C$. From (2.9) it follows that $w = 0$ in $D + C$; that is, $u_1 = u_2$. This proves our next theorem.

THEOREM 2.3   *A solution of the mixed boundary value problem (2.8) with $h \geq 0$ and h not identically zero is uniquely determined.*

It is important to note that Green's identity (2.3) also enables us to establish a necessary condition for the existence of a solution of the Neumann problem (2.6). If we interchange the role of u and v in (2.3), and set $v = 1$, we obtain

(2.11) $$\int_C \frac{\partial u}{\partial n} \, ds = \iint_D \Delta u \, dx \, dy$$

Thus, if the problem (2.6) has a solution u, then application of (2.11) yields

(2.12) $$\int_C \frac{\partial u}{\partial n} \, ds = \int_C f \, ds = 0$$

This shows that if the problem (2.6) is to have a solution, then the integral of f over the boundary C must vanish. In terms of our physical interpretation of the problem, condition (2.12) simply says that in a steady-state heat flow, the net supply of heat at the boundary of D must be zero.

In the case where problem (2.6) involves Poisson's equation, $\Delta u = q$ in D, application of (2.11) gives the necessary condition

(2.13) $$\iint_D q(x, y) \, dx \, dy = \int_C f \, ds$$

for the existence of a solution of such a problem. Consequently, if the condition (2.12) or (2.13) is not satisfied, then the Neumann problem for Laplace's equation or Poisson's equation cannot have a solution.

Exercises 7.1

1. Reduce the Dirichlet, the Neumann, and the Robin problems for Poisson's equation to a problem involving Laplace's equation and indicate the corresponding boundary conditions.

2. Show that if u is a solution of the Robin problem

$$\Delta u = q(x, y) \qquad \text{in } D$$

$$\frac{\partial u}{\partial n} + hu = f(x, y) \qquad \text{on } C$$

then

$$\int_C hu \, ds = \int_C f \, ds - \iint_D q \, dx \, dy$$

3. Prove that the Dirichlet problem

$$\Delta u + ku = q(x, y) \qquad \text{in } D$$
$$u = f(x, y) \qquad \text{on } C$$

has a unique solution if $k > 0$.

4. Prove that the Neumann problem

$$\Delta u + ku = q(x, y) \qquad \text{in } D$$

$$\frac{\partial u}{\partial n} = f(x, y) \qquad \text{on } C$$

has a unique solution if $k < 0$.

5. Prove that the Robin problem

$$\Delta u + ku = q(x, y) \qquad \text{in } D$$

$$\frac{\partial u}{\partial n} + hu = f(x, y) \qquad \text{on } C$$

has a unique solution if $k < 0$ and $h > 0$.

6. Show that if u is a solution of the problem

$$Lu \equiv \frac{\partial}{\partial x}\left(x^2 \frac{\partial u}{\partial x}\right) + \frac{\partial}{\partial y}\left(e^y \frac{\partial u}{\partial y}\right) = 0 \qquad \text{in } D$$

$$u = 0 \qquad \text{on } C$$

then $u \equiv 0$ throughout D. *Hint:* Consider $uLu = (\partial/\partial x)(x^2 uu_x) + (\partial/\partial y)$ $(e^y uu_y) - x^2 u_x^2 - e^y u_y^2$ and use Green's theorem.

7. Show that the problem

$$\frac{\partial}{\partial x}[(1 + x^2)u_x] + \frac{\partial}{\partial y}[(1 + y^2)u_y] + ku = q(x, y)$$

in D, $k \geq 0$, and $u = f(x, y)$ on C has at most one solution.

8. Show that the problem

$$\Delta u = q(x, y) \qquad \text{in } D$$

$$u = f(x, y) \qquad \text{on } C_1$$

$$\frac{\partial u}{\partial n} + hu = 0 \qquad \text{on } C_2$$

where C_1 is a part of the boundary of D and C_2 the remainder, and where h is a positive constant, has at most one solution.

9. Formulate and establish the theorems of Section 2 in three dimensions. Note that Green's first identity in three dimensions is of the form

$$\iiint_V (u \, \Delta v + u_x v_x + u_y v_y + u_z v_z) \, dV = \iint_S u \frac{\partial v}{\partial n} \, ds$$

where S is a smooth surface bounding the domain V, and Δ is the Laplacian in three-space dimensions.

3. Maximum Principle for Harmonic Functions

A function u is called a harmonic function in a domain D if u has continuous second-order derivatives and satisfies Laplace's equation at each point in D. In this section we shall prove a maximum principle for harmonic functions, which is much the same as the maximum principle we proved for functions satisfying the heat equation.

THEOREM 3.1 (Maximum Principle) *Let u be a harmonic function in a bounded domain D with boundary C. If u is continuous in $D + C$, then the maximum value of u over $D + C$ is attained on the boundary C of D.*

Proof: We prove first that any function u that is continuous in $D + C$ and satisfies the differential inequality

(3.1) $u_{xx} + u_{yy} > 0 \qquad \text{in } D$

must attain its maximum value on the boundary C. Let u be a continuous function in $D + C$ that satisfies (3.1) and suppose that u assumed its maximum value at an interior point (x_0, y_0) of D. Then, at such a point, we would have

$$u_{xx}(x_0, y_0) \leq 0, \qquad u_{yy}(x_0, y_0) \leq 0$$

so that

$$u_{xx}(x_0, y_0) + u_{yy}(x_0, y_0) \leq 0$$

This contradicts the fact that u satisfies (3.1) in D. Therefore, a function continuous in $D + C$ and satisfying (3.1) attains its maximum value on C.

Now suppose that u is a harmonic function in D and continuous in $D + C$. Let M denote its maximum value on C and consider the function

$$v(x, y) = u(x, y) + \varepsilon(x^2 + y^2)$$

where $\varepsilon > 0$ is an arbitrary number. It is clear that v is continuous in $D + C$ and

$$\Delta v = \Delta u + 4\varepsilon = 4\varepsilon > 0 \qquad \text{in } D$$

Hence, by the previous result, the maximum value of v is attained on C. Thus, at any point in D, we have

$$v(x, y) \leq \max_{\text{on } C} v(x, y) \leq M + \varepsilon R$$

where $R = \max(x^2 + y^2)$ for all (x, y) in $D + C$. Since $u(x, y) = v(x, y) - \varepsilon(x^2 + y^2) \leq v(x, y)$, it follows that

$$u(x, y) \leq v(x, y) \leq M + \varepsilon R$$

for all (x, y) in $D + C$, and for any number $\varepsilon > 0$. Letting $\varepsilon \to 0$, we then find $u(x, y) \leq M$, which establishes the theorem.

By applying the maximum principle to the harmonic function $v = -u$, we obtain an analogous result for the minimum value of u. Thus, a harmonic function in a bounded domain that is continuous throughout the closure of the domain attains its maximum and minimum values on the boundary of that domain. Of course, if u is a constant, its maximum (which coincides with its minimum) is attained at every point in D. As a matter of fact, a constant is the only harmonic function that can attain a maximum at an interior point of a domain, bounded or unbounded. This is the strong version of the maximum principle, which we shall establish in Section 6.

By using the maximum principle for harmonic functions, it is possible to give an alternative proof of Theorem 2.1 for the uniqueness of solution of Dirichlet problem for Laplace's equation. In fact, if u_1 and u_2 are two solutions of the problem (1.7), then their difference $u = u_1 - u_2$ is a harmonic function that vanishes on the boundary C. Then, by the maximum and minimum principle, u cannot be greater than or less than zero in D. Hence, u must vanish identically in $D + C$; that is, $u_1 = u_2$.

The maximum principle also enables us to establish continuous dependence of the solution of Dirichlet problem for Laplace's equation on the boundary data. We state this result as a theorem.

THEOREM 3.2 *If u and v are two harmonic functions in a bounded domain D with boundary C such that $|u - v| \leq \varepsilon$ on C, then*

$$|u - v| \leq \varepsilon \qquad \text{in } D$$

The proof is simple and is left as an exercise.

In sections to follow, solutions of the problem (1.7) in rectangular and circular domains will be determined. Thus, for these types of domains, Theorems 3.1 and 3.2 imply that the Dirichlet problem is well posed for the Laplace's equation.

Exercises 7.2

1. Express the Laplace's equation $\Delta u = 0$ in polar coordinates r and θ, where

    $$x = r \cos \theta, \qquad y = r \sin \theta$$

2. Show that if u is a harmonic function in D, then

    $$v(x, y) = u\left(\frac{x}{r^2}, \frac{y}{r^2}\right)$$

    is also harmonic at all points in D, where $r \neq 0$.

3. Show that by introducing the new variables $\xi = \ln(a/r)$, $\eta = \theta$, Laplace's equation in polar coordinates is transformed into the equation $u_{\xi\xi} + u_{\eta\eta} = 0$. Thus, determine the problem into which the Dirichlet problem for a sector

    $$\Delta u = 0 \qquad\qquad (r < a, 0 < \theta < b)$$
    $$u(r, 0) = f(r) \qquad\qquad (0 < r < a)$$
    $$u(a, \theta) = 0$$
    $$u(r, b) = 0$$

    is transformed by the change of variables.

4. Under the change of variables $\xi = \ln(1/r)$, $\eta = \theta$, show that the Dirichlet problem for an infinite sector

    $$\Delta u = 0 \qquad\qquad (r > 0, 0 < \theta < b)$$
    $$u(r, 0) = 0 \qquad\qquad (r > 0)$$
    $$u(r, b) = f(r) \qquad\qquad (r > 0)$$

    (u is bounded for $r \geq 0$) is transformed into the problem

    $$v_{\xi\xi} + v_{\eta\eta} = 0 \qquad (-\infty < \xi < \infty, 0 < \eta < b)$$
    $$v(\xi, 0) = 0 \qquad\qquad (-\infty < \xi < \infty)$$
    $$v(\xi, b) = f(e^{-\xi}) \qquad\qquad (-\infty < \xi < \infty)$$

5. Let u be a harmonic function in D and continuous on C. Show that if $u > 0$ on C, then $u > 0$ in D.

6. Let u, v, and w be three harmonic functions in D and continuous on C. Show that if $u \leq v \leq w$ on C, then $u \leq v \leq w$ in D.

7. Let u and v be continuous in D and on C such that u is harmonic and $\Delta v \geq 0$ in D. Show that if $u = v$ on C, then $u \geq v$ in D.

8. Show that a solution of the Poisson's equation $\Delta u = q$ in a domain D cannot attain its maximum at any point in D if $q > 0$, nor its minimum if $q < 0$.

9. Let u be a solution of

    $$\Delta u - hu = 0 \qquad \text{in } D$$

where $h > 0$. If u is continuous in $D + C$ and $u \leq$ on C, show that $u \leq 0$ in D. *Hint:* Show that u cannot attain a positive maximum in D.

10. Prove Theorem 3.2 of this section.

11. Show that if u is a solution of the three-dimensional Laplace's equation

$$\Delta u = u_{xx} + u_{yy} + u_{zz} = 0$$

is a domain D bounded by a surface S, and u is continuous in $D + S$, then u satisfies a maximum principle.

4. Dirichlet Problem in a Rectangle

Beginning with this section we shall consider solutions of the Dirichlet and Neumann problems for the Laplace's equation in simple domains such as a rectangle and a disk. It will be seen that for this type of domain, the method of separation of variables can be used to obtain a solution of the Dirichlet or the Neumann problem. We first consider in this section the Dirichlet problem in a rectangular domain R (Fig. 7.2): $0 < x < a, 0 < y < b$. We seek a solution of the Laplace's equation

(4.1) $$u_{xx} + u_{yy} = 0 \qquad \text{in } R$$

which satisfies the boundary conditions

(4.2)
$$u(0, y) = 0, \qquad u(a, y) = 0 \qquad (0 \leq y \leq b)$$
$$u(x, 0) = 0, \qquad u(x, b) = f(x) \qquad (0 \leq x \leq a)$$

This problem may be interpreted physically as finding the equilibrium temperature throughout a thin rectangular body R when its sides $x = 0, x = a$, $y = 0$ are kept at zero temperature and the side $y = b$ is maintained at given temperature distribution $f(x), 0 \leq x \leq a$.

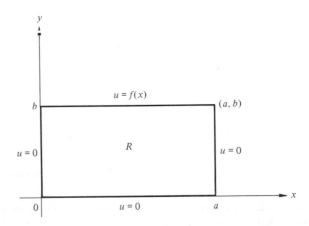

FIG. 7–2 *The Dirichlet problem in a rectangle.*

In accordance with the method of separation of variables, we assume nontrivial solutions of (4.1) of the form

(4.3) $$u(x, y) = X(x)Y(y)$$

which satisfy the three homogeneous boundary conditions in (4.2). Substituting (4.3) in (4.1) and separating variables, we obtain

$$\frac{X''}{X} = -\frac{Y''}{Y} = -\lambda$$

This leads to the two ordinary differential equations

(4.4) $$X'' + \lambda X = 0, \qquad Y'' - \lambda Y = 0$$

which are to be satisfied by the functions X and Y, respectively. In order for (4.3) to satisfy the three homogeneous boundary conditions for (4.2), we must have

(4.5) $$X(0) = 0, \qquad X(a) = 0, \qquad Y(0) = 0$$

Thus, the function X and Y must be determined from the now familiar eigenvalue problem

(4.6) $$X'' + \lambda X = 0, \qquad X(0) = 0, \qquad X(a) = 0$$

and the initial value problem

(4.7) $$Y'' - \lambda Y = 0, \qquad Y(0) = 0$$

When we encountered problem (4.6) before, we found the eigenvalues $\lambda_n = n^2\pi^2/a^2$ with the corresponding eigenfunctions

$$X_n(x) = \sin \frac{n\pi}{a} x \qquad\qquad (n = 1, 2, \ldots)$$

For each $\lambda_n = n^2\pi^2/a^2$, a solution of (4.7) is given by

$$Y(y) = \frac{1}{2} \left[e^{(n\pi/a)y} - e^{-(n\pi/a)y} \right]$$

$$= \sinh \frac{n\pi}{a} y \qquad\qquad (n = 1, 2, \ldots)$$

It follows that the functions

$$u_n(x, y) = \sin \frac{n\pi x}{a} \sinh \frac{n\pi y}{a} \qquad\qquad (n = 1, 2, \ldots)$$

are all particular solutions of the Laplace's equation vanishing at $x = 0$, $x = a$, and $y = 0$. These functions are called rectangular harmonics.

To obtain a solution of the problem (4.1), (4.2) we now form the series

(4.8) $$u(x, y) = \sum_{n=1}^{\infty} c_n \sin \frac{n\pi x}{a} \sinh \frac{n\pi y}{a}$$

where the coefficients c_n are constants yet to be determined. Formally setting $y = b$ and using the boundary condition in (4.2), we obtain

$$f(x) = u(x, b)$$

(4.9)
$$= \sum_{n=1}^{\infty} \left(c_n \sinh \frac{n\pi b}{a} \right) \sin \frac{n\pi x}{a}$$

$$= \sum_{n=1}^{\infty} b_n \sin \frac{n\pi x}{a}$$

where

(4.10)
$$b_n = c_n \sinh \frac{n\pi b}{a} \qquad\qquad (n = 1, 2, \ldots)$$

The last expression in (4.9) is the Fourier sine series expansion of f over $(0, a)$, and therefore

(4.11)
$$b_n = \frac{2}{a} \int_0^a f(x) \sin \frac{n\pi x}{a} \, dx \qquad\qquad (n = 1, 2, \ldots)$$

Substituting c_n from (4.10) in (4.8), we then obtain

(4.12)
$$u(x, y) = \sum_{n=1}^{\infty} b_n \frac{\sinh(n\pi y/a)}{\sinh(n\pi b/a)} \sin \frac{n\pi x}{a}$$

for the solution of the problem (4.1), (4.2). The coefficients b_n are given by (4.11).

If we assume that f is continuous, piecewise smooth on $0 \le x \le a$, and vanishes at $x = 0$ and $x = a$, we can verify that (4.12) indeed gives the solution of our problem (4.1), (4.2) by the same method used in Section 4 of Chapter 6. Notice that the inequality

$$\frac{\sinh(n\pi y/a)}{\sinh(n\pi b/a)} = \frac{e^{n\pi y/a} - e^{-n\pi y/a}}{e^{n\pi b/a} - e^{-n\pi b/a}}$$

$$= e^{-n\pi(b-y)/a} \frac{1 - e^{-2n\pi y/a}}{1 - e^{-2n\pi b/a}}$$

$$\le \frac{e^{-n\pi(b-y)/a}}{1 - e^{-2\pi b/a}}$$

may be used to prove uniform convergence of the series (4.12) and the second-order partial derivatives of that series with respect to x and y for $0 \le x \le a$, $0 \le y \le y_0$ with any $y_0 < b$.

The general Dirichlet problem

(4.13)
$$u_{xx} + u_{yy} = 0 \qquad \text{in } R$$
$$u(x, 0) = f_1(x), \qquad u(x, b) = f_2(x) \qquad (0 < x < a)$$
$$u(0, y) = f_3(y), \qquad u(a, y) = f_4(y) \qquad (0 < y < b)$$

in the rectangular domain R can be solved by superposition of the four functions u_1, u_2, u_3, and u_4, where each u_i ($1 \leq i \leq 4$) denotes the solution of (4.13) when all boundary data, except f_i, are zero.

Example 4.1. Find the solution of the problem (4.1), (4.2) when $R: 0 < x < \pi$, $0 < y < \pi$, and $f(x) = \sin^3 x$.

Solution: We recall from trigonometry that

$$\sin^3 x = \tfrac{3}{4} \sin x - \tfrac{1}{4} \sin 3x$$

so that from (4.9) we see that $b_1 = 3/4$, $b_3 = -1/4$, and $b_n = 0$ for all other values of n. Hence, by (4.12), the solution is

$$u(x, y) = \frac{3}{4} \frac{\sinh y}{\sinh \pi} \sin x - \frac{1}{4} \frac{\sinh 3y}{\sinh 3\pi} \sin 3x$$

The general Neumann problem for the Laplace's equation in the rectangle R,

$$u_{xx} + u_{yy} = 0 \quad \text{in } R$$

(4.14)
$$u_y(x, 0) = f(x), \qquad u_y(x, b) = h(x) \qquad (0 \leq x \leq a)$$
$$u_x(0, y) = k(y), \qquad u_x(a, y) = g(y) \qquad (0 \leq y \leq b)$$

can also be solved in the same manner, provided the boundary data satisfy the necessary condition (2.12), which means in the present case that

(4.15)
$$\int_0^a [f(x) - h(x)] \, dx + \int_0^b [g(y) - k(y)] \, dy = 0$$

We illustrate the situation in this case by means of the following example.

Example 4.2. Find a solution of the Neumann problem

$$\Delta u = 0 \qquad\qquad (0 < x < \pi, 0 < y < \pi)$$
$$u_y(x, 0) = x - \frac{\pi}{2} \qquad\qquad (0 \leq x \leq \pi)$$
$$u_y(x, \pi) = 0 \qquad\qquad (0 \leq x \leq \pi)$$
$$u_x(0, y) = u_x(\pi, y) = 0 \qquad (0 \leq y \leq \pi)$$

Solution: Here we note that condition (4.15) is fulfilled by the boundary datum $f(x) = x - \pi/2$. The method of separation of variables $u(x, y) = X(x)Y(y)$ leads to the Sturm-Loiuville problem

$$X'' + \lambda X = 0, \qquad X'(0) = 0, \qquad X'(\pi) = 0$$

for the function X. This has the eigenvalues $\lambda_n = n^2$ and the corresponding eigenfunction $X_n(x) = \cos nx$, $n = 0, 1, 2, \ldots$. For each eigenvalue $\lambda_n = n^2$, the initial value problem for the function Y,

$$Y'' - n^2 Y = 0, \qquad Y'(\pi) = 0$$

gives $Y_n(y) = \cosh n(\pi - y)$. Therefore, to solve the problem, we assume a series solution in the form

$$u(x, y) = A_0 + \sum A_n \cosh n(y - \pi) \cos nx$$

consisting of the functions $X_n Y_n$, $n \geq 1$. Differentiating this formally with respect to y and applying the boundary condition at $y = 0$, we find

$$x - \frac{\pi}{2} = -\sum_{n=1}^{\infty} nA_n \sinh n\pi \cos nx$$

$$= \sum_{n=1}^{\infty} a_n \cos nx$$

where $a_n = -nA_n \sinh n\pi$, $n = 1, 2, \ldots$. In view of the fact that $\int_0^\pi (x - (\pi/2)) \, dx = 0$, we see that the constant term a_0 in the Fourier cosine series expansion of the function $f(x) = x - (\pi/2)$ is zero. Therefore, the series given above is precisely the Fourier cosine series of the function, and so

$$a_n = \frac{2}{\pi} \int_0^\pi \left(x - \frac{\pi}{2} \right) \cos nx \, dx$$

$$= \frac{2}{\pi} \frac{(-1)^n - 1}{n^2} \qquad\qquad (n = 1, 2, \ldots)$$

Hence,

$$A_n = -\frac{2}{\pi} \frac{(-1)^n - 1}{n^3 \sinh n\pi}$$

or

$$A_{2k-1} = \frac{4}{\pi(2k - 1)^3 \sinh(2k - 1)\pi} \qquad (k = 1, 2, \ldots)$$

so that a solution of the given Neumann problem is

$$u(x, y) = A_0 + \frac{4}{\pi} \sum_{k=1}^{\infty} \frac{\cosh(2k - 1)(y - \pi)}{(2k - 1)^3 \sinh(2k - 1)\pi} \cos nx$$

and A_0 is an arbitrary constant.

Exercises 7.3

1. Solve the Dirichlet problem

$$\Delta u = 0 \qquad\qquad (0 < x < a, 0 < y < b)$$
$$u(x, 0) = f(x) \qquad\qquad (0 \leq x \leq a)$$
$$u(x, b) = 0 \qquad\qquad (0 \leq x \leq a)$$
$$u(0, y) = u(a, y) = 0 \qquad\qquad (0 \leq y \leq b)$$

In particular, find the solution when $f(x) = \sin(\pi x/a)$.

2. By interchanging the role of x and y, deduce from (4.12) the solution of the problem

$$\Delta u = 0 \qquad\qquad (0 < x < a, 0 < y < b)$$
$$u(x, 0) = u(x, b) = 0 \qquad\qquad (0 \le x \le a)$$
$$u(0, y) = 0, \qquad u(a, y) = g(y) \qquad\qquad (0 \le y \le b)$$

In particular, find the solution when $g(y) = \sin(2\pi y)/b$.

3. Find the solution of the problem

$$\Delta u = 0 \qquad\qquad (0 < x < \pi, 0 < y < \pi)$$
$$u(x, 0) = \sin 2x, \qquad u(x, \pi) = 0 \qquad\qquad (0 \le x \le \pi)$$
$$u(0, y) = 0, \qquad u(\pi, y) = \sin 2y \qquad\qquad (0 \le y \le \pi)$$

4. Solve the nonhomogeneous problem

$$\Delta u = -1 \qquad\qquad (0 < x < \pi, 0 < y < \pi)$$
$$u(x, 0) = u(x, \pi) = 0 \qquad\qquad (0 \le x \le \pi)$$
$$u(0, y) = u(\pi, y) = 0 \qquad\qquad (0 \le y \le \pi)$$

Hint: Introduce the new variable

$$w(x, y) = \frac{x(\pi - x)}{2} - u(x, y)$$

5. Solve the nonhomogeneous problem

$$\Delta u = -\sin x \qquad\qquad (0 < x < \pi, 0 < y < 1)$$
$$u_y(x, 0) = u(x, 1) = 0 \qquad\qquad (0 \le x \le \pi)$$
$$u(0, y) = u(\pi, y) = 0 \qquad\qquad (0 \le y \le 1)$$

6. Solve the problem

$$\Delta u = x - y \qquad\qquad (0 < x < 1, 0 < y < 1)$$
$$u(x, 0) = u_y(x, 1) = 0 \qquad\qquad (0 \le x \le 1)$$
$$u_x(0, y) = 0, \qquad u(1, y) = 0 \qquad\qquad (0 \le y \le 1)$$

7. Let u be a solution of the problem

$$\Delta u = 0 \qquad\qquad (0 < a < x, 0 < y < a)$$
$$u(x, 0) = 0, \qquad u(x, a) = -f(x) \qquad\qquad (0 \le x \le a)$$
$$u(0, y) = 0, \qquad u(a, y) = f(y) \qquad\qquad (0 \le y \le a)$$

Show that $u(x, y) = -u(y, x)$; thus, deduce $u(x, x) = 0$.

8. Use the result of Problem 7 to find the harmonic function for the right isosceles triangle bounded by the lines $y = 0$, $x = \pi$, $x = y$ which satisfies the boundary conditions

$$u(x, 0) = 0, \qquad u(\pi, y) = \sin^3 y, \qquad u(x, x) = 0$$

9. Find the harmonic function for the right isosceles triangle of the preceding problem which satisfies the boundary conditions $u_y(x, 0) = 0$, $u(\pi, y) = f(y)$, $(\partial u/\partial n)(x, x) = 0$.

10. Find the solution of the problem

$$\Delta u - hu = 0 \qquad (h \text{ a positive constant}; 0 < x < \pi, 0 < y < \pi)$$
$$u(x, 0) = 0, \qquad u(x, \pi) = f(x) \qquad\qquad (0 \le x \le \pi)$$
$$u(0, y) = u(\pi, y) = 0 \qquad\qquad\qquad (0 \le y \le \pi)$$

11. Solve the Neumann problem

$$\Delta u = 0 \qquad\qquad (0 < x < a, 0 < y < b)$$
$$u_y(x, 0) = u_y(x, b) = 0 \qquad\qquad (0 \le x \le a)$$
$$u_x(0, y) = g(y), \qquad u_x(a, y) = 0 \qquad (0 \le y \le b)$$

assuming that $\int_0^b g(y)\, dy = 0$.

12. Solve the problem

$$\Delta u = 0 \qquad\qquad (0 < x < a, 0 < y < b)$$
$$u_x(0, y) = 0, \qquad u_x(a, y) = g(y) \qquad (0 \le y \le b)$$
$$u_y(x, 0) = f(x), \qquad u_y(x, b) = 0 \qquad (0 \le x \le a)$$

assuming that

$$\int_0^a f(x)\, dx = 0 \qquad \text{and} \qquad \int_0^b g(y)\, dy = 0$$

13. Find the solution of the Neumann problem

$$\Delta u = 0 \qquad\qquad (0 < x < \pi, 0 < y < \pi)$$
$$u_x(0, y) = u_x(\pi, y) = 0 \qquad\qquad (0 \le y \le \pi)$$
$$u_y(x, 0) = x/\pi, \qquad u_y(x, \pi) = 1 - x/\pi \qquad (0 \le x \le \pi)$$

14. Find the solution of the Neumann problem

$$\Delta u = 0 \qquad\qquad (0 < x < \pi, 0 < y < \pi)$$
$$u_x(0, y) = \cos y, \qquad u_x(\pi, y) = 0 \qquad (0 \le y \le \pi)$$
$$u_y(x, 0) = 1 - 2x/\pi, \qquad u_y(x, \pi) = 0 \qquad (0 \le x \le \pi)$$

15. Solve the mixed boundary value problem

$$\Delta u = 0 \qquad\qquad (0 < x < \pi, 0 < y < \pi)$$
$$u(x, 0) = 0, \qquad u(x, \pi) = f(x) \qquad (0 \le x \le \pi)$$
$$u_x(0, y) = u_x(\pi, y) = 0 \qquad\qquad (0 \le y \le \pi)$$

In particular, find the solution when $f(x) = 4\cos 2x$.

16. Solve the mixed boundary value problem

$$\Delta u = 0 \qquad\qquad (0 < x < \pi, 0 < y < \pi)$$
$$u_x(0, y) = g(y), \qquad u(\pi, y) = 0 \qquad (0 \le y \le \pi)$$
$$u(x, 0) = f(x), \qquad u_y(x, \pi) = 0 \qquad (0 \le x \le \pi)$$

5. Dirichlet Problem in a Disk

Let D and C denote respectively the interior and boundary of the disk $x^2 + y^2 \leq a^2$ (Fig. 7.3) with radius a and center at the origin. We seek a harmonic function u in D, which assumes the prescribed values $u = f$ on the boundary C; that is,

(5.1) $u_{xx} + u_{yy} = 0$ in D, $u = f$ on C

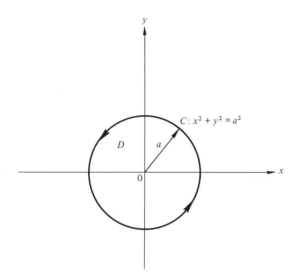

FIG. 7–3   *Dirichlet problem in a circular region.*

In order to be able to apply the method of separation of variables to this problem, we introduce polar coordinates

$$x = r \cos \theta, \qquad y = r \sin \theta \qquad (0 \leq \theta \leq 2\pi, \ 0 < r \leq a)$$

to transform the Laplace's equation into the form

(5.2) $$u_{rr} + \frac{1}{r} u_r + \frac{1}{r^2} u_{\theta\theta} = 0$$

The boundary condition in (5.1) becomes

(5.3) $$u(a, \theta) = f(\theta) \qquad\qquad (0 \leq \theta \leq 2\pi)$$

Thus, the problem (5.1) is reduced to the equivalent problem (5.2), (5.3), where now the separation-of-variables method can be applied. Accordingly, we assume particular solutions of (5.2) in the form

$$u(r, \theta) = R(r) \, \Theta(\theta)$$

Substituting this in (5.2) and separating variables, we obtain

$$r^2 \frac{R''(r)}{R(r)} + r \frac{R'(r)}{R(r)} = -\frac{\Theta''(\theta)}{\Theta(\theta)} = \lambda$$

where λ is our separation constant. This leads to the two ordinary differential equations

(5.4) $r^2 R''(r) + r R'(r) - \lambda R(r) = 0$

and

(5.5) $\Theta''(\theta) + \lambda \Theta(\theta) = 0$

for the functions R and Θ, respectively.

In order for the solution of the problem (5.2), (5.3) to be single-valued, it is necessary to require the solution to be periodic in θ, of periodic 2π; that is,

$$u(r, \theta + 2\pi) = u(r, \theta)$$

This requirement is clearly met if Θ is periodic, of period 2π. Hence, we impose the "periodic" boundary conditions

(5.6) $\Theta(-\pi) - \Theta(\pi) = 0, \qquad \Theta'(-\pi) - \Theta'(\pi) = 0$

for the function Θ. Equation (5.5) together with the conditions (5.6) constitute an eigenvalue problem [Problem 15, Exercises 4.4] for which the eigenvalues are $\lambda = n^2$, $n = 0, 1, 2, \ldots$, and the corresponding eigenfunctions are

$$\Theta_n(\theta) = C_n \cos n\theta + D_n \sin n\theta$$

When $\lambda = 0$, equation (5.4) has the general solution

$$R_0(r) = A_0 + B_0 \ln r$$

and when $\lambda = n^2$, $n = 1, 2, \ldots$, it has the general solution

$$R_n(r) = A_n r^n + B_n r^{-n}$$

Therefore, all the functions

(5.7)
$$u_n(r, \theta) = A_0 + B_0 \ln r$$
$$+ (A_n r^n + B_n r^{-n})(C_n \cos n\theta + D_n \sin n\theta)$$

$n = 0, 1, 2, \ldots, r > 0$ which are periodic of period 2π, satisfy Laplace's equation (5.2) in polar coordinates. These functions are called the *circular harmonics*.

We shall form a suitable infinite combination of the functions (5.7) for our solution of the problem (5.2), (5.3). Since the solution must be continuous in D, which contains the origin $r = 0$, we must exclude from our consideration the logarithmic term and the terms involving negative powers of r. We therefore choose $B_n = 0$, $n = 0, 1, 2, \ldots$ in (5.7) and consider the infinite series

$$(5.8) \qquad u(r, \theta) = \frac{\alpha_0}{2} + \sum_{n=1}^{\infty} r^n(\alpha_n \cos n\theta + \beta_n \sin n\theta)$$

where we have relabeled the constants. To determine the constants α_0, α_n, and β_n, $n \geq 1$, we set $r = a$ and apply the boundary condition (5.3) to obtain

$$(5.9) \qquad f(\theta) = \frac{\alpha_0}{2} + \sum_{n=1}^{\infty} a^n(\alpha_n \cos \theta + \beta_n \sin n\theta)$$

This is the Fourier series expansion of f on the interval $[-\pi, \pi]$, for which the coefficients are given by

$$(5.10) \qquad a_n = a^n\alpha_n = \frac{1}{\pi} \int_{-\pi}^{\pi} f(\theta) \cos n\theta \, d\theta \qquad (n = 0, 1, 2, \ldots)$$

$$b_n = a^n\beta_n = \frac{1}{\pi} \int_{-\pi}^{\pi} f(\theta) \sin n\theta \, d\theta \qquad (n = 1, 2, \ldots)$$

Substituting for α_n and β_n in (5.8), we obtain

$$(5.11) \qquad u(r, \theta) = \frac{a_0}{2} + \sum_{n=1}^{\infty} \left(\frac{r}{a}\right)^n (a_n \cos n\theta + b_n \sin n\theta)$$

where a_n and b_n are the Fourier coefficients of f on $[-\pi, \pi]$, given by the integrals in (5.10).

Formula (5.11) together with (5.10) gives the solution of our problem (5.2), (5.3). To verify this, we now assume that f is continuous, piecewise smooth, and periodic of period 2π on $[-\pi, \pi]$. Let

$$M = \frac{1}{\pi} \int_{-\pi}^{\pi} |f(\theta)| \, d\theta$$

so that $|a_n| \leq M$ and $|b_n| \leq M$, and define

$$u_n(r, \theta) = \left(\frac{r}{a}\right)^n (a_n \cos n\theta + b_n \sin n\theta) \qquad (n = 1, 2, \ldots)$$

with $u_0 = a_0/2$. Then, for $r \leq r_0$ with any $r_0 < a$,

$$(5.12) \qquad |u_n(r, \theta)| \leq \left(\frac{r}{a}\right)^n [|a_n| + |b_n|] \leq 2M \left(\frac{r}{a}\right)^n$$

The series consisting of the terms $2M(r/a)^n$ converges uniformly for $r \leq r_0$. By Theorem 6.1 of Chapter 5, the series (5.11) also converges uniformly for

$r = a$. Therefore, the series (5.11) converges uniformly to $u(r, \theta)$ for $r \leq a$, and thus $u(r, \theta)$ is continuous for $0 \leq r \leq a, 0 \leq \theta \leq 2\pi$. Since

$$u(a, \theta) = \frac{a_0}{2} + \sum_{n=1}^{\infty} (a_n \cos n\theta + b_n \sin n\theta) = f(\theta)$$

the boundary condition (5.3) is met.

To show that u satisfies the Laplace's equation (5.2), we note that the series (5.11) and its first and second partial derivatives are dominated by some constant multiple of the series $\sum 2Mn^2(r/a)^{n-2}$. This series converges uniformly for $r \leq r_0 < a$. Hence, u has continuous first- and second-order derivatives for $r < a$, which can be obtained by termwise differentiation of the series (5.11). It follows that

$$\frac{\partial^2 u}{\partial r^2} + \frac{1}{r} \frac{\partial u}{\partial r} + \frac{1}{r^2} \frac{\partial^2 u}{\partial \theta^2} = \sum_{n=1}^{\infty} \frac{1}{r^2} u_n(r, \theta)[n(n - 1) + n - n^2] = 0$$

thus verifying that u satisfies (5.2).

Example 5.1. Solve the Dirichlet problem

$$u_{rr} + \frac{1}{r} u_r + \frac{1}{r^2} u_{\theta\theta} = 0 \qquad\qquad (r < a)$$

$$u(a, \theta) = a \cos^2 \theta \qquad\qquad (0 \leq \theta \leq 2\pi)$$

Solution: We note that

$$a \cos^2 \theta = a(\tfrac{1}{2} + \tfrac{1}{2} \cos 2\theta)$$

Therefore, by (5.11), we have

$$u(r, \theta) = \frac{1}{2} \left(a + \frac{r^2}{a} \cos 2\theta \right)$$

Example 5.2. Find the solution of the Dirichlet problem

$$u_{xx} + u_{yy} = 0 \qquad \text{for } x^2 + y^2 < 1$$
$$u = y^2 \qquad \text{for } x^2 + y^2 = 1$$

Solution: Considering the problem in polar coordinates, we see that the boundary condition becomes $u(1, \theta) = \sin^2 \theta = \tfrac{1}{2}(1 - \cos 2\theta)$. Thus, by (5.1), we have

$$u(r, \theta) = \tfrac{1}{2}(1 - r^2 \cos 2\theta)$$

Reverting back to rectangular coordinates, we find

$$u(x, y) = \tfrac{1}{2}(1 - x^2 + y^2)$$

which is the solution of the problem.

Exercises 7.4

1. Find the solution of the Dirichlet problem

$$\Delta u \equiv u_{rr} + \frac{1}{r} u_r + \frac{1}{r^2} u_{\theta\theta} = 0 \qquad (r < a)$$

$$u(a, \theta) = a^3 \sin^3 \theta \qquad (0 \le \theta \le 2\pi)$$

2. Find the solution of the problem

$$\Delta u = 0 \qquad (r < 1)$$

$$u(1, \theta) = \sin \theta + \cos^2 \theta \qquad (0 \le \theta \le 2\pi)$$

3. Solve the Dirichlet problem

$$\Delta u = u_{xx} + u_{yy} = 0 \qquad (x^2 + y^2 < a^2)$$

$$u(x, y) = x^2, \qquad x^2 + y^2 = a^2 \qquad (x^2 + y^2 = a^2)$$

4. Solve the problem

$$\Delta u = 0 \qquad (x^2 + y^2 < 4)$$

$$u(x, y) = y^4 \qquad (x^2 + y^2 = 4)$$

5. Show that if the boundary data f in (5.3) is an odd function of θ (that is, $f(-\theta) = -f(\theta)$), then so is the solution $u(r, \theta)$ of the problem (5.2), (5.3)—that is, $u(r, -\theta) = -u(r, \theta)$—and thus $u(r, 0) = 0$ and $u(r, \pi) = 0$. *Hint:* Set $v(r, \theta) = u(r, \theta) + u(r, -\theta)$.

6. Use the result of Problem 5 to find the solution of the problem

$$\Delta u = 0 \qquad (r < a, 0 < \theta < \pi)$$

$$u(r, 0) = u(r, \theta) = 0 \qquad (0 \le r \le a)$$

$$u(a, \theta) = 4 \sin \theta \cos \theta \qquad (0 \le \theta \le \pi)$$

7. Show that if the boundary data f in (5.3) is an odd function of θ and is periodic of period π, then so is the solution $u(r, \theta)$ of the problem (5.2), (5.3). Thus, deduce that u vanishes for $\theta = 0, \pi$, and $\pm \pi/2$.

8. Use the result of Problem 7 to find the solution of the problem

$$\Delta u = 0 \qquad (0 < r < a, 0 < \theta < \pi/2)$$

$$u(r, 0) = u(r, \pi/2) = 0 \qquad (0 \le r \le a)$$

$$u(a, \theta) = 2a \sin 2\theta \cos 2\theta \qquad (0 \le \theta \le \pi/2)$$

9. Find the solution of the problem

$$\Delta u = 0 \qquad (r < 2, 0 < \theta < \pi/2)$$

$$u(r, 0) = u_\theta(r, \pi/2) = 0 \qquad (0 < r < 2)$$

$$u(2, \theta) = 4 \sin^3 \theta$$

10. Solve the Dirichlet problem for an annular domain

$$\Delta u = 0 \qquad (a < r < b)$$

$$u(a, \theta) = 0 \qquad (0 \le \theta \le 2\pi)$$

$$u(b, \theta) = g(\theta) \qquad (0 \le \theta \le 2\pi)$$

11. Solve Problem 10 when the boundary conditions are

$$u(a, \theta) = f(\theta) \qquad\qquad (0 \leq \theta \leq 2\pi)$$
$$u(b, \theta) = 0 \qquad\qquad (0 \leq \theta \leq 2\pi)$$

12. Find the solution of the problem

$$\Delta u = 0 \qquad\qquad (a < r < b, 0 < \theta < \pi)$$
$$u(r, 0) = u(r, \pi) = 0 \qquad\qquad (a \leq r \leq b)$$
$$u(a, \theta) = 0, \quad u(b, \theta) = f(\theta) \qquad\qquad (0 \leq \theta \leq \pi)$$

13. Solve the problem

$$\Delta u = 0 \qquad\qquad (a < r < b, 0 < \theta < \pi)$$
$$u(r, 0) = f(r), \quad u(r, \pi) = 0 \qquad\qquad (a \leq r \leq b)$$
$$u(a, \theta) = u(b, \theta) = 0 \qquad\qquad (0 \leq \theta \leq \pi)$$

Hint: $r^{i\lambda} = e^{i\lambda \ln r} = \cos(\lambda \ln r) + i \sin(\lambda \ln r)$.

14. Solve the problem

$$\Delta u = 0 \qquad\qquad (a < r < b, 0 < \theta < \pi)$$
$$u_\theta(r, 0) = 0, \quad u_\theta(r, \pi) = f(r) \qquad\qquad (a \leq r \leq b)$$
$$u(a, \theta) = u(b, \theta) = 0 \qquad\qquad (0 \leq \theta \leq \pi)$$

6. Poisson's Integral Formula

The solution (5.11) of the Dirichlet problem in a disk can be expressed in the form of an integral from which we can deduce several important and useful properties of harmonic functions. This is accomplished by substituting the formulas (5.10) for the Fourier coefficients a_n and b_n in (5.11). We obtain

$$
\begin{aligned}
u(r, \theta) &= \frac{1}{2\pi} \int_{-\pi}^{\pi} f(\phi) \, d\phi \\
&\quad + \frac{1}{\pi} \sum_{n=1}^{\infty} \left(\frac{r}{a}\right)^n \int_{-\pi}^{\pi} f(\phi)(\cos n\phi \cos n\theta + \sin n\phi \sin n\theta) \, d\phi \\
\text{(6.1)} \quad
&= \frac{1}{2\pi} \int_{-\pi}^{\pi} f(\phi) \, d\phi + \frac{1}{\pi} \sum_{n=1}^{\infty} \left(\frac{r}{a}\right)^n \int_{-\pi}^{\pi} f(\phi) \cos n(\theta - \phi) \, d\phi \\
&= \frac{1}{\pi} \int_{-\pi}^{\pi} f(\phi) \left[\frac{1}{2} + \sum_{n=1}^{\infty} \left(\frac{r}{a}\right)^n \cos n(\theta - \phi)\right] d\phi
\end{aligned}
$$

where we have interchanged the order of summation and integration. This interchange is justified, since by (5.12) the series

$$\text{(6.2)} \qquad\qquad \frac{1}{2} + \sum_{n=1}^{\infty} \left(\frac{r}{a}\right)^n \cos n(\theta - \phi)$$

converges uniformly for $r < a$ and $-\pi \leq \theta \leq \pi$.

Let us calculate the sum of the series (6.2). We let $z = \rho e^{i\alpha} = \rho(\cos \alpha + i \sin \alpha)$, where $|z| = \rho < 1$, and consider the series

$$\frac{1}{2} + \sum_{n=1}^{\infty} z^n$$

Since $|z| < 1$, we have

$$\frac{1}{2} + \sum_{n=1}^{\infty} z^n = \frac{1}{2} + \frac{z}{1 - z} = \frac{1 + z}{2(1 - z)}$$

$$= \frac{1 + \rho \cos \alpha + i\rho \sin \alpha}{2(1 - \rho \cos \alpha - i\rho \sin \alpha)}$$

(6.3)

$$= \frac{(1 + \rho \cos \alpha + i\rho \sin \alpha)(1 - \rho \cos \alpha + i\rho \sin \alpha)}{2[(1 - \rho \cos \alpha)^2 + \rho^2 \sin^2 \alpha]}$$

$$= \frac{1 - \rho^2 + 2i\rho \sin \alpha}{2(1 - 2\rho \cos \alpha + \rho^2)}$$

On the other hand, since

$$z^n = \rho^n e^{in\alpha} = \rho^n(\cos n\alpha + i \sin n\alpha)$$

we have

(6.4) $$\frac{1}{2} + \sum_{n=1}^{\infty} z^n = \frac{1}{2} + \sum_{n=1}^{\infty} \rho^n(\cos n\alpha + i \sin n\alpha)$$

Thus, by equating the real parts of the right-hand sides of (6.3) and (6.4), we find

(6.5) $$\frac{1}{2} + \sum_{n=1}^{\infty} \rho^n \cos n\alpha = \frac{1 - \rho^2}{2(1 - 2\rho \cos \alpha + \rho^2)}$$

It follows that (6.2) has the sum

$$\frac{1}{2} + \sum_{n=1}^{\infty} \left(\frac{r}{a}\right)^n \cos n(\theta - \phi) = \frac{a^2 - r^2}{2(a^2 - 2ar \cos(\theta - \phi) + r^2)}$$

so that (6.1) becomes

(6.6) $$u(r, \theta) = \frac{1}{2\pi} \int_{-\pi}^{\pi} \frac{(a^2 - r^2)}{a^2 - 2ar \cos(\theta - \phi) + r^2} f(\phi) \, d\phi$$

This is known as Poisson's integral formula for the solution of the Dirichlet problem in a disk.

We recall that in (5.11), f was assumed continuous and piecewise smooth in addition to being periodic of period 2π. In the integral formula (6.6), it is sufficient to require that f be continuous and periodic. For then the function u defined by (6.6) for $r < a$ and by $u(a, \theta) = f(\theta)$ for $r = a$ is continuous throughout the disk $r \leq a$. Moreover, u has continuous derivatives of all orders with respect to r and θ for $r < a$, which can all be obtained by differentiation within the integral sign. By a straightforward calculation, it is easily seen that the function

$$(6.7) \qquad K(a, r, \theta - \phi) = \frac{1}{2\pi} \frac{a^2 - r^2}{a^2 - 2ar\cos(\theta - \phi) + r^2}$$

satisfies (5.2) for $r < a$, $0 \le \theta \le 2\pi$. Thus, the integral formula (6.6) with $u(a, \theta) = f(\theta)$ represents the unique solution of the Dirichlet problem (5.2), (5.3). Frequently, this formula is more convient to use than the series (5.11).

The function (6.7) is often called Poisson's kernel. This function is positive for $0 \le r < a$, $-\pi \le \theta \le \pi$. Indeed, since $a^2 - r^2 > 0$, we see that

$$a^2 - 2ar\cos(\theta - \phi) + r^2 = (a - r)^2 + 2ar[1 - \cos(\theta - \phi)]$$

$$= (a - r)^2 + 4ar\sin^2\frac{(\theta - \phi)}{2}$$

$$> 0$$

Further, Poisson's kernel satisfies the interesting property

$$(6.8) \qquad 1 = \frac{1}{2\pi} \int_{-\pi}^{\pi} \frac{(a^2 - r^2)\, d\phi}{a^2 - 2ar\cos(\theta - \phi) + r^2}$$

This result follows from (6.6) when $f(\phi) = 1$ and the fact that in such a case $u(r, \theta) = 1$ by the maximum principle.

If we set $r = 0$ in (6.6), we then obtain the very important result

$$u(0, 0) = \frac{1}{2\pi} \int_{-\pi}^{\pi} f(\phi)\, d\phi$$

or

$$(6.9) \qquad u(0, 0) = \frac{1}{2\pi a} \int_{-\pi}^{\pi} u(a, \phi)\, ds$$

since $u(a, \phi) = f(\phi)$ and $ds = a\, d\phi$. This formula expresses the well-known mean-value property of harmonic functions. Let us state this property as a theorem in a more general setting.

THEOREM 6.1. *Let u be a harmonic function in a domain D. Then the value of u at the center of any disk lying in D is equal to the mean or average of the values of u on the boundary of the disk.*

It is noteworthy that the mean-value property of a harmonic function can be established by using merely the harmonicity of the function without resorting to Poisson's integral formula. To see this, let D_r be a disk of radius r and center (x, y) lying in D. Then each point (ξ, η) in D_r can be expressed in polar coordinates

$$\xi = x + \rho\cos\theta \qquad\qquad (0 \le \rho \le r)$$

$$\eta = y + \rho\sin\theta \qquad\qquad (0 \le \theta \le 2\pi)$$

with pole at (x, y). Applying the identity (2.11) to the domain D_r, we obtain

(6.10) $$\int_0^{2\pi} \frac{\partial u}{\partial r}(x + r \cos \theta, y + r \sin \theta) r \, d\theta = \iint_{D_r} \Delta u \rho \, d\rho \, d\theta$$

Since u is harmonic, $\Delta u = 0$ and thus (6.10) becomes

(6.11) $$\int_0^{2\pi} \frac{\partial u}{\partial r}(x + r \cos \theta, y + r \sin \theta) \, d\theta = 0$$

Let us set

(6.12) $$U(x, y; r) = \int_0^{2\pi} u(x + r \cos \theta, y + r \sin \theta) \, d\theta$$

Since u and its derivatives are continuous in D_r, so is U together with its first derivatives. It follows that we can calculate $\partial U / \partial r$ by differentiating (6.12) under the integral sign. In view of (6.11), we find

$$\frac{\partial U}{\partial r} = \int_0^{2\pi} \frac{\partial u}{\partial r}(x + r \cos \theta, y + r \sin \theta) \, d\theta = 0$$

This implies that U is independent of r; in particular, we have

(6.13) $$U(x, y; 0) = U(x, y; r) \qquad\qquad (0 \le r \le a)$$

Now, from (6.12), we see that

$$U(x, y, 0) = \lim_{r \to 0} \int_0^{2\pi} u(x + r \cos \theta, y + r \sin \theta) \, d\theta$$

$$= \int_0^{2\pi} u(x, y) \, d\theta$$

$$= 2\pi u(x, y)$$

Therefore, by (6.12) and (6.13), we finally obtain

(6.14) $$u(x, y) = \frac{1}{2\pi} \int_{-\pi}^{\pi} u(x + r \cos \theta, y + r \sin \theta) \, d\theta$$

which proves Theorem 6.1.

This yields the special case (6.9) when the point (x, y) happens to be the origin.

It is interesting to note that the converse of Theorem 6.1 is also true. That is, if u is continuous and satisfies the mean-value property (6.4) for any r in a domain D, then u is harmonic in D. As a matter of fact, under the continuity requirement it can be shown that u, as expressed by the formula (6.14), has continuous derivatives of all orders in D which themselves also satisfy the mean-value property. This implies that a harmonic function necessarily has derivatives of all orders. Here, we shall show only that $\Delta u = 0$ in D.

Suppose that there is a point (x, y) in D at which $\Delta u \ne 0$; say, $\Delta u(x, y) > 0$. Since u is continuous, there is a disk D_r about (x, y) with radius r and lying in

D such that $\Delta u > 0$ throughout D_r. Then, applying the formula (2.11) to D_r, we find

$$0 < \iint_{D_r} \Delta u \, d\xi \, d\eta$$

$$= \int_0^r \int_0^{2\pi} \Delta u \rho \, d\rho \, d\theta$$

$$= \int_0^{2\pi} \frac{\partial u}{\partial r} r \, d\theta$$

$$= r \frac{\partial}{\partial r} \int_0^{2\pi} u(x + r \cos \theta, y + r \sin \theta) \, d\theta$$

which, by (6.14), yields

$$0 < \iint_{D_r} \Delta u \, d\xi \, d\eta = r \frac{\partial}{\partial r} [u(x, y)] = 0$$

a contradiction. Therefore, $\Delta u = 0$ throughout D.

Because of Theorem 6.1 we are now in position to establish the statement made in Section 3 to the effect that a constant is the only harmonic function that can attain a maximum inside a domain. We shall state and prove this fact as a theorem.

THEOREM 6.2. *Let u be a harmonic function in a domain D. If u attains its maximum value at a point inside D, then u is a constant.*

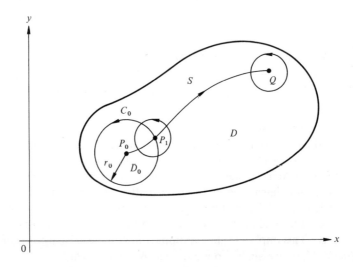

FIG. 7–4 *The strong maximum principle.*

Proof: Let M denote the maximum value of u in D (Fig. 7.4), which is attained at a point P_0: (x_0, y_0) inside D. We shall prove that $u = M$ identically in D. Let Q be any other point inside D and join P_0 and Q by a smooth curve S lying in D. Beginning from the point P_0 and moving toward the point Q, we shall construct a finite number of disks lying in D and with centers on S such that the center of each disk lies inside the preceding disk. We shall prove that $u = M$ throughout each of the disks. Thus, let D_0 be a disk with center at P_0 and radius r_0 such that D_0 lies in D. Then, by the mean-value property of u, we have

$$(6.15) \qquad M = u(P_0) = \frac{1}{2\pi} \int_0^{2\pi} u(r_0, \theta) \, d\theta$$

Now, on the circumference C_0 of D_0, we have $u(r_0, \theta) \leq M$. If $u(r_0, \theta) < M$ for some point on C_0, then by the continuity we would have $u < M$ over some arc of C_0 containing that point; consequently,

$$\frac{1}{2\pi} \int_0^{2\pi} u(r_0, \theta) \, d\theta < M$$

which contradicts (6.15). Therefore, $u = M$ identically on C_0. But the preceding argument holds as well for any concentric disk with radius r for $0 \leq r \leq r_0$. Hence, $u = M$ identically in D_0.

Now let P_1 be the point of intersection of C_0 with the curve S so that $u(P_1) = M$. Let D_1 be a disk about P_1 with radius r_1 such that D_1 lies in D. By repeating the preceding argument, we again conclude that $u = M$ throughout D_1. Proceeding in this manner, it follows that after a finite number of steps we shall reach a disk D_n that contains the point Q and for which $u = M$ identically in D_n. Thus, $u(Q) = M$, and since the point Q is arbitrary in D, it follows that $u = M$ throughout D.

Exercises 7.5

1. Deduce from (6.3) and (6.4) the identity

$$\sum_{n=1}^{\infty} \rho^n \sin nt = \frac{\rho \sin t}{(1 - 2\rho \cos t + \rho^2)}$$

2. Verify directly the relation (6.8) by making use of the formula

$$\int_0^{2\pi} \frac{d\phi}{1 - A \cos \phi} = \frac{2\pi}{(1 - A^2)^{1/2}} \qquad (|A| < 1)$$

3. Let m and M be the minimum and maximum values of u, respectively, on the circle $r = a$, $0 \leq \theta \leq 2\pi$. Using (6.6) and (6.8), obtain the inequality $m \leq u(r, \theta) \leq M$ for $0 \leq r \leq a$, $0 \leq \theta \leq 2\pi$.

4. By using (6.6), prove that if u is a nonnegative harmonic function for $r < a$; then u satisfies the Harnack's inequality

$$\frac{a - r}{a + r} u(0, 0) \le u(r, \theta) \le \frac{a + r}{a - r} u(0, 0)$$

5. By using Harnack's inequality, prove that if $u \ge 0$ is harmonic in the entire xy-plane, then u must be a constant.

6. Show that if the function f in (6.6) is odd with respect to y (that is, $f(2\pi - \theta) = -f(\theta)$), then (6.6) can be written as

$$u(r, \theta) = \int_0^\pi [K(a, r, \theta - \phi) - K(a, r, \theta + \phi)] f(\phi) \, d\phi$$

where $K(a, r, \theta - \phi)$ is defined by (6.7). Show that this solves the Dirichlet problem $\Delta u = 0$, $0 < r < a$, $0 < \theta < \pi$; $u(r, 0) = u(r, \pi) = 0$, $0 \le r \le a$; and $u(a, \theta) = f(\theta)$, $0 \le \theta \le \pi$.

7. Show that if the function f is even with respect to ϕ, then (6.6) can be written as

$$u(r, \theta) = \int_0^\pi [K(a, r, \theta - \phi) + K(a, r, \theta + \phi)] f(\phi) \, d\phi$$

which solves the Dirichlet problem for the semicircular domain $0 < r < a$, $0 < \theta < \pi$, satisfying the conditions: $u_\theta(r, 0) = u_\theta(r, \pi) = 0$, $0 \le r \le a$; $u(a, \theta) = f(\theta)$, $0 \le \theta \le \pi$.

8. Obtain from the result of Problem 6 an integral formula for the solution of the problem

$$\Delta u = 0 \qquad\qquad (0 < r < a, 0 < \theta < \pi/2)$$
$$u(r, 0) = u(r, \pi/2) = 0 \qquad\qquad (0 \le r \le a)$$
$$u(a, \theta) = f(\theta) \qquad\qquad (0 \le \theta \le \pi/2)$$

(See Problem 7, Exercises 7.4.)

9. Show that the exterior Dirichlet problem for a disk

$$\Delta u = 0 \qquad (r > a, 0 < \theta < 2\pi; u \text{ bounded as } r \text{ tends to } \infty)$$
$$u(a, \theta) = f(\theta) \qquad\qquad (0 \le \theta \le 2\pi)$$

has the solution

$$u(r, \theta) = \frac{-1}{2\pi} \int_{-\pi}^\pi \frac{(a^2 - r^2) f(\phi) \, d\phi}{a^2 - 2ar \cos(\theta - \phi) + r^2}$$

10. By multiplying both sides of equation (6.14) by $r \, dr$ and integrating from 0 to a, prove that the value of a harmonic function at the center of a disk is equal to the average value of the function on the disk. That is,

$$u(x, y) = \frac{1}{\pi a^2} \iint_D u(\xi, \eta) \, d\xi \, d\eta, \qquad D: (x - \xi)^2 + (y - \eta)^2 \le a^2$$

11. Let $S(x, y, z; a)$ denote a sphere with center (x, y, z) and radius a. For each point (ξ, η, ζ) within the sphere, introduce the spherical coordinates $\xi = x + r \sin \phi \cos \theta$, $\eta = y + r \sin \phi \sin \theta$, $\zeta = z + r \cos \phi$, $0 \leq \phi \leq \pi$, $0 \leq \theta \leq 2\pi$, $r \leq a$. Let u be a function defined on the sphere $S(x, y, z; a)$. The integral

$$U(x, y, z; a) = \frac{1}{4\pi a^2} \int_0^{2\pi} \int_0^{\pi} u(\xi, \eta, \zeta) a^2 \sin \phi \, d\phi \, d\theta$$

is called the mean value of u on the sphere S. Prove that if u is a harmonic function in the xyz-space, then $u(x, y, z) = U(x, y, z; a)$. (This is the mean-value property of harmonic functions in three-dimensional space.)

12. Let u be a continuous function of x, y, z, with continuous first- and second-order derivatives in a domain D. Prove that if u has the mean-value property stated in the preceding exercise, then u is harmonic in D.

7. Neumann Problem in a Disk

We now consider the Neumann problem

(7.1) $$u_{xx} + u_{yy} = 0 \quad \text{in } D, \quad \frac{\partial u}{\partial n} = f \quad \text{on } C$$

where D denotes the interior and C the boundary of the disk $x^2 + y^2 \leq a^2$. In polar coordinates (r, θ) this problem is transformed into

(7.2)
$$u_{rr} + \frac{1}{r} u_r + \frac{1}{r^2} u_{\theta\theta} = 0 \qquad (r < a)$$

$$\frac{\partial u}{\partial r} (a, \theta) = f(\theta) \qquad (0 \leq \theta \leq 2\pi)$$

We require the function f to satisfy the condition

(7.3) $$\int_0^{2\pi} f(\theta) \, d\theta = 0$$

which is necessary if the problem (7.2) is to have a solution.

As in Section 5, we assume a series solution of the form

(7.4) $$u(r, \theta) = \frac{\alpha_0}{2} + \sum_{n=1}^{\infty} r^n(\alpha_n \cos n\theta + \beta_n \sin n\theta)$$

Differentiating (7.4) with respect to r and applying the boundary condition in (7.2) for $r = a$, we find

(7.5)
$$f(\theta) = \sum_{n=1}^{\infty} na^{n-1}(\alpha_n \cos n\theta + \beta_n \sin n\theta)$$

$$= \sum_{n=1}^{\infty} (a_n \cos n\theta + b_n \sin n\theta)$$

where we have set $na^{n-1}\alpha_n = a_n$ and $na^{n-1}\beta_n = b_n$ for $n \geq 1$. This is precisely the Fourier series expansion of f on the interval $-\pi \leq \theta \leq \pi$, with its constant term a_0 being zero because of the condition (7.3). Therefore,

(7.6)

$$\alpha_n = \frac{1}{na^{n-1}\pi} \int_{-\pi}^{\pi} f(\theta) \cos n\theta \, d\theta$$

$$\beta_n = \frac{1}{na^{n-1}\pi} \int_{-\pi}^{\pi} f(\theta) \sin n\theta \, d\theta$$

where $n = 1, 2, \ldots$. Substituting these in (7.4), we obtain

$$u(r, \theta) = \frac{\alpha_0}{2} + \frac{a}{\pi} \sum_{n=1}^{\infty} \frac{1}{n} \left(\frac{r}{a}\right)^n \int_{-\pi}^{\pi} [\cos n\theta \cos n\phi + \sin n\theta \sin n\phi] f(\phi) \, d\phi$$

(7.7)

$$= \frac{\alpha_0}{2} + \frac{a}{\pi} \sum_{n=1}^{\infty} \frac{1}{n} \left(\frac{r}{a}\right)^n \int_{-\pi}^{\pi} f(\phi) \cos n(\theta - \phi) \, d\phi$$

$$= \frac{\alpha_0}{2} + \frac{a}{\pi} \int_{-\pi}^{\pi} \left[\sum_{n=1}^{\infty} \frac{1}{n} \left(\frac{r}{a}\right)^n \cos n(\theta - \phi)\right] f(\phi) \, d\phi$$

where α_0 remains an arbitrary constant. Notice that the interchange in the order of summation and integration in (7.7) is justified, since for $r < a$, the series

(7.8)

$$\sum_{n=1}^{\infty} \frac{1}{n} \left(\frac{r}{a}\right)^n \cos n(\theta - \phi)$$

converges uniformly with respect to ϕ.

We now calculate the sum of the series (7.8). From (6.5) we recall that, for $|\rho| < 1$,

$$\sum_{n=1}^{\infty} \rho^n \cos n\alpha = \frac{1 - \rho^2}{2(1 - 2\rho \cos \alpha + \rho^2)} - \frac{1}{2}$$

$$= \frac{\rho \cos \alpha - \rho^2}{(1 - 2\rho \cos \alpha + \rho^2)}$$

and hence

$$\sum_{n=1}^{\infty} \rho^{n-1} \cos n\alpha = \frac{\cos \alpha - \rho}{1 - 2\rho \cos \alpha + \rho^2}$$

The last series converges uniformly for $|\rho| < 1$ so that, by termwise integration, we find

$$\sum_{n=1}^{\infty} \frac{1}{n} \rho^n \cos n\alpha = \sum_{n=1}^{\infty} \cos n\alpha \int_0^{\rho} \zeta^{n-1} \, d\zeta$$

$$= \int_0^{\rho} \frac{(\cos \alpha - \zeta) \, d\zeta}{1 - 2\zeta \cos \alpha + \zeta^2}$$

$$= -\tfrac{1}{2} \ln(1 - 2\rho \cos \alpha + \rho^2) \qquad (|\rho| < 1)$$

Hence, the series (7.8) has the sum

(7.9) $\displaystyle\sum_{n=1}^{\infty} \frac{1}{n} \left(\frac{r}{a}\right)^n \cos n(\theta - \phi) = -\frac{1}{2} \ln \left[\frac{a^2 - 2ar \cos(\theta - \phi) + r^2}{a^2}\right]$

and the solution (7.7) becomes

(7.10) $\displaystyle u(r, \theta) = \frac{\alpha_0}{2} - \frac{a}{2\pi} \int_{-\pi}^{\pi} f(\phi) \ln[a^2 - 2ar \cos(\theta - \phi) + r^2]\, d\phi$

where we have used (7.3) to drop the factor $1/a^2$ in the argument of the logarithm.

When f is continuous and satisfies condition (7.3), formula (7.10) provides a solution of the Neumann problem (7.1), (see Problem 6). In accordance with Theorem 2.2 of this chapter, this solution is unique up to an additive constant $C = \alpha_0/2$.

Example 7.1.   Find the solution of the problem

$$\Delta u = 0 \qquad\qquad\qquad\qquad (r < 1)$$

$$\frac{\partial u}{\partial n} = \sin \theta \qquad\qquad\qquad (0 \le \theta \le 2\pi)$$

Solution: We note that

$$\int_0^{2\pi} \sin \theta \, d\theta = 0$$

so that condition (7.3) holds. From (7.6) we see that $\alpha_n = \beta_n = 0$ for $n \ge 1$, except $\beta_1 = 1$. Hence, by (7.4), the solution is

$$u(r, \theta) = r \sin \theta + C$$

where C is an arbitrary constant.

Example 7.2.   Find the solution of the problem

$$\Delta u = 0, \qquad x^2 + y^2 < 4$$

$$\frac{\partial u}{\partial n} = xy \text{ on } x^2 + y^2 = 4$$

Solution: In polar coordinates we note that the boundary condition becomes $(\partial u/\partial r)(2, \theta) = 2 \sin 2\theta$, for which condition (7.3) holds. From (7.6) it follows that the only nonzero coefficient in (7.4) is $\beta_2 = 1/2$. Hence, the solution is

$$u(r, \theta) = \frac{r^2}{2} \sin 2\theta + C$$

which, in rectangular coordinates, becomes $u(x, y) = xy + C$, with arbitrary constant C.

It is interesting to note that the Neumann problem in the xy-plane can be reduced to a Dirichlet problem by utilizing certain elementary results from the theory of complex variables. It is known that if v is a harmonic function in a simply connected domain D, there is another harmonic function u in D, called the harmonic conjugate of v, such that

$$(7.11) \qquad\qquad u_x = v_y, \qquad u_y = -v_x$$

These equations are known as the Cauchy-Riemann conditions for analytic functions. From (7.11) it follows that

$$du = \frac{\partial u}{\partial x}\,dx + \frac{\partial u}{\partial y}\,dy = \frac{\partial v}{\partial y}\,dx - \frac{\partial v}{\partial x}\,dy$$

Thus, if v is a harmonic function in a domain D, then its harmonic conjugate u is given by the line integral

$$(7.12) \qquad\qquad u(x, y) = \int_{(x_0,y_0)}^{(x,y)} \left(\frac{\partial v}{\partial \eta}\,d\xi - \frac{\partial v}{\partial \xi}\,d\eta \right)$$

along any path lying in D that joins an arbitrary point (x_0, y_0) to (x, y).

Now suppose that u is a solution of the Neumann problem

$$(7.13) \qquad\qquad \Delta u = 0 \quad \text{in } D, \quad \frac{\partial u}{\partial n} = f \quad \text{on } C$$

which is continuous together with its first derivatives in $D + C$. Since u is harmonic, we know that its harmonic conjugate v exists. Let the boundary C of D be given parametrically by the equations $x = x(s)$, $y = y(s)$, $0 \le s \le s_0$, where s denotes the arc length of C. By the Cauchy-Riemann conditions (7.11), we see that on C,

$$(7.14) \qquad \frac{\partial v}{\partial s} = \frac{\partial v}{\partial x}\frac{dx}{ds} + \frac{\partial v}{\partial y}\frac{dy}{ds} = \frac{-\partial u}{\partial y}\frac{dx}{ds} + \frac{\partial u}{\partial x}\frac{dy}{ds} = \frac{\partial u}{\partial n}$$

That is, the tangential derivative of v on C is equal to the normal derivative of u on C. Hence, the harmonic conjugate v of the solution of the problem (7.13) satisfies the equation

$$(7.15) \qquad\qquad \frac{\partial v}{\partial s} = f \quad \text{on } C$$

It follows that v is given on C by the formula

$$(7.16) \qquad\qquad v(x, y) = \int_{(x_0,y_0)}^{(x,y)} f\,ds = \phi(x, y)$$

with (x_0, y_0) being an arbitrary point on C. Thus, v is a solution of the Dirichlet problem

$$(7.17) \qquad\qquad \Delta v = 0 \quad \text{in } D, \quad v = \phi \quad \text{on } C$$

where ϕ is given by (7.16). Having found v from (7.17), we can then determine its harmonic conjugate u by (7.12). Because of (7.14) and (7.15), it follows that

u is a solution of the problem (7.13). As an illustration, we consider the next example.

Example 7.3. Solve the problem

$$\Delta u = 0 \qquad \text{in } x^2 + y^2 < a^2$$

$$\frac{\partial u}{\partial n} = x^2 - y^2 \qquad \text{on } x^2 + y^2 = a^2$$

by first reducing it to a Dirichlet problem.

Solution: In polar coordinates we see that on the circumference $r = a$, (7.16) gives

$$v(a, \theta) = \int_0^\theta a^2(\cos^2 \phi - \sin^2 \phi)a \, d\phi$$

$$= a^3 \int_0^\theta \cos 2\phi \, d\phi = \frac{a^3 \sin 2\theta}{2}$$

Therefore, the corresponding Dirichlet problem is

$$\Delta v = 0 \qquad \text{in } x^2 + y^2 < a^2$$

$$v(a, \theta) = \frac{a^3 \sin 2\theta}{2} \qquad \text{on } x^2 + y^2 = a^2$$

which, by (5.11), has the solution

$$v(r, \theta) = \frac{ar^2}{2} \sin 2\theta = axy$$

Hence, by (7.12), the solution of our original problem is

$$u(x, y) = \int^{(x,y)} (v_y \, dx - v_x \, dy)$$

$$= a \int^{(x,y)} (x \, dx - y \, dy) = \frac{a(x^2 - y^2)}{2} + C$$

where C is an arbitrary constant.

Exercises 7.6

1. State why the Neumann problem

$$\Delta u = 0 \qquad\qquad (r < 1)$$

$$\frac{\partial u}{\partial r} = \sin^2 \theta \qquad\qquad (0 \le \theta \le 2\pi)$$

does not have a solution. Does the problem

$$\Delta u = 1 \qquad\qquad (r < 1)$$

$$\frac{\partial u}{\partial r} = \sin^2 \theta \qquad\qquad (0 \le \theta \le 2\pi)$$

have a solution? If so, find the solution.

2. Solve the problem

$$\Delta u = 0 \qquad (r < 2)$$

$$\frac{\partial u}{\partial r} = 2 \sin^3 \theta \qquad (0 \leq \theta \leq 2\pi)$$

3. Solve the problem

$$\Delta u = 0 \qquad (r < 1)$$

$$\frac{\partial u}{\partial r} = \sin 2\theta \qquad (0 \leq \theta \leq 2\pi)$$

4. Find the solution of the problem

$$u_{xx} + u_{yy} = 0 \qquad (x^2 + y^2 < 4)$$

$$\frac{\partial u}{\partial n} = y^3 \qquad (x^2 + y^2 = 4)$$

5. Find the solution of the problem

$$u_{xx} + u_{yy} = 0 \qquad (x^2 + y^2 < 1)$$

$$\frac{\partial u}{\partial n} = x^3 - 3xy^2 \qquad (x^2 + y^2 = 1)$$

6. By differentiating (7.10) with respect to r within the integral sign, show that

$$\frac{\partial u}{\partial r} = \frac{a}{r} \int_{-\pi}^{\pi} K(a, r, \theta - \phi) f(\phi) \, d\phi$$

where K is the Poisson's kernel given in (6.7), and thus deduce that

$$\lim_{r \to a} \frac{\partial u}{\partial r} = f(\theta) \qquad (r < a)$$

7. (a) Let f be a periodic function such that $\int_{-\pi}^{\pi} f(\theta) \, d\theta = 0$. Define

$$F(\phi) = \int_{0}^{\phi} f(\theta) \, d\theta$$

Show that $F(\pi) - F(-\pi) = 0$.
(b) Replace $f(\phi)$ in (7.10) by $F'(\phi)$ and integrate by parts to show that (7.10) can be written as

$$u(r, \theta) = \frac{-a^2 r}{\pi} \int_{-\pi}^{\pi} \frac{F(\phi) \sin(\theta - \phi) \, d\phi}{a^2 - 2ar \cos(\theta - \phi) + r^2}$$

8. Find a solution of the exterior Neumann problem for a disk

$$\Delta u = 0 \qquad (r > a)$$

$$\frac{\partial u}{\partial r} = f(\theta)$$

$$(0 \leq \theta \leq 2\pi; \ u \text{ bounded as } r \to \infty)$$

9. Show that if the function f in (7.10) is odd with respect to y, then (7.10) can be written as

$$u(r, \theta) = \frac{-a}{2\pi} \int_0^\pi f(\phi) \ln \frac{a^2 - 2ar \cos(\theta - \phi) + r^2}{a^2 - 2ar \cos(\theta + \phi) + r^2} d\phi$$

which solves the mixed boundary value problem $\Delta u = 0$, $r < a$, $0 < \theta < \pi$; $u(r, 0) = u(r, \pi) = 0$; $\partial u/\partial r = f(\theta)$, $0 \le \theta \le \pi$, $r = a$.

10. Deduce from (7.10) the solution of the boundary value problem

$$\Delta u = 0 \qquad\qquad (r < a, 0 < \theta < \pi)$$
$$u_\theta(r, 0) = u_\theta(r, \pi) = 0$$
$$\frac{\partial u}{\partial r} = f(\theta) \qquad\qquad (0 \le \theta \le \pi, r = a)$$

where $\int_0^\pi f(\theta) \, d\theta = 0$.

8. Problems in Infinite Domains

In this section we shall consider boundary value problems for the Laplace's equation in an infinite domain of the xy-plane. We shall again use the method of Fourier transform, as we did in the case of the heat equation. We consider first the Dirichlet problem in the upper half-plane $y > 0$, namely,

(8.1)
$$u_{xx} + u_{yy} = 0 \qquad\qquad (-\infty < x < \infty, y > 0)$$
$$u(x, 0) = f(x) \qquad\qquad (-\infty < x < \infty)$$

We take the Fourier transform of the solution u with respect to the variable x, treating y as a parameter. Following the by-now familiar procedure, we assume that the problem (8.1) has a solution u that, together with its first- and second-order partial derivatives, is piecewise smooth and absolutely integrable on $-\infty < x < \infty$ for $y > 0$. Then the Fourier transform of u,

(8.2)
$$U(s, y) = \frac{1}{\sqrt{2\pi}} \int_{-\infty}^\infty u(x, y)e^{-isx} \, dx$$

exists and

(8.3)
$$u(x, y) = \frac{1}{\sqrt{2\pi}} \int_{-\infty}^\infty U(s, y)e^{isx} \, ds$$

Differentiating (8.2) under the integral sign twice with respect to y and using Laplace's equation, we obtain

$$U_{yy}(s, y) = \frac{1}{\sqrt{2\pi}} \int_{-\infty}^\infty u_{yy}(x, y)e^{-isx} \, dx$$

$$= \frac{-1}{\sqrt{2\pi}} \int_{-\infty}^\infty u_{xx}(x, y)e^{-isx} \, dx$$

As usual, we require that both u and u_x tend to zero as $|x| \to \infty$. Then integration by parts twice yields the equation

$$(8.4) \qquad U_{yy}(s, y) = s^2 U(s, y)$$

for the transform (8.2). This has the general solution

$$(8.5) \qquad U(s, y) = C_1(s)e^{-sy} + C_2(s)e^{sy}$$

involving two arbitrary functions C_1 and C_2. From the boundary condition in (8.1) we get one condition to be satisfied by (8.5). We therefore need another condition in order to be able to determine the functions C_1 and C_2 uniquely. A physically plausible condition is that our solution u be bounded as y becomes infinite. This requires (8.5) to be bounded for large values of y. Consequently, when $s > 0$, we must choose $C_2 = 0$ so that (8.5) becomes

$$(8.6) \qquad U(s, y) = C_1(s)e^{-sy} \qquad\qquad (s > 0)$$

Setting $y = 0$ in (8.2) and (8.6) and using the boundary condition given in (8.1), we see that

$$U(s, 0) = C_1(s) = F(s)$$

where F denotes the Fourier transform of f. Hence, when $s > 0$, (8.6) becomes

$$(8.7) \qquad U(s, y) = F(s)e^{-sy}$$

In the same manner, when $s < 0$, we find

$$(8.8) \qquad U(s, y) = F(s)e^{sy}$$

The formulas (8.7) and (8.8) can be jointly written as

$$(8.9) \qquad U(s, y) = F(s)e^{-|s|y}$$

for all values of s and $y \geq 0$. Substituting this in (8.3), we then obtain

$$(8.10) \qquad \begin{aligned} u(x, y) &= \frac{1}{\sqrt{2\pi}} \int_{-\infty}^{\infty} F(s)e^{isx - |s|y}\, ds \\ &= \frac{1}{2\pi} \int_{-\infty}^{\infty} f(\xi) \int_{-\infty}^{\infty} e^{is(x - \xi) - |s|y}\, ds\, d\xi \end{aligned}$$

where we have introduced the definition of $F(s)$ and formally interchanged the order of integrations. The inner integral with respect to s can be evaluated to give

$$(8.11) \qquad \begin{aligned} \int_{-\infty}^{\infty} e^{is(x - \xi) - |s|y}\, ds &= \int_{-\infty}^{0} e^{is(x - \xi) + sy}\, ds + \int_{0}^{\infty} e^{is(x - \xi) - sy}\, ds \\ &= \int_{0}^{\infty} e^{-is(x - \xi) - sy}\, ds + \int_{0}^{\infty} e^{is(x - \xi) - sy}\, ds \\ &= 2 \int_{0}^{\infty} e^{-sy} \cos s(x - \xi)\, ds \\ &= \frac{2y}{(x - \xi)^2 + y^2} \end{aligned}$$

Here we have observed that $2 \cos \alpha = e^{i\alpha} + e^{-i\alpha}$. Thus, (8.10) simplifies to

$$(8.12) \qquad u(x, y) = \frac{y}{\pi} \int_{-\infty}^{\infty} \frac{f(\xi) \, d\xi}{(x - \xi)^2 + y^2} \qquad (y > 0)$$

This is known as Poisson's integral formula for the half-plane $y > 0$.

Under the assumption that f is continuous and bounded for $-\infty < x < \infty$, it can be shown that the integral (8.12), together with its partial derivatives of any order taken under the integral sign, converges uniformly in x and y for $y \geq y_0$, $-1/y_0 \leq x \leq 1/y_0$ with any $y_0 > 0$. This means that u has continuous partial derivatives of all orders. By a straightforward calculation, it is readily shown that u satisfies Laplace's equation for $y > 0$. Moreover, by making the change of variable $x - \xi = y \tan t$, (8.12) becomes

$$u(x, y) = \frac{1}{\pi} \int_{-\pi/2}^{\pi/2} f(x - y \tan t) \, dt$$

which can be shown to have the limit

$$\lim_{y \to 0^+} u(x, y) = \lim_{y \to 0^+} \frac{1}{\pi} \int_{-\pi/2}^{\pi/2} f(x - y \tan t) \, dt$$

$$= f(x)$$

If we define u by (8.12) for $y > 0$ and $u(x, 0) = f(x)$ for $y = 0$, then u represents the unique bounded solution of the problem (8.1).

It should be pointed out that the requirement that u be bounded, which was imposed in the determination of (8.9), is an essential condition if the problem (8.1) is to have a unique solution. For we see that the function

$$v(x, y) = (e^y - e^{-y}) \sin x$$

which is unbounded for $y > 0$, satisfies Laplace's equation and vanishes at $y = 0$. Hence, the superposition of (8.12) and v is also a solution of the problem (8.1), and so the problem does not have a unique solution.

It is noteworthy that the problem (8.1) can also be solved by considering the Fourier sine transform of its solution with respect to the variable y. That is, we set

$$(8.13) \qquad U_s(x, s) = \left(\frac{2}{\pi} \right)^{\frac{1}{2}} \int_0^{\infty} u(x, y) \sin sy \, dy$$

Then, differentiating (8.13) twice with respect to x and using the differential equation together with the boundary condition in (8.1), we obtain

$$\frac{\partial^2 U_s}{\partial x^2}(x, s) = -\left(\frac{2}{\pi} \right)^{\frac{1}{2}} \int_0^{\infty} u_{yy}(x, y) \sin sy \, dy$$

$$= -\left(\frac{2}{\pi} \right)^{\frac{1}{2}} sf(x) - s^2 U_s(x, y)$$

Here we have assumed as usual that u and u_y vanish as $y \to \infty$. Thus, the transform U_s satisfies the equation

(8.14)
$$\frac{\partial^2 U_s}{\partial x^2} + s^2 U_s = - \left(\frac{2}{\pi}\right)^{\frac{1}{2}} sf(x)$$

Further, we assume that u is bounded for $|x| < \infty$, $0 < y < \infty$, and vanishes as $|x| \to \infty$. This requires that U_s satisfy the boundary condition

(8.15)
$$U_s(x, s) \to 0 \qquad \text{as } |x| \to \infty$$

Equation (8.14) together with the condition (8.15) constitutes a singular Sturm-Liouville problem. By the method of Section 2, Chapter 4, the Green's function (Problem 17, Exercises 4.2) for this problem is given by

$$G(x; \xi) = -\frac{1}{2s} e^{-s|x-\xi|}$$

Therefore,

$$U_s(x, s) = -\left(\frac{2}{\pi}\right)^{\frac{1}{2}} s \int_{-\infty}^{\infty} f(\xi)G(x; \xi) \, d\xi$$

$$= \frac{1}{\sqrt{2\pi}} \int_{-\infty}^{\infty} f(\xi)e^{-s|x-\xi|} \, d\xi$$

Substituting this in formula (8.8) of Chapter 5 for the inverse Fourier sine transform, we find

(8.16)
$$u(x, y) = \left(\frac{2}{\pi}\right)^{\frac{1}{2}} \int_0^{\infty} U_s(x, s) \sin sy \, ds$$

$$= \frac{1}{\pi} \int_{-\infty}^{\infty} f(\xi) \int_0^{\infty} e^{-s|x-\xi|} \sin sy \, ds \, d\xi$$

after an interchange in the order of integration. Since

$$\int_0^{\infty} e^{-st} \sin sy \, ds = \frac{y}{t^2 + y^2} \qquad\qquad (t > 0)$$

We see that (8.16) leads back to the solution (8.12).

Next, we consider the Dirichlet problem in a semi-infinite strip D; $0 < x < \infty$, $0 < y < b$; that is

(8.17)
$$\begin{aligned}
\Delta u &= 0 & &\text{in } D \\
u(x, 0) &= f(x) & &(x \geq 0) \\
u(x, b) &= 0 & &(x \geq 0) \\
u(0, y) &= 0 & &(0 \leq y \leq b)
\end{aligned}$$

where we require that u be bounded as $x \to \infty$. It is appropriate for this problem to use Fourier sine transform in the variable x, treating y as a parameter.

Thus, we set

(8.18) $$U_s(s, y) = \left(\frac{2}{\pi}\right)^{\frac{1}{2}} \int_0^\infty u(x, y) \sin sx \, dx \qquad (s > 0)$$

Then, differentiating (8.18) twice with respect to y and using the differential equation, we obtain

$$\frac{\partial^2 U_s}{\partial y^2} = -\left(\frac{2}{\pi}\right)^{\frac{1}{2}} \int_0^\infty u_{xx}(x, y) \sin sx \, dx$$

This leads to the differential equation for U_s,

(8.19) $$\frac{\partial^2 U_s}{\partial y^2} - s^2 U_s = 0$$

under the usual assumption that u and u_x vanish as $x \to \infty$. From the boundary conditions in (8.17), we have

(8.20) $$U_s(s, 0) = F_s(s), \qquad U_s(s, b) = 0$$

where $F_s(s)$ denotes the Fourier sine transform of $f(s)$.

Now equation (8.19) has the general solution

(8.21) $$U_s(s, y) = C_1(s)e^{sy} + C_2(s)e^{-sy}$$

which satisfies the second condition in (8.20) if we choose

$$C_1 = \frac{C(s)}{2} e^{-sb} \qquad \text{and} \qquad C_2 = -\frac{C(s)}{2} e^{sb}$$

for arbitrary function $C(s)$. Thus, (8.21) can be written as

(8.22) $$U_s(s, y) = C(s) \sinh s(b - y)$$

Using the first condition in (8.20), we readily see that

$$C(s) = \frac{F_s(s)}{\sinh sb}$$

and hence (8.22) becomes

(8.23) $$U_s(s, y) = F_s(s) \frac{\sinh s(b - y)}{\sinh sb}$$

By inverting (8.23), the solution of the problem (8.17) is therefore given by

(8.24) $$u(x, y) = \frac{2}{\pi} \int_0^\infty \frac{\sinh s(b - y)}{\sinh sb} \sin sx \int_0^\infty f(\xi) \sin \xi s \, d\xi \, ds$$

If the boundary conditions in (8.17) are such that the nonhomogeneous part is prescribed on the side $x = 0$, the solution can be obtained by the method described in Section 5 of Chapter 6. For example, suppose we wish to solve the problem

$$\Delta u = 0 \qquad\qquad (0 < x < \infty, 0 < y < b)$$

(8.25) $$u(x, 0) = u(x, b) = 0 \qquad\qquad (x \geq 0)$$

$$u(0, y) = g(y) \qquad\qquad (0 \leq y \leq b)$$

We observe that the method of separation of variables $u(x, y) = X(x)Y(y)$ leads to an eigenvalue problem for the function Y, whose eigenvalues are $\lambda_n = n^2\pi^2/b^2$; the corresponding eigenfunctions are $Y_n = \sin(n\pi/b)y$, $n = 1, 2, \ldots$. Accordingly, we assume a solution of the problem in the form

(8.26) $$u(x, y) = \sum_{n=1}^{\infty} B_n(x) \sin \frac{n\pi}{b} y$$

where

(8.27) $$B_n(x) = \frac{2}{b} \int_0^b u(x, y) \sin \frac{n\pi}{b} y \, dy$$

Then, differentiating (8.27) twice with respect to x and using the differential equation together with the homogeneous boundary conditions in (8.25), we obtain the equation

(8.28) $$B_n''(x) - \left(\frac{n\pi}{b}\right)^2 B_n(x) = 0$$

for the functions B_n. From the boundary conditions in (8.25) we have

(8.29) $$B_n(0) = \frac{2}{b} \int_0^b g(y) \sin \frac{n\pi}{b} y \, dy = b_n \qquad (n = 1, 2, \ldots)$$

which are the Fourier sine coefficients of g on $(0, b)$. Now equation (8.28) has the general solution

(8.30) $$B_n(x) = C_1(y)e^{-(n\pi/b)x} + C_2(y)e^{(n\pi/b)x}$$

In order that (8.26) is bounded as x tends to ∞, $B_n(x)$ must be bounded; hence, we choose $C_2 = 0$ in (8.30). By the condition (8.29) we thus see that $C_1 = b_n$. Therefore, the solution of the problem (8.19) is

(8.31) $$u(x, y) = \sum_{n=1}^{\infty} b_n e^{-(n\pi/b)x} \sin \frac{n\pi}{b} y$$

where the constants b_n are given by (8.29).

For example, when $g(y) = \sin y$ and $b = \pi$ in (8.19), we have the solution

$$u(x, y) = e^{-x} \sin y$$

In the case of the Neumann problem

$$\Delta u = 0 \qquad\qquad (-\infty < x < \infty, y > 0)$$

(8.32)

$$\frac{\partial u}{\partial y}(x, 0) = f(x) \qquad\qquad (-\infty < x < \infty)$$

in the half-plane, it is possible by a simple device to reduce the problem (8.32) to a Dirichlet problem and thereby obtain a solution. In fact, suppose u is a solution of (8.32). Let $v(x, y) = \partial u(x, y)/\partial y$. Then, clearly,

$$\Delta v(x, y) = \Delta u_y(x, y)$$

$$= \frac{\partial}{\partial y} \Delta u(x, y) = 0 \qquad\qquad (y > 0)$$

and

$$v(x, 0) = \frac{\partial u}{\partial y}(x, 0) = f(x) \qquad\qquad (-\infty < x < \infty)$$

so that v solves a Dirichlet problem in the half-plane, $y > 0$. Therefore, by (8.12), we have

(8.33) $$v(x, y) - \frac{y}{\pi} \int_{-\infty}^{\infty} \frac{f(\xi)\, d\xi}{(x - \xi)^2 + y^2} \qquad\qquad (y > 0)$$

and from the definition it follows that

(8.34)
$$u(x, y) = \int^y v(x, \eta)\, d\eta$$

$$= \int^y \frac{\eta}{\pi} \int_{-\infty}^{\infty} \frac{f(\xi)\, d\xi}{(x - \xi)^2 + \eta^2}\, d\eta$$

$$= \frac{1}{\pi} \int_{-\infty}^{\infty} f(\xi) \int^y \frac{\eta\, d\eta}{(x - \xi)^2 + \eta^2}\, d\xi$$

$$= \frac{1}{2\pi} \int_{-\infty}^{\infty} f(\xi) \ln[(x - \xi)^2 + y^2]\, d\xi$$

The interchange in the order of integration in (8.34) is valid in view of the fact that the integral (8.33) is uniformly convergent in y for $|y| \geq \varepsilon$, as we observed earlier in connection with (8.12).

Under the assumption that f is continuous and satisfies an order relation $|x^k f(x)| < M$ for $-\infty < x < \infty$, where $k > 1$ and M is a constant, it can be verified that (8.34) is a solution of the Neumann problem (8.32), which is unique up to an additive constant.

Exercises 7.7

1. Verify that

$$\frac{1}{\pi} \int_{-\infty}^{\infty} \frac{d\xi}{(x - \xi)^2 + y^2} = 1 \qquad (-\infty < x < \infty, 0 < y < \infty)$$

2. Show that if f is an odd function, formula (8.12) can be written as

$$u(x, y) = \frac{y}{\pi} \int_0^{\infty} \left(\frac{1}{(x - \xi)^2 + y^2} - \frac{1}{(x + \xi)^2 + y^2} \right) f(\xi)\, d\xi$$

which solves the Dirichlet problem $\Delta u = 0$ in the first quadrant $x > 0$, $y > 0$ with the boundary conditions: $u(0, y) = 0$, $y > 0$; $u(x, 0) = f(x)$, $x \geq 0$. In particular, when $f(x) = 1$ for $x > 0$ and $f(x) = -1$ for $x < 0$, show that $u = (2/\pi) \arctan(x/y)$.

3. Deduce from formula (8.12) the solution of the problem

$$\Delta u = 0 \qquad\qquad (x > 0, y > 0)$$
$$u_x(0, y) = 0 \qquad\qquad (y \geq 0)$$
$$u(x, 0) = f(x) \qquad\qquad (x \geq 0)$$

where f is bounded and continuous for $x \geq 0$.

4. By interchanging the role of x and y in (8.12), a solution formula for the Dirichlet problem $\Delta u = 0$ for the right half-plane $x > 0$, $-\infty < y < \infty$, with boundary condition $u(0, y) = f(y)$, $-\infty < y < \infty$, is obtained. As a special case of this formula, deduce the solution of the problem

$$\Delta u = 0 \qquad\qquad (x > 0, y > 0)$$
$$u(0, y) = f(y) \qquad\qquad (y \geq 0)$$
$$u(x, 0) = 0 \qquad\qquad (x \geq 0)$$

u bounded for $x \geq 0$, $y \geq 0$.

5. Find the solution of the Dirichlet problem

$$\Delta u = 0 \qquad\qquad (x > 0, y > 0)$$
$$u(x, 0) = f(x) \qquad\qquad (x \geq 0)$$
$$u(0, y) = g(y) \qquad\qquad (y \geq 0)$$

by assuming it is bounded for $x > 0$, $y > 0$.

6. Find the solution of the problem

$$\Delta u = 0 \qquad\qquad (0 < x < \infty, 0 < y < b)$$
$$u(0, y) = 0 \qquad\qquad (0 \leq y \leq b)$$
$$u_y(x, 0) = 0, \qquad u(x, b) = f(x) \qquad\qquad (x \geq 0)$$

u bounded as $x \to \infty$.

7. Solve the problem

$$\Delta u = 0 \qquad\qquad (x > 0, 0 < y < \pi)$$
$$u_x(0, y) = g(y) \qquad\qquad (0 \leq y \leq \pi)$$
$$u_y(x, 0) = u(x, \pi) = 0 \qquad\qquad (x \geq 0)$$

u bounded as $x \to \infty$.

8. Solve the problem

$$\Delta u = 0 \qquad\qquad (x > 0, 0 < y < \pi)$$
$$u_x(0, y) = 0 \qquad\qquad (0 \leq y \leq \pi)$$
$$u(x, 0) = 0, \qquad u_y(x, \pi) = f(x) \qquad\qquad (x > 0)$$

u bounded as $x \to \infty$.

9. Find the solution of the problem for sector

$$u_{rr} + \frac{1}{r} u_r + \frac{1}{r^2} u_{\theta\theta} = 0 \qquad\qquad (r < 1, 0 < \theta < b)$$

$$u_\theta(r, 0) = 0, \qquad u(r, b) = f(r) \qquad\qquad (0 \le r \le 1)$$

$$u(1, \theta) = 0 \qquad\qquad (0 \le \theta \le b)$$

by introducing the new variable $\xi = \ln(1/r)$, $\eta = \theta$. (See Exercises 7.2.)

10. Solve the problem

$$\Delta u - hu = 0 \qquad\qquad (x > 0, 0 < y < \pi)$$

$$u(0, y) = 0 \qquad\qquad (0 \le y \le \pi)$$

$$u(x, 0) = 0, \qquad u(x, \pi) = f(x) \qquad\qquad (x \ge 0)$$

u bounded as $x \to \infty$; h a positive constant.

11. Solve the problem

$$\Delta u - hu = 0 \qquad\qquad (x > 0, 0 < y < \pi)$$

$$u(0, y) = g(y) \qquad\qquad (0 \le y \le \pi)$$

$$u(x, 0) = u(x, \pi) = 0 \qquad\qquad (x \ge 0)$$

u bounded as $x \to \infty$; h a positive constant.

12. Deduce from (8.34) the solution formula

$$u(x, y) = \frac{1}{2\pi} \int_0^\infty \ln \frac{(x - \xi)^2 + y^2}{(x + \xi)^2 + y^2} f(\xi)\, d\xi$$

for the problem $\Delta u = 0$, $x > 0$, $y > 0$; $u(0, y) = 0$, $y \ge 0$; $u_y(x, 0) = f(x)$, $x \ge 0$.

13. Deduce from formula (8.34) a solution of the Neumann problem

$$\Delta u = 0 \qquad\qquad (x > 0, y > 0)$$

$$u_x(0, y) = 0 \qquad\qquad (y \ge 0)$$

$$u_y(x, 0) = f(x) \qquad\qquad (x \ge 0)$$

14. Find a solution of the mixed problem

$$\Delta u = 0 \qquad\qquad (x > 0, y > 0)$$

$$u(x, 0) = 0 \qquad\qquad (x \ge 0)$$

$$u_x(0, y) = g(y) \qquad\qquad (y \ge 0)$$

u bounded for $x \ge 0$, $y \ge 0$.

15. Solve the Neumann problem

$$\Delta u = 0 \qquad\qquad (x > 0, y > 0)$$

$$u_y(x, 0) = 0 \qquad\qquad (x \ge 0)$$

$$u_x(0, y) = g(y) \qquad\qquad (y \ge 0)$$

16. Find a solution of the Neumann problem

$$\Delta u = 0 \qquad\qquad (x > 0, y > 0)$$
$$u_x(0, y) = g(y) \qquad\qquad (y \geq 0)$$
$$u_y(x, 0) = f(x) \qquad\qquad (x \geq 0)$$

u bounded for $x \geq 0$, $y \geq 0$.

9. Fundamental Solution and Green's Function

Let (ξ, η) and (x, y) denote an arbitrary fixed point and a variable point, respectively, in the *xy*-plane. We recall that in polar coordinates with pole at (ξ, η), Laplace's equation takes the form

$$(9.1) \qquad \Delta u = \frac{\partial^2 u}{\partial r^2} + \frac{1}{r}\frac{\partial u}{\partial r} + \frac{1}{r^2}\frac{\partial^2 u}{\partial \theta^2} = 0$$

where

$$r = \sqrt{(x - \xi)^2 + (y - \eta)^2}$$

and

$$\theta = \tan^{-1}\frac{(y - \eta)}{(x - \xi)}$$

If *u* is a solution of (9.1) that depends only on *r*, then *u* satisfies the ordinary differential equation

$$(9.2) \qquad \frac{d^2 u}{dr^2} + \frac{1}{r}\frac{du}{dr} = \frac{1}{r}\frac{d}{dr}\left(r\frac{du}{dr}\right) = 0$$

Thus, *u* must be of the form

$$(9.3) \qquad u(r, \theta) = C_1 \ln r + C_2$$

where C_1 and C_2 are arbitrary constants. If we choose $C_1 = 1/2\pi$ and $C_2 = 0$, then the particular solution

$$(9.4) \qquad U(r, \theta) = \frac{1}{2\pi} \ln r$$

is called the fundamental solution of the two-dimensional Laplace's equation. The fundamental solution has the property of being harmonic throughout the *xy*-plane except at the pole (ξ, η), where it becomes logarithmically infinite. It is the simplest conceivable solution having this type of singularity at a point.

The essential role played by the fundamental solution (9.4) is that it leads to an integral formula that expresses the value of any harmonic function *u* inside a domain in terms of the values of *u* and its normal derivative $\partial u/\partial n$ on the boundary of the domain. This makes it possible for us to obtain explicit representations for the solutions of the Dirichlet problem and the Neumann problem in terms of kernel functions known as Green's function and Neumann's function, respectively.

Our basic tool is the Green's second identity

$$(9.5) \qquad \iint_D (u \, \Delta v - v \, \Delta u) \, dx \, dy = \int_C \left(u \, \frac{\partial v}{\partial n} - v \, \frac{\partial u}{\partial n} \right) ds$$

over a domain D with a smooth boundary C. The functions u and v together with their first- and second-order derivatives are assumed continuous in D. We shall take v in (9.5) to be the fundamental solution U with the pole (ξ, η) in D. Since U is singular at the pole, we delete from D a small disk about (ξ, η) with radius ε and boundary C_0 (Fig. 7.5).

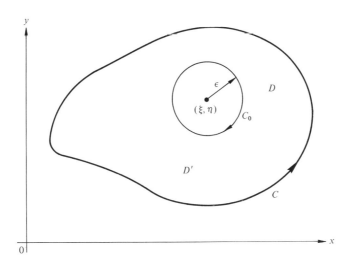

FIG. 7-5   *The fundamental solution.*

Applying (9.5) to the punctured domain D' bounded by C and C_0, and noting that $\Delta U = 0$ throughout D', we find

$$(9.6) \qquad -\iint_D (\ln r) \, \Delta u \, dx \, dy = \int_{C+C_0} \left[u \, \frac{\partial}{\partial n} (\ln r) - \ln r \, \frac{\partial u}{\partial n} \right] ds$$

where we have dropped the common factor $1/2\pi$. This relation holds for all values of ε no matter how small. We shall show that the integral along C_0 yields the value $-2\pi u(\xi, \eta)$ when ε is allowed to approach zero.

On C_0 we note that $r = \varepsilon = $ const and the outward normal vector is opposite in direction to the radius vector. Thus,

$$\frac{\partial}{\partial n} (\ln r) \bigg|_{r=\varepsilon} = -\frac{d}{dr} \ln r \bigg|_{r=\varepsilon} = -\frac{1}{\varepsilon}$$

so, by introducing polar coordinates, we see that

$$\lim_{\varepsilon \to 0} \int_{C_0} u \frac{\partial}{\partial n} (\ln r) \, ds = \lim_{\varepsilon \to 0} \int_0^{2\pi} u(\xi + \varepsilon \cos \theta, \eta + \varepsilon \sin \theta)$$

(9.7)

$$\cdot \left(-\frac{1}{\varepsilon} \right) \varepsilon \, d\theta$$

$$= -2\pi u(\xi, \eta)$$

Since the first derivatives of u are continuous in D, there is a constant M such that $\partial u / \partial n \leq M$ on C_0. Therefore,

(9.8)
$$\left| \int_{C_0} \frac{\partial u}{\partial n} \ln r \, ds \right| \leq M \int_0^{2\pi} |\ln \varepsilon| \, \varepsilon \, d\theta \leq 2\pi M \varepsilon \, |\ln \varepsilon|$$

which tends to zero with ε. Thus, letting ε approach zero in (9.6) and using (9.7) and (9.8), we obtain the integral formula

(9.9) $\quad u(\xi, \eta) = \dfrac{1}{2\pi} \displaystyle\int_C \left[u \frac{\partial}{\partial n} (\ln r) - \ln r \frac{\partial u}{\partial n} \right] ds + \dfrac{1}{2\pi} \iint_D (\Delta u) \ln r \, dx \, dy$

This expresses the value of u at any point in D in terms of the values of u and $\partial u / \partial n$ on the boundary C and of Δu in D. In particular, when $u = 1$, we obtain an important property of the fundamental solution, namely,

(9.10)
$$\frac{1}{2\pi} \int_C \frac{\partial}{\partial n} (\ln r) \, ds = 1$$

Formula (9.9) does not immediately yield a representation for the solution of the Dirichlet problem or the Neumann problem, since it involves the values of both u and its normal derivative $\partial u / \partial n$ on C. We shall therefore convert it into an integral formula from which it will be possible to eliminate u or $\partial u / \partial n$.

Let $g = g(x, y; \xi, \eta)$ be a function of (x, y) that depends on the pole (ξ, η) such that g is harmonic throughout the domain D. Applying (9.5) for the function u and g, we then have

(9.11)
$$\int_C \left(u \frac{\partial g}{\partial n} - g \frac{\partial u}{\partial n} \right) ds + \int_D g \, \Delta u \, dx \, dy = 0$$

Combining this with (9.9), we thus obtain

(9.12)
$$u(\xi, \eta) = \int_C \left(u \frac{\partial G}{\partial n} - G \frac{\partial u}{\partial n} \right) ds + \iint_D G \, \Delta u \, dx \, dy$$

where we have written $G = G(x, y; \xi, \eta)$ with

(9.13)
$$G(x, y; \xi, \eta) = \frac{1}{2\pi} \ln r + g(x, y; \xi, \eta)$$

Now, if the harmonic function g can be determined in such a way that G or $\partial G/\partial n$ vanishes on C, the term involving $\partial u/\partial n$ or u in (9.12) disappears, and the resulting formula yields a representation for the solution of the corresponding Dirichlet or Neumann problem.

We focus our attention here on the problem of determining the function g such that G vanishes on the boundary C of the domain D. It is clear that if g is a solution of the boundary value problem

(9.14)
$$\frac{\partial^2 g}{\partial x^2} + \frac{\partial^2 g}{\partial y^2} = 0 \quad \text{in } D$$

$$g(x, y; \xi, \eta) = \frac{-1}{2\pi} \ln r \quad \text{on } C$$

for each point (ξ, η) in D, then the function G defined by (9.13) vanishes when (x, y) lies on C. Thus, we obtain from (9.12) the specific representation formula

(9.15)
$$u(\xi, \eta) = \int_C u(x, y) \frac{\partial G}{\partial n}(x, y; \xi, \eta)\, ds + \iint_D G(x, y; \xi, \eta)\, \Delta u\, dx\, dy$$

for the solution u of the Dirichlet problem

(9.16)
$$\Delta u = q(x, y) \quad \text{in } D, \quad u = f(x, y) \quad \text{on } C$$

in terms of the function (9.13) and its normal derivative on the boundary.

Let us state our result as a theorem.

THEOREM 9.1. *If u denotes the solution of the problem (9.16), then u has the representation*

(9.17)
$$u(x, y) = \int_C f(\xi, \eta) \frac{\partial G}{\partial n}(\xi, \eta; x, y)\, ds$$

$$+ \iint_D q(\xi, \eta) G(\xi, \eta; x, y)\, d\xi\, d\eta$$

where G is the function defined by (9.13) and (9.14) with the role of (x, y) and (ξ, η) interchanged.

The function G defined by (9.13) and (9.14) is called the Green's function. It is clear that the Green's function, whenever it exists for a given domain, is uniquely determined. This follows from the uniqueness of the function g as a solution of (9.14), which is a Dirichlet problem. It might also be seen from the fact that if G_1 and G_2 are two distinct Green's functions for a given domain, then their difference $G_1 - G_2$ is a harmonic function throughout that domain which vanishes on the boundary, and so, by the maximum principle, must vanish identically.

Let us note the following important properties that characterize the Green's function G:

(i) For each (ξ, η) in D, G satisfies the Laplace's equation

$$\frac{\partial^2 G}{\partial x^2} + \frac{\partial^2 G}{\partial y^2} = 0 \qquad \text{for all } (x, y) \text{ in } D$$

except at (ξ, η).

(9.18)

(ii) $G(x, y; \xi, \eta) = 0$ when (x, y) lies on the boundary C.

(iii) G has a logarithmic singularity at (ξ, η) such that

$$\int_c \frac{\partial G}{\partial n} \, ds = 1$$

(iv) G is symmetric with respect to the points (x, y) and (ξ, η); that is,

$$G(\xi, \eta; x, y) = G(x, y; \xi, \eta)$$

The first two of these properties clearly follow from the definition of the Green's function. The third property is a consequence of (9.10) and (2.11), g being harmonic in D. The last of the properties can be proved by setting

$$u(x, y) = G(x, y: \xi, \eta), \qquad v(x, y) = G(x, y; \zeta, \tau)$$

in Green's second identity (9.5) over the domain D' bounded by C, C_1, and C_2, where C_1 and C_2 are small circles of radius ε about the poles (ξ, η) and (ζ, τ), Figure 7.6. We note that since $\Delta u = 0$ and $\Delta v = 0$ in D', and u and v vanish on C, (9.5) yields

(9.19) $$\int_{C_1} \left(u \frac{\partial v}{\partial n} - v \frac{\partial u}{\partial n} \right) ds + \int_{C_2} \left(u \frac{\partial v}{\partial n} - v \frac{\partial u}{\partial n} \right) ds = 0$$

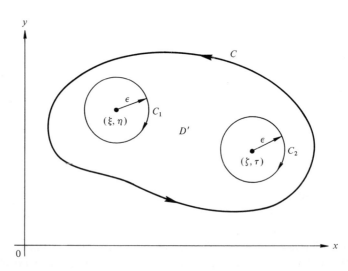

FIG. 7–6 *Proof of symmetry of the Green's function.*

By using the definition (9.13) together with (2.11), and by a calculation quite like our derivation of (9.9), we see that

(9.20)
$$\lim_{\varepsilon \to 0} \int_{C_1} \left(u \frac{\partial v}{\partial n} - v \frac{\partial u}{\partial n} \right) ds = v(\xi, \eta)$$

$$\lim_{\varepsilon \to 0} \int_{C_2} \left(u \frac{\partial v}{\partial n} - v \frac{\partial u}{\partial n} \right) ds = -u(\zeta, \tau)$$

Thus, from (9.19), we have $u(\zeta, \tau) = v(\xi, \eta)$, or $G(\zeta, \tau; \xi, \eta) = G(\xi, \eta; \zeta, \tau)$.

10. Examples of Green's Functions

In this section we shall present examples of Green's functions for the Laplace's equation for special domains in the xy-plane. We determine first the Green's function for the interior D of the disk (Fig. 7.7),

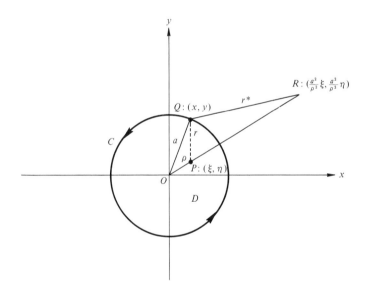

FIG. 7-7   *Inverse points with respect to a circle.*

(10.1) $$x^2 + y^2 \leq a^2$$

Let $P: (\xi, \eta)$ denote the pole of the Green's function $G = G(x, y; \xi, \eta)$ in D, with $Q: (x, y)$ being a variable point, and let

$$r = \sqrt{(x - \xi)^2 + (y - \eta)^2}$$

denote the distance of the point Q from the pole P. We wish to determine a function $g = g(x, y; \xi, \eta)$, which is harmonic throughout D and which assumes the value $-(1/2\pi) \ln r$ when $x^2 + y^2 = a^2$. If $(\xi, \eta) = (0, 0)$, then clearly $g = (-1/2\pi) \ln a$ fulfills the requirement. Hence, by (9.13), the Green's function for the disk (10.1) with pole at (0, 0) is given by

$$G(x, y; 0, 0) = \frac{1}{2\pi} \ln r - \frac{1}{2\pi} \ln a$$

(10.2)

$$= \frac{1}{2\pi} \ln \frac{r}{a} \qquad\qquad (r = \sqrt{x^2 + y^2})$$

Suppose now that $(\xi, \eta) \neq (0, 0)$ and denote by $\rho = \sqrt{\xi^2 + \eta^2}$, the distance of the pole P from the center of the disk. Let

$$R: \left(\frac{a^2}{\rho^2} \xi, \frac{a^2}{\rho^2} \eta \right)$$

denote the inverse of the point P with respect to the circle $C: x^2 + y^2 = a^2$ (that is, $OP \cdot OR = a^2$ with P and R lying on the same line from O). When the point Q is located on the circle C, we see that the triangles OPQ and OQR are similar. This is true because the two triangles have an angle at O in common, and the corresponding sides forming that angle are proportional; that is,

$$\frac{\overline{OP}}{\overline{OQ}} = \frac{\overline{OQ}}{\overline{OR}} \qquad\qquad (\overline{OQ} = a)$$

in view of the relation $\overline{OP} \cdot \overline{OR} = a^2$. Hence,

$$\frac{\overline{PQ}}{\overline{QR}} = \frac{\overline{OP}}{a} = \frac{a}{\overline{OR}}$$

from which we obtain

(10.3)
$$\overline{PQ} = \frac{\overline{OP}}{a} \cdot \overline{QR} = \frac{a}{\overline{OR}} \cdot \overline{QR}$$

Thus,

(10.4)
$$r = \frac{\rho}{a} \left[\left(x - \frac{a^2}{\rho^2} \xi \right)^2 + \left(y - \frac{a^2}{\rho^2} \eta \right)^2 \right]^{1/2}$$

whenever $x^2 + y^2 = a^2$.

Now consider the function

(10.5)
$$g(x, y; \xi, \eta) = -\frac{1}{2\pi} \ln \frac{\rho}{a} \left[\left(x - \frac{a^2}{\rho^2} \xi \right)^2 + \left(y - \frac{a^2}{\rho^2} \eta \right)^2 \right]^{1/2}$$

It is easily verified by direct differentiation that this function satisfies the Laplace's equation for all (x, y) in D. Moreover, in view of (10.4), the function assumes the value $-(1/2\pi) \ln r$ whenever (x, y) lies on the boundary C of D. Hence, (10.5) is the solution of the Dirichlet problem (9.14) for the disk (10.1).

By (9.13) the Green's function for the disk (10.1) is therefore given by

(10.6) $$G(x, y; \xi, \eta) = \frac{1}{2\pi} \ln r - \frac{1}{2\pi} \ln \frac{\rho}{a} r^* = \frac{1}{2\pi} \ln \frac{ar}{\rho r^*}$$

where we have written

(10.7) $$r^* = \left[\left(x - \frac{a^2}{\rho^2}\xi\right)^2 + \left(y - \frac{a^2}{\rho^2}\eta\right)^2\right]^{1/2}$$

Since we have found the Green's function, the solution of the nonhomogeneous Dirichlet problem (9.16) for any disk is now immediate, by Theorem 9.1. In particular, when $q = 0$, we have

(10.8) $$u(x, y) = \int_C f(\xi, \eta) \frac{\partial G}{\partial n} (\xi, \eta; x, y) \, ds$$

where we have interchanged the role of (x, y) and (ξ, η) in (10.6). Let us show that this agrees with the Poisson's integral formula (6.6), which was previously obtained in Section 6. We have to calculate the normal derivative of the Green's function (10.6) for $\xi^2 + \eta^2 = a^2$. For this purpose, it is convenient to introduce polar coordinates to describe the points (x, y) and (ξ, η). Thus, let $x = \rho \cos \theta$, $y = \rho \sin \theta$, and $\xi = v \cos \phi$, $\eta = v \sin \phi$. Then

$$r^2 = (\xi - x)^2 + (\eta - y)^2$$
$$= v^2 - 2\rho v \cos (\phi - \theta) + \rho^2$$

(10.9) $$r^{*2} = \left(\xi - \frac{a^2}{\rho^2}x\right)^2 + \left(\eta - \frac{a^2}{\rho^2}y\right)^2$$
$$= v^2 - 2\frac{a^2 v}{\rho} \cos (\phi - \theta) + \frac{a^4}{\rho^2}$$

Since the outward normal derivative of a function on a circle coincides with the derivative in the radial direction, it follows from (10.6) and (10.9) that

$$\frac{\partial G}{\partial n} (v, \phi; \rho, \theta) = \frac{1}{2\pi} \left[\frac{\partial}{\partial v} (\ln r) - \frac{\partial}{\partial v} (\ln r^*)\right]$$

$$= \frac{1}{4\pi} \left[\frac{\partial}{\partial v} (\ln r^2) - \frac{\partial}{\partial v} (\ln r^{*2})\right]$$

(10.10)

$$= \frac{1}{4\pi} \left[\frac{1}{r^2} \frac{\partial r^2}{\partial v} - \frac{1}{r^{*2}} \frac{\partial r^{*2}}{\partial v}\right]$$

$$= \frac{1}{2\pi} \left[\frac{v - \rho \cos(\phi - \theta)}{r^2} - \frac{v - (a^2/\rho) \cos(\phi - \theta)}{r^{*2}}\right]$$

This yields

(10.11) $$\frac{\partial G}{\partial n} (a, \phi; \rho, \theta) = \frac{1}{2\pi a} \frac{a^2 - \rho^2}{a^2 - 2a\rho \cos(\phi - \theta) + \rho^2}$$

upon setting $v = a$ and noting that $r^* = (ar)/\rho$. Substituting this result in (10.8) and noting that $ds = a\,d\phi$, we indeed obtain the Poisson's integral formula (6.6).

We take up next the determination of the Green's function for Laplace's operator for the half-plane $y > 0$ (Fig. 7.8). Again let $P: (\xi, \eta)$ denote the

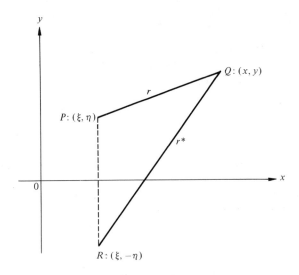

FIG. 7–8   *Green's function in the half-plane $y > 0$.*

pole of the Green's function in the half-plane $y > 0$ and let $Q: (x, y)$, $y > 0$, be any point whose distance from the pole is denoted by r. Consider the reflected image $R: (\xi, -\eta)$ of the point P with respect to the x-axis. It is clear that when Q is located on the boundary $y = 0$ of the half-plane $y \geq 0$, Q is equidistant from P and R. Thus, we take

(10.12)
$$g(x, y; \xi, \eta) = \frac{-1}{2\pi} \ln r^*$$

where

(10.13)
$$r^* = \sqrt{(x - \xi)^2 + (y + \eta)^2}$$

Clearly, this function is harmonic for all (x, y) in the half-plane $y \geq 0$ and reduces to $-(1/2\pi) \ln r$ on $y = 0$. Therefore, the Green's function for the half-plane $y \geq 0$ is given by

(10.14)
$$G(x, y; \xi, \eta) = \frac{1}{2\pi} \ln r - \frac{1}{2\pi} \ln r^* = \frac{1}{2\pi} \ln \frac{r}{r^*}$$

Thus, we can formally state the following theorem, which corresponds to Theorem 9.1.

THEOREM 10.1. *If u denotes the solution of the Dirichlet problem*

(10.15)
$$\Delta u = q(x, y) \qquad (-\infty < x < \infty, y > 0)$$
$$u(x, 0) = f(x) \qquad (-\infty < x < \infty)$$

then u has the representation

$$u(x, y) = -\int_{-\infty}^{\infty} f(\xi) \frac{\partial G}{\partial \eta} (\xi, 0; x, y) \, d\xi$$

(10.16)
$$+ \int_{0}^{\infty} \int_{-\infty}^{\infty} q(\xi, \eta) G(\xi, \eta; x, y) \, d\xi \, d\eta$$

$$= \frac{y}{\pi} \int_{-\infty}^{\infty} \frac{f(\xi) \, d\xi}{(\xi - x)^2 + y^2}$$

$$+ \int_{0}^{\infty} \int_{-\infty}^{\infty} q(\xi, \eta) G(\xi, \eta; x, y) \, d\xi \, d\eta$$

where G is the Green's function (10.14).

   When $q = 0$, (10.16) leads back to the Poisson's integral formula (8.12) for the half-plane $y > 0$.

Exercises 7.8

1. Establish the results given in (9.20).
2. Verify that the function g defined in (10.5) satisfies Laplace's equation in the variables x and y.
3. Verify directly that the Green's function (10.6) is symmetric with respect to the point (x, y) and the pole (ξ, η).
4. Show that by introducing the polar coordinates $x = v \cos \theta$, $y = v \sin \theta$ and $\xi = \rho \cos \phi$, $\eta = \rho \sin \phi$, the Green's function (10.6) takes the form

$$G(v, \theta; \rho, \phi) = \frac{1}{4\pi} \ln \frac{a^2(v^2 - 2v\rho \cos(\theta - \phi) + \rho^2)}{(a^4 - 2a^2 v\rho \cos(\theta - \phi) + v^2\rho^2)}$$

    and thus verify that $G = 0$ when $v = a$.
5. Determine the harmonic function (10.5) by actually solving the Dirichlet problem

$$\frac{\partial^2 g}{\partial v^2} + \frac{1}{v} \frac{\partial g}{\partial v} + \frac{1}{v^2} \frac{\partial^2 g}{\partial \theta^2} = 0 \qquad (v < a)$$

$$g(a, \theta; \rho, \phi) = -\frac{1}{4\pi} \ln [a^2 - 2a\rho \cos(\theta - \phi) + \rho^2] \qquad (v = a)$$

    for fixed ρ and ϕ. *Hint:* Assume a solution g analogous to (5.8) and use the series (7.9) for the boundary data.

6. Let $G(v, \theta; \rho, \phi)$ and $G(v, \theta; \rho, -\phi)$ be the Green's functions for a disk of radius a with poles at the points (ρ, ϕ) and $(\rho, -\phi)$, respectively. Show that

$$G^*(v, \theta; \rho, \phi) = G(v, \theta; \rho, \phi) - G(v, \theta; \rho, -\phi)$$

   is the Green's function for the semicircular domain $r \leq a, 0 \leq \theta \leq \pi$. What is the harmonic function $g(v, \theta; \rho, \phi)$ in this case?

7. By using the Green's function G^* obtained in Problem 6, and by a similar procedure, obtain the Green's function for the quarter-disk $0 \leq r \leq a, 0 \leq \theta \leq \pi/2$.

8. Find the Green's function for the sector $0 \leq r \leq a, 0 \leq \theta \leq \pi/3$. *Hint:* Let $v' = r^3, \theta' = 3\theta$, and use the results of Problem 6.

9. Prove that the Green's function $G(\rho, \phi; v, \theta)$ satisfies the relation

$$\frac{a^2 - v^2}{4} = \int_0^{2\pi} \int_0^a G(\rho, \phi; v, \theta)\rho \, d\rho \, d\phi$$

   Hint: Take $f = 0$ and $q = 1$ in (9.16) and obtain a solution by inspection; then use (9.17).

10. Determine the harmonic function (10.12) by actually solving the Dirichlet problem

$$\Delta g = 0 \qquad\qquad (y > 0, -\infty < x < \infty)$$

$$g(x, y; \xi, \eta) = -\frac{1}{4\pi} \ln[(x - \xi)^2 + \eta^2] \qquad\qquad (y = 0)$$

   for each fixed $(\xi, \eta), \eta > 0$.

11. By a procedure similar to that used in Problem 6, find the Green's function for the quadrant $x \geq 0, y \geq 0$.

11. Neumann's Function and Examples

In Section 9 of the present chapter we obtained from the basic formula (9.12) an explicit representation for the solution of the Dirichlet problem (9.16) in terms of the normal derivative of the Green's function (9.13). In this section we shall derive from (9.12) a similar representation formula for the solution of the nonhomogeneous Neumann problem

(11.1) $\Delta u = q(x, y)$ in D, $\dfrac{\partial u}{\partial n} = f(x, y)$ on C

Let us rewrite (9.12) in different notation as

(11.2) $u(\xi, \eta) = \displaystyle\int_C \left(u \frac{\partial H}{\partial n} - H \frac{\partial u}{\partial n}\right) ds + \iint_\Delta \Delta u H \, dx \, dy$

where

(11.3) $H(x, y; \xi, \eta) = \dfrac{1}{2\pi} \ln r + h(x, y; \xi, \eta)$

with h being an arbitrary harmonic function throughout D. In order for (11.2) to represent a solution of the problem (11.1), it seemed natural to choose the function h so that $\partial H/\partial n$ vanishes on C, thus eliminating from (11.2) the term that involves the values of u on the boundary C. This would mean that h is a solution of the special Neumann problem

$$\Delta h = 0 \quad \text{in } D$$

$$\frac{\partial h}{\partial n} = -\frac{1}{2\pi}\frac{\partial}{\partial n}(\ln r) \quad \text{on } C$$

But this problem cannot have a solution because, by (9.10),

$$\int_C \frac{\partial h}{\partial n}\, ds = -1$$

which violates the necessary condition (2.12) for solvability of the Neumann problem.

Let us determine h so that $\partial H/\partial n = $ const on C; say, $\partial H/\partial n = b \neq 0$. Then, from (11.3), we have

$$\int_C \frac{\partial H}{\partial n}\, ds = \frac{1}{2\pi}\int_C \frac{\partial}{\partial n}(\ln r)\, ds + \int_C \frac{\partial h}{\partial n}\, ds$$

which, by (9.10) and (2.11), yields

$$b\int_C ds = 1$$

This implies that

(11.4) $$b = \frac{1}{L}$$

where L denotes the perimeter of the domain D. This means that we must determine h as a solution of the Neumann problem

(11.5)
$$\Delta h = 0 \quad \text{in } D$$

$$\frac{\partial h}{\partial n} = \frac{1}{L} - \frac{1}{2\pi}\frac{\partial}{\partial n}(\ln r) \quad \text{on } C$$

Notice that here the condition (2.12) is satisfied. So, if the function h in (11.3) is a solution of (11.5), then substitution of (11.3) in (11.2) yields the specific representation

(11.6)
$$u(\xi, \eta) = -\int_C H(x, y; \xi, \eta)\frac{\partial u}{\partial n}\, ds$$
$$+ \iint_D H(x, y; \xi, \eta)\, \Delta u\, dx\, dy + \frac{1}{L}\int_C u\, ds$$

for a solution of the Neumann problem (11.1). The last term on the right of (11.6) is simply an additive constant, representing the average value $\bar{u}$ of the solution. Thus, we have the following representation theorem for (11.1).

THEOREM 11.1. *Let u denote a solution of the nonhomogeneous Neumann problem (11.1) for which the compatibility condition (2.13) holds. Then u has the representation*

(11.7)
$$u(x, y) = - \int_C H(\xi, \eta; x, y) f(\xi, \eta) \, ds$$
$$+ \iint_D q(\xi, \eta) H(\xi, \eta; x, y) \, d\xi \, d\eta + \bar{u}$$

where H is defined by (11.3) and (11.5) with the role of (x, y) and (ξ, η) interchanged, and where $\bar{u}$ is an arbitrary constant equal to the average value of u.

The function H defined by (11.3) and (11.5) is called a Neumann's function for the Laplace's equation. Unlike the Green's function, a Neumann's function is unique up to an additive constant. This is due to the fact that a solution of (11.5) is uniquely determined up to an additive constant. However, if we choose the additive constant in such a way that the normalization condition

(11.8)
$$\int_C H(x, y; \xi, \eta) \, ds = 0$$

holds, then H becomes uniquely determined. In this discussion we shall assume that our Neumann's function satisfies (11.8).

It is of interest to note the following characteristic properties of the Neumann's function:

    (i) H satisfies Laplace's equation for all (x, y) in D, except at (ξ, η).

    (ii) $\partial H / \partial n = 1/L$ on C, where L is the perimeter of D.

    (iii) H has a logarithmic singularity at (ξ, η) such that

(11.9)
$$\int_C \frac{\partial H}{\partial n} \, ds = 1$$

    (iv) H is symmetric with respect to the points (x, y) and (ξ, η); that is, $H(x, y; \xi, \eta) = H(\xi, \eta; x, y)$.

The symmetric property (iv) can be established with the help of (11.8) in exactly the same manner we established the symmetry of the Green's function, and is therefore left as an exercise (Problem 1).

Let us now consider the construction of the Neumann's function (11.3) for the interior of the disk $x^2 + y^2 \leq a^2$. Using the same notation as in (10.6) we set

(11.10)
$$H(x, y; \xi, \eta) = \frac{1}{2\pi} \ln r + \frac{1}{2\pi} \ln r^* + A(\xi, \eta)$$

where A is a harmonic function. It is clear that the function (11.10) is harmonic in the interior of the disk for all points (x, y) except at the pole (ξ, η). Moreover, from the calculation in (10.10), we readily verify that when (x, y) lies on the circumference of the disk, we have

$$\frac{\partial H}{\partial n}(x, y; \xi, \eta) = \frac{1}{2\pi a} = \frac{1}{L}$$

Thus, the first three properties listed for the Neumann's function are fulfilled. To ensure symmetry of the Neumann's function, we have introduced the harmonic function $A(\xi, \eta)$ in (11.10). The function A will be determined by requiring (11.10) to satisfy the normalization condition (11.8). In this way, we shall also have ensured uniqueness of our Neumann's function.

Thus, applying (11.8) to (11.10) and noting that on the circumference C of the disk, $r = \rho r^*/a$, we have

(11.11)
$$\int_C H(x, y; \xi, \eta)\, ds = \frac{1}{2\pi} \int_C (\ln rr^* + 2\pi A)\, ds$$
$$= \frac{1}{2\pi} \int_C \left(\ln \frac{\rho}{a} r^{*2} + 2\pi A \right) ds$$
$$= 0$$

Now the integrand in the last integral of (11.11) is a harmonic function of (x, y) throughout the disk. Hence, by the mean-value property of harmonic function (Theorem 6.1), the integral in (11.11) is equal to the value of the integrand at the center $(x, y) = (0, 0)$ of the disk. Thus, we find

$$\ln \frac{\rho}{a} \frac{a^4}{\rho^4} (\xi^2 + \eta^2) + 2\pi A = 0$$

or

(11.12)
$$A(\xi, \eta) = \frac{1}{2\pi} \ln \frac{\rho}{a^3}$$

Therefore, our Neumann's function for the disk $x^2 + y^2 \leq a^2$ is

(11.13)
$$H(x, y; \xi, \eta) = \frac{1}{2\pi} \left[\ln r + \ln r^* + \ln \frac{\rho}{a^3} \right]$$
$$= \frac{1}{2\pi} \ln \frac{rr^*\rho}{a^3}$$

where $r = [(x - \xi)^2 + (y - \eta)^2]^{1/2}$,

$$r^* = \left[\left(x - \frac{a^2}{\rho^2} \xi \right)^2 + \left(y - \frac{a^2}{\rho^2} \eta \right)^2 \right]^{1/2}$$

and $\rho = (\xi^2 + \eta^2)^{1/2}$. Thus, a solution of the Neumann problem (11.1) for a disk is immediately known by Theorem 11.1. In the particular case where $q = 0$, it is easily shown that, in polar coordinates,

$$(11.14) \qquad u(x, y) = - \int_C H(\xi, \eta; x, y)f(\xi, \eta) \, ds$$

where H is given by (11.13) with the role of (x, y) and (ξ, η) interchanged, agrees with formula (7.10) previously obtained.

Neumann's function for the half-plane $y > 0$ is given by

$$(11.15) \qquad H(x, y; \xi, \eta) = \frac{1}{2\pi} [\ln r + \ln r^*] = \frac{1}{2\pi} \ln rr^*$$

where we have used the same notation as in (10.14). Clearly, this function is harmonic throughout the upper half-plane except at the pole (ξ, η). Moreover, $\partial H/\partial y = 0$, as to be expected, since the boundary here is of infinite length. The function (11.15) is unique up to an additive constant. Thus, a solution of the nonhomogeneous Neumann problem

$$(11.16) \qquad \begin{aligned} \Delta u &= q(x, y) & (-\infty < x < \infty, \, y > 0) \\ \frac{\partial u}{\partial y} &= f(x) & (-\infty < x < \infty) \end{aligned}$$

has the representation

$$(11.17) \qquad \begin{aligned} u(x, y) &= \frac{1}{2\pi} \int_{-\infty}^{\infty} f(\xi) \ln[(x - \xi)^2 + y^2] \, d\xi \\ &+ \frac{1}{2\pi} \int_0^{\infty} \int_{-\infty}^{\infty} \ln(rr^*)q(\xi, \eta) \, d\xi \, d\eta + C \end{aligned}$$

where C is an arbitrary constant. When $q = 0$, this formula reduces to (8.34).

Exercises 7.9

1. Show that the Neumann's function (11.3) satisfying the normalization condition (11.8) is symmetric with respect to the points (x, y) and (ξ, η).

2. Verify that the function (11.10) satisfies the relation

$$\frac{\partial H}{\partial n}(x, y; \xi, \eta) = \frac{1}{2\pi a}$$

   when $x^2 + y^2 = a^2$.

3. Verify directly that the Neumann's function (11.13) for a disk is symmetric with respect to (x, y) and (ξ, η).

4. Introduce the polar coordinates $x = v \cos \theta$, $y = v \sin \theta$ and $\xi = \rho \cos \phi$, $\eta = \rho \sin \phi$, and show that the formula (11.14) agrees with (7.10) except for an additive constant.

5. Show that the Neumann's function (11.13) satisfies the relation

$$\frac{\partial H}{\partial a} = \frac{1}{2\pi a} [K(a, \rho, \theta - \phi) - 1]$$

where K is the Poisson's kernel given in (6.7).

6. Find a Neumann's function for the quadrant $x > 0$, $y > 0$.

Some Selected References

1. Berg, P., and J. L. McGregor. 1966. *Elementary Partial Differential Equations.* San Francisco: Holden-Day, Inc.
2. Boyce, W. E., and R. DiPrima. 1969. *Elementary Differential Equations and Boundary Value Problems.* New York: John Wiley & Sons, Inc.
3. Churchill, R. 1963. *Fourier Series and Boundary Value Problems.* New York: McGraw-Hill Book Co., Inc.
4. Dennemeyer, R. 1968. *Introduction to Partial Differential Equations and Boundary Value Problems.* New York: McGraw-Hill Book Co., Inc.
5. Dettman, J. 1969. *Mathematical Methods in Physics and Engineering.* New York: McGraw-Hill Book Co., Inc.
6. Duff, G. F. D., and D. Naylor. 1966. *Differential Equations of Applied Mathematics.* New York: John Wiley & Sons, Inc.
7. Greenspan, D. 1961. *Introduction to Partial Differential Equations.* New York: McGraw-Hill Book Co., Inc.
8. Hildebrand, F. 1962. *Advanced Calculus for Applications.* Englewood Cliffs, N.J.: Prentice-Hall, Inc.
9. Petrovskii, I. G. 1967. *Partial Differential Equations.* Philadelphia: W. B. Saunders Co.
10. Sagan, H. 1961. *Boundary and Eigenvalue Problems in Mathematical Physics.* New York: John Wiley & Sons, Inc.
11. Sneddon, I. 1959. *Elements of Partial Differential Equations.* New York: McGraw-Hill Book Co., Inc.
12. Tikhonov, A., and A. Samarskii. 1955. *Equations in Mathematical Physics.* New York: Pergamon Press.
13. Tolstov, G. 1965. *Fourier Series.* Englewood Cliffs, N.J.: Prentice-Hall, Inc.
14. Weinberger, H. 1965. *A First Course in Partial Differential Equations.* Waltham, Mass.: Blaisdell Publishing Co.

Solutions of the Exercises

Chapter 1

Exercises 1.1

1. (a) Continuous and piecewise smooth.
   (b) Piecewise continuous and piecewise smooth.

2. The extension of f is piecewise continuous if f is piecewise continuous on $[-L, L]$; the extension is continuous if f is continuous on $[-L, L]$ and $f(-L) = f(L)$. The periodic extension of f is piecewise smooth if f is piecewise smooth; the extension is smooth if f is smooth on $[-L, L]$ and $f(-L) = f(L)$.

5. No.   6. No.

Exercises 1.2

1. $u_x = 2xy + y^2$; $u_y = x^2 + 2xy$.

2. $u_x = e^x \cos y + y$; $u_y = -e^x \sin y + x$.

3. $u_x = \dfrac{2x}{x^2 + y^2}$; $u_y = \dfrac{2y}{x^2 + y^2}$.

4. $u_x = \dfrac{2y}{(x + y)^2}$; $u_y = \dfrac{-2x}{(x + y)^2}$.

5. $u_x = \dfrac{1}{y} \sec^2 \dfrac{x}{y}$; $u_y = -\dfrac{x}{y^2} \sec^2 \dfrac{x}{y}$.

313

7. $u_x = \left(\dfrac{y}{x}\right)^{1/2} \dfrac{1}{x + y}$; $u_y = -\left(\dfrac{x}{y}\right)^{1/2} \dfrac{1}{x + y}$.

11. $u_{xx} = \dfrac{y^2}{(x^2 + y^2)^{3/2}}$; $u_{xy} = -\dfrac{xy}{(x^2 + y^2)^{3/2}}$; $u_{yy} = \dfrac{x^2}{(x^2 + y^2)^{3/2}}$.

12. $u_{xx} = a^2 e^{ax+by}$; $u_{xy} = abe^{ax+by}$; $u_{yy} = b^2 e^{ax+by}$.

13. $u_{xx} = e^x \sin y$; $u_{xy} = e^x \cos y$; $u_{yy} = -e^x \sin y$.

14. $u_{xx} = \dfrac{-2xy}{(x^2 + y^2)^2}$; $u_{xy} = \dfrac{x^2 - y^2}{(x^2 + y^2)^2}$; $u_{yy} = \dfrac{2xy}{(x^2 + y^2)^2}$.

17. $u_{xy} = x^{y-1} + y(\ln x)x^{y-1}$.

21. For $(x, y) \neq (0, 0)$, $u_{xy} = \dfrac{x^2 - y^2}{x^2 + y^2}$.

Exercises 1.3

1. $\dfrac{du}{dt} = t \ln(1 - t) - \dfrac{t^2}{2(1 - t)}$.

2. $du/dt = [\cos(\sin t) + t \sin t]/t - [(\ln t) \sin(\sin t) - t] \cos t$.

3. $du/dt = 1$.   **4.** $du/dt = 2 \tanh 2t$.

5. $du/dx = (1 + 3x^2) \ln x + (1 + x^2)$.

6. $du/dx = 4x$.   **7.** $u_r = -2r$; $u_s = 10s$.

8. $u_r = 0$; $u_s = e^s$.   **9.** $u_r = 2r$; $u_s = 0$.

10. $u_r = \dfrac{2(r^2 + s^2)}{r - s} + 4r \ln(r - s)$; $u_s = \dfrac{-2(r^2 + s^2)}{r - s} + 4s \ln(r - s)$.

11. $u_{xx} - u_{yy} = u_{st}$.   **12.** $u_{xx} + u_{yy} = u_{rr} + \dfrac{1}{r} u_r + \dfrac{1}{r^2} u_{\theta\theta}$.

14. $u_x = \dfrac{x}{r} u_r - \dfrac{y}{r^2} u_\theta$; $u_y = \dfrac{y}{r} u_r + \dfrac{x}{r^2} u_\theta$.

15. $u_r = u_x \cos \theta + u_y \sin \theta$; $u_\theta = -ru_x \sin \theta + ru_y \cos \theta$.

Exercises 1.4

1. $\phi'(x) = \dfrac{\pi x \cos(\pi/2)x - 2 \sin(\pi/2)x}{2x^2}$.

2. $\phi'(x) = x(\pi/2 - \ln 2)$.

3. $\phi'(x) = (1 + \cos x)/(1 + x + \sin x)$.

4. $(2\pi x)/(x^2 - 1)^2$.   **5.** $\phi'(x) = (3 \sin^3 x - 2 \sin x^2)/x$.

8. $\phi(x) = \ln(1 + x)$.

Exercises 1.5

5. For each $x \geq a > 0$, $e^{-nx} \leq e^{-na}$ and $\sum_{n=1}^{\infty} e^{-na} = e^{-a}/(1 - e^{-a})$.

8. For each $|x| \leq a < 1$, $|x^{2n}| \leq a^{2n}$ and $\sum_{n=0}^{\infty} a^{2n} = 1/(1 - a^2)$. Then

$$\int_0^x \frac{dt}{1 + t^2} = \sum_{n=0}^{\infty} (-1)^n \frac{x^{2n+1}}{2n + 1}$$

10. $\displaystyle\sum_{n=1}^{\infty} \frac{(-1)^{n+1}}{(2n - 1)^3}$.

14. The series for u_t, u_x, u_{xx} are all uniformly convergent for $0 \leq x \leq \pi, 0 < t_0 \leq t$.

Exercises 1.6

1. $\left| \dfrac{1}{x^2 + t^2} \right| \leq \dfrac{1}{a^2 + t^2}$ for all t, and $\displaystyle\int_0^{\infty} \frac{dt}{a^2 + t^2} = \frac{\pi}{2a}$.

2. $\left| \dfrac{\sin t}{x^2 + t^2} \right| \leq \dfrac{1}{x^2 + t^2}$.

4. $|e^{-xt} \cos t| \leq e^{-at}$ for $0 < a \leq x, 0 \leq t < \infty$ and $\int_0^{\infty} e^{-at} \, dt = 1/a$.

6. For $0 < a \leq x \leq b$, $e^{-t} t^{x-1} \leq e^{-t} t^{b-1} \leq A/t^2$ for some constant A.

7. Integrate under the integral sign from 0 to ∞.

10. For all x, $|e^{-t^2} \cos xt| \leq e^{-t^2}$ and $\int_0^{\infty} e^{-t^2} \, dt = \sqrt{\pi}/2$.

Exercises 1.7

1. (a) $du/ds = 6\sqrt{2}$;   (b) $du/ds = \sqrt{3} - (1 + \sqrt{3})e$.

2. $\dfrac{du}{ds} = \dfrac{32}{\sqrt{17}} + \dfrac{4}{\sqrt{17}} (\sin 2 + \cos 2)$.

3. $du/ds = -72/\sqrt{17}$.   **4.** $\theta = 45°$; $du/ds = 3\sqrt{2}$ (max).

5. $du/ds = 194/\sqrt{97}$ (max).   **6.** $\partial u/\partial n = 4$.

7. $\partial u/\partial n = 2/r$.

Exercises 1.8

1. 0.   **2.** $\frac{1}{4}$

3. 0.   **4.** 5/42.

5. (a) 2π;   (b) 2π.

Chapter 2

Exercises 2.1

1. (a) and (f) are second order, linear; (b), (c), and (e) are second order, nonlinear; (d) first order, linear.

Exercises 2.2

1. (a) $u = 3xy + y^2/2 + f(x)$.   (b) $u = \ln x + xe^y + f(y)$.
   (c) $u = -y \cos x + f(y)$.   (d) $u = xy^2/2 + y \tan x + f(x)$.
   (e) $u = yf(x) + g(x)$.   (f) $u = \int_a^x g(t)\, dt + f(y)$.

2. (a) $u = -e^{x-y} + f(x) + g(y)$.   (b) $u = x^2y/2 + xy^2 + f(x) + g(y)$.
   (c) $u = ye^x + xf(y) + g(y)$.   (d) $u = y^4/4 \sin x + yf(x) + g(x)$.
   (e) $u = \int_a^x f(\xi)\, d\xi \int_b^y g(\eta)\, d\eta + h(x) + k(y)$.

3. (a) $u = f(x + 2y) + g(x - 2y)$.   (b) $u = f(x + y) + g(5x + y)$.
   (c) $u = f(2x - y) + xg(2x - y)$.   (d) $u = f(x + y) + xg(x + y)$.
   (e) $u = f(2x + iy) + g(2x - iy)$.
   (f) $u = f[(2 + 3i)x + y] + g[(2 - 3i)x + y]$.

4. (a) $u = 2(x - (1/y)) + e^{-xy}f(y)$.   (b) $u = -(\cos x/y) + y^2f(x)$.
   (c) $u = f(y)e^{2xy} + g(y)e^{-2xy} - 3x/4y^2$.
   (d) $u = f(y)e^{xy} + g(y)e^{-3xy}$.   (e) $u = f(x)e^{xy} + g(x)ye^{xy}$.

5. $u = xe^y + (1/x)f(y) + g(x)$.   6. $u = x(x - 1) + \sin y$.

7. $u = \sinh x + \cos y - 1$.   8. $u = 1 - \cos x + y^2 + x^2y^2/4$.

9. $u = x - y + e^y - 1 + \dfrac{x^3 \sin y}{3}$.

Exercises 2.3

3. $u = 2e^{-9t/4} \sin(3x/2) - 4e^{-25t/4} \sin(5x/2)$.

4. $u = \tfrac{3}{4}e^{-(1+k)t} \cos x + \tfrac{1}{4}e^{-(9+k)t} \cos 3x$.

5. $u = \tfrac{3}{4} \cos(\sqrt{1 + c^2}t) \sin x - \tfrac{1}{4} \cos(\sqrt{9 + c^2}t) \sin 3x$.

6. $u = -\dfrac{\sinh \pi(y - 1) \sin \pi x}{\sinh \pi} + \dfrac{3 \sinh 2\pi(y - 1) \sin 2\pi}{\sinh 2\pi}$.

Exercises 2.4

1. $u = e^x f(x - y)$.   2. $u = f(3x + 2y) + x^2/4$.

3. $u = \dfrac{\sin x - \cos x}{2} + y + 2 + e^{-x}f(2x + y)$.

4. $u = x^2 - 6x + \tfrac{1}{2}x^2y - \tfrac{3}{2}xy + \tfrac{9}{4}y + \tfrac{2}{5}e^x + 14 + e^{-2x/3}f(4x + 3y)$.

5. $u = -\tfrac{1}{3}e^{2x} \sin 3y + e^{2x}f(x + y)$.

7. $u = \ln x + f(y/x)$.   8. $u = 2e^x \ln x - xy + e^x f(xy)$.

9. $u = x + f(x^2 - y^2)$.   10. $u = e^{y/x}f(xy)$.

11. $u = x + x^3/y^2 + (1/y^2)f(x^2 + y^2)$.

12. $u = \dfrac{x}{x + y}\, e^{-x/(x+y)} + e^{-x/(x+y)}f(x + y)$.

13. $u = x \ln x + xf(x^2 + y^2)$.

14. If $A \neq 0$, then $u = e^{-Dx/A}f(Bx - Ay, Cy - Bz)$. If $A = 0$, but $B \neq 0$, then $u = e^{-Dy/B}f(Cy - Bz, x)$. If $A = B = 0$ and $C \neq 0$, then $u = e^{-Dz/C}f(x, y)$.

15. (a) $u = e^{-x}f(2x - y, 3y + 2z)$.
    (b) $u = e^{-3x/2}f(x + 2y, 2y + z)$.

16. $u = y + e^{x-y}$.　　　　　　17. $u = e^{2x-y}[1 + \cos(x - y)]$.

18. $u = e^{-2x} \sin \dfrac{5x + 2y}{2} + e^{(1/2)(x+y)} + \tfrac{1}{4}x^2 - \tfrac{1}{4}x + \tfrac{1}{8}$.

19. $u = -\cos x + \cos(\sin x - y) - \sin x + y$. 　$\cos(\sin z - y)$
    　　　　　　　　　　　　　　　　　　　　　　　$= \cos(y - \sin z)$

20. $u = x/2 + \sqrt{x}\, y^{3/2} - y/2$.

21. $u = e^y(4 - x^2 - y^2)^{1/2}e^{-(4-x^2-y^2)^{1/2}}$.

22. $u = e^{y^2-(x^2+y^2)^{1/2}} \sin(x^2 + y^2)^{1/2}$.

23. $u = e^{-x^2}f(x^2 + y^2)$, where f is any differentiable function such that $f(a^2) = k$.

24. $\phi(x) = e^x[(x^2 + 1)^{1/2} + k]$.

Exercises 2.5

1. $u = e^{-y}f(x) + e^{-x}g(y)$.　　　　2. $u = f(x + y) + e^x g(x - y)$.

3. $u = f(x - iy) + g(x + iy)$.　　　　4. $u = f(x - y) + xg(x - y)$.

5. $u = f(x) + e^{-3x}g(2x + y)$.　　　6. $r^2u = f(r + ct) + g(r - ct)$.

7. $u = f(x + iy) + g(x - iy) + h(x + y) + k(x - y)$.

8. $u = f(x + y) + xg(x + y) + h(x - y) + xk(x - y)$.

10. $u = x^3/6 - y^3/24$.　　　　11. $u = xy^4/108 + y^5/810$.

12. $u = \tfrac{1}{2}ye^{x-y}$.

13. $u = -\tfrac{1}{2}[\cos(2x + y) + \sin(2x + y)]$.

15. (a) $u = f(xy) + g(x/y) + \tfrac{1}{6}\ln^3 x$.
    (b) $u = (1/y)f(x) + (1/x)g(y) + xy/4$.
    (c) $u = xf(x/y) + x^n g(x/y) + [(x + y)/(1 - n)]\ln x,\ n \neq 1$;
    $u = xf(x/y) + (x \ln x)g(x/y) + [(x + y)/2]\ln^2 x,\ n = 1$.

16. (a) $u = f(x + y) + g(x - z)$.
    (b) $u = f(x + y, y + z) + e^{-x}g(2x - y)$.
    (c) $u = f(x - y, y - z) + xg(x - y, y - z)$.

Exercises 2.6

9. Hyperbolic for $x^2 + y^2 > 1$, parabolic for $x^2 + y^2 = 1$, and elliptic for $x^2 + y^2 < 1$.

10. Hyperbolic for $x^2 - 4y > 0$, parabolic for $x^2 - 4y = 0$, and elliptic for $x^2 - 4y < 0$.

Exercises 2.7

1. $48(u_{\xi\xi} - u_{\eta\eta}) + u_\xi + 4u_\eta = 0$.　　2. $u_{\xi\xi} - u_{\eta\eta} - u_\eta = -\eta(\xi + \eta)$.

3. $75u_{\xi\eta} + u = -(\xi - \eta)^2/25$.　　　5. $2u_{\xi\eta} + u_\eta + 1 = 0$.

6. $4u_{\xi\xi} - u_\xi - 2u_\eta = 0$.　　　　7. $u_{\xi\xi} + u_\eta = \xi(\eta - 3\xi)$.

8. $9u_{\xi\xi} - u = 0$.　　　　　　　9. $u_{\xi\xi} - 4u = 0$.

10. $4(u_{\xi\xi} + u_{\eta\eta}) + u = 0$.　　　11. $27(u_{\xi\xi} + u_{\eta\eta}) - \eta u_\xi = 0$.

12. $u_{\xi\xi} + u_{\eta\eta} + (\xi - \eta)(u_\xi + u_\eta) = 0.$

13. $6(u_{\xi\xi} + u_{\eta\eta}) - u = 0.$

14. $12(u_{\xi\xi} + u_{\eta\eta}) + 7u_\xi + \sqrt{3}\, u_\eta + u = 0.$

15. $u_{\xi\xi} + u_{\eta\eta} - e^\eta u = \sin(2\eta - \xi).$ **16.** $u = f(x + y) + g(2x - 3y).$

17. $u = f[(1 - 3i)x - 5y] + g[(1 + 3i)x - 5y].$

18. $u = f(2x - y) + xg(2x - y).$

19. $u = f[(2 + i)x + y] + g[(2 - i)x + y].$

Chapter 3

Exercises 3.1

2. $w_{tt} - c^2 w_{xx} = -v_{tt} + c^2 v_{xx};\ w(x, 0) = f(x) - v(x, 0);\ w_t(x, 0) = g(x) - v_t(x, 0);$
$w(0, t) = 0,\ w(L, t) = 0.$

3. Suppose u_1 and u_2 are two solutions and set $u = u_1 - u_2$.

Exercises 3.2

1. $u(x, 0) = \sin x;\ u_t(x, 0) = -c \cos x.$

2. $u(x, 0) = x^2;\ u_t(x, 0) = 2cx.$

3. $u = \sin 2x \cos 4t + \frac{1}{2} \cos x \sin 2t.$

4. $u = x \sin x \cos 3t + 3t \cos x \sin 3t + \frac{1}{6} \cos 2x \sin 6t.$

5. $u = \dfrac{1 + x^2 + t^2}{[1 + (x + t)^2][1 + (x - t)^2]} + e^x \sinh t.$

6. $u = e^{-x} \cosh t + \frac{1}{2}[\arctan(x + t) - \arctan(x - t)].$

7. $u = \cos(\pi/2)x \cos(\pi/2)t + (1/a) \sinh ax \sinh at.$

8. $u = \sin 3x \cos 3t + \frac{1}{2} \sin 2x \sin 2t - \sin x \sin t.$

9. $u(1/8, 11/8) = 0;\ u(1/4, 1) = 1/2.$

10. $u(-\pi/12, 7\pi/12) = 1/2 - \sqrt{3}/4;\ u(-\pi/2, 5\pi/6) = \sqrt{3}/4.$

11. $u(0, 3/4) = 45/64;\ u(-1/2, 3/4) = 211/384;\ u(9/8, 7/8) = 117/384.$

12. $u(-\pi/6, 5\pi/6) = \dfrac{e^{-1} + e^{-2/3}}{2} + 1.$

$u(3\pi/8, 5\pi/8) = \dfrac{e^{-1/4} + e^{-1}}{2} + \dfrac{1}{2} + \dfrac{\sqrt{2}}{4}.$

Exercises 3.3

1. $u = x^2 + t^2 + xt^2.$ **2.** $u = xt(t - 1) - t^3/\ + \sin x \cos t.$

3. $u = e^x \sinh t + xt^3/6.$ **4.** $u = \cos(x - t) + (e^x/4)(\cosh t - 1).$

5. $u = (e^x/4)(\cosh t - 1) + \frac{1}{2}[\arctan(x + t) - \arctan(x - t)] + t - \sin t.$

6. $u = -x^3 - 3xt^2 + x^2 + t^2 - \frac{1}{9} \sin x \sin t + \frac{1}{3}t \sin x.$

7. $u = x - \sin x \cos t + \sin x$.

8. $u = -x \sin x \cos t - t \cos x \sin t + x \sin x$.

9. $u = \frac{1}{3}(3x^2 t + t^3) - x^2 \ln(1 + t)$.

10. Write

$$v(x, t) = \frac{1}{2c} \int_0^t \int_{x-c(t-\tau)}^{x+c(t-\tau)} F(\xi, \tau) \, d\xi \, d\tau$$

Then

$$v_t = \frac{1}{2} \int_0^t [F(x + c(t - \tau), \tau) + F(x - c(t - \tau), \tau)] \, d\tau$$

$$v_x = \frac{1}{2c} \int_0^t [F(x + c(t - \tau), \tau) - F(x - c(t - \tau), \tau)] \, d\tau$$

$$v_{tt} = F(x, t) + \frac{c}{2} \int_0^t [F_\alpha(x + c(t - \tau), \tau) - F_\beta(x - c(t - \tau), \tau)] \, d\tau$$

$$v_{xx} = \frac{1}{2c} \int_0^t [F_\alpha(x + c(t - \tau), \tau) - F_\beta(x - c(t - \tau), \tau)] \, d\tau$$

where $\alpha = x + c(t - \tau)$ and $\beta = x - c(t - \tau)$.

12. $u = \frac{1}{2} [f(x - t) + e^{\alpha t} f(x + t)]$

$$+ \frac{1}{2} e^{-(\alpha x/2) + (\alpha t/2)} \int_{x-t}^{x+t} e^{\alpha s/2} \left[g(s) - \frac{\alpha}{2} f(s) \right] ds.$$

Exercises 3.4

1. $E'(t) = \displaystyle\int_{-\infty}^{\infty} [u_t u_{tt} + c^2 u_x u_{xt}] \, dx$

$$= \int_{-\infty}^{\infty} u_t(u_{tt} - c^2 u_{xx}) \, dx + c^2 u_x u_t \Big|_{-\infty}^{\infty}$$

$$= 0$$

by the differential equation and the assumption on u_x and u_t as $|x| \to \infty$. Thus $E(t) = $ const for $t \geq 0$.

2. If u_1 and u_2 are two solutions, then $u = u_1 - u_2$ satisfies $u_{tt} - c^2 u_{xx} = 0$, $u(x, 0) = 0$ and vanishes together with its first derivatives as $|x| \to \infty$. Since $E(t) = $ const and $E(0) = 0$, it follows that $E(t) = 0$ for $t \geq 0$. Therefore, $u_t^2 + c^2 u_x^2 = 0$, which implies $u \equiv 0$.

5. $u(x, t) = \begin{cases} \dfrac{1}{2} [f(x + ct) - f(ct - x)] + \dfrac{1}{2c} \displaystyle\int_{ct-x}^{x+ct} g(s) \, ds & (x < ct) \\[4mm] \dfrac{1}{2} [f(x + ct) + f(x - ct)] + \dfrac{1}{2c} \displaystyle\int_{x-ct}^{x+ct} g(s) \, ds & (x > ct) \end{cases}$

6. Let u be the solution of (2.1), (2.2) where f and g are even, and set $v(x, t) = u(-x, t)$. Then v is also a solution of (2.1), (2.2). Since the solution is unique, $u(x, t) = v(x, t)$, or $u(x, t) = u(-x, t)$.

7. $u(x, t) = \dfrac{1}{2} [f(x + ct) + f(ct - x)] + \dfrac{1}{c} \displaystyle\int_0^{ct-x} g(s)\, ds$

$$3x - \tfrac{1}{3}(6xt) \qquad\qquad + \dfrac{1}{2c} \int_{ct-x}^{x+ct} g(s)\, ds \qquad (x < ct)$$

8. $u(x, t) = \begin{cases} 3xt - \tfrac{1}{3}(x^3 + 3xt^2) & (x \le t) \\ x^2 + xt + t^2 - \tfrac{1}{3}(3x^2 t + t^2) & (x > t) \end{cases}$

$u(1/4, 1) = 47/128$.

9. $u(x, t) = xt + \sin(\pi x/2) \cos(\pi t/2)$.

10. (a) $u(x, t) = \cos(\pi x/2) \cos(\pi t/2) + x^2 t + t^3/3$;
   (b) $u(x, t) = \tfrac{1}{2}[e^{-|x-t|} + e^{-|x+t|}] + \cos x \sin t$.

12. $u(x, t) = \sin x \cos t + \tfrac{1}{2}xt^2$.   **13.** $u(x, t) = \cos x \sin t + t^3/6$.

Exercises 3.5

1. If f is odd about $x = 0$ and $x = L$, then $f(x + 2L) = f[2L - (-x)] = -f(-x) = f(x)$.

2. If f is odd about $x = 0$ and even about $x = L$, then

$$f(x + 4L) = f[2L - (-2L - x)]$$
$$= f(-2L - x) = -f(2L + x)$$
$$= -f(-x) = f(x)$$

3. Write $\displaystyle\int_a^{a+2L} g(x)\, dx = \int_a^{-L} g(x)\, dx + \int_{-L}^{L} g(x) + \int_L^{a+2L} g(x)\, dx.$

The first and the third integrals on the right cancel out. In fact, set $s = x + 2L$. Then

$$\int_a^{-L} g(x)\, dx = \int_{a+2L}^{L} g(s - 2L)\, ds = \int_{a+2L}^{L} g(s)\, ds$$

since g is of period $2L$.

4 Let u be the solution of (2.1), (2.2) where f and g are odd about $x = 0$ and $x = L$. To show u is odd about $x = L$, set $v(x, t) = -u(2L - x, t)$. Then v is also a solution of (2.1), (2.2). Since u is unique, $u(x, t) = v(x, t) = -u(2L - x, t)$.

7. Let g denote the odd periodic extension of $u_t(x, 0) = x(1 - x^2)$ of period 2. Then

$$u(x, t) = \sin \pi x \cos \pi t + \dfrac{1}{2} \int_{x-t}^{x+t} g(s)\, ds$$

and

$$u\left(\dfrac{5}{8}, \dfrac{9}{8}\right) = -\dfrac{\sqrt{2}}{4} - \dfrac{1105}{2048}$$

8. $u(3/4, 2) = 3/16$.

9. $u(x, t) = (1/2)[f(x - t) + f(x + t)] + (2/\pi) \cos(\pi/2)x \sin(\pi/2)t$ where f is the extension of $u(x, 0) = x^2(1 - x^2)$ such that f is even about $x = 0$ and odd about $x = 1$.

10. $u(x, t) = \frac{1}{2}(1 - \cos 2\pi x \cos 2\pi t)$.

13. $u(1/2, 3/2) = \frac{1}{2}[3e - 2e^{1/2} - 1]$.

14. $u(1/4, 2) = 87/128$.

Exercises 3.6

1. $u(5/8, 19/8) = 273/32$.   **2.** $u(1/4, 3/2) = -11/128$.

3.   (a) $u(x, t) = \begin{cases} (t - x)e^{-(t-x)} - e^{-t} \sinh x & (x < t) \\ e^{-x} \cosh t - 1 & (x > t) \end{cases}$

     (b) $u(x, t) = \begin{cases} \sin 2(t - x) + \sin x \cos t & (x \leq t) \\ \sin x \cos t & (x \geq t) \end{cases}$

4.   (a) $u(1/4, 3/2) = \frac{1}{2}[e^{3/4} - e^{1/4} - 2e + 1]$.

     (b) $u(3/4, 3/2) = -11/192 + \cos(5\pi/8)$.

6. $u(x, t) = \sum_{n \geq 0} k\left(t + \dfrac{x - (2n + 1)L}{c}\right) - \sum_{n \geq 0} k\left(t - \dfrac{x + (2n + 1)L}{c}\right)$

     with $k(t) = 0$ for $t < 0$.

7. $u(x, t) = -c \int_0^{t - x/c} h(s)\, ds + v(x, t)$ for $x < ct$ where v is the solution of Problem 7, Exercises 3.4.

8. $u(x, t) = \begin{cases} \frac{1}{2}[f(x + ct) + f(ct - x)] - ke^{k(x-ct)} \displaystyle\int_0^{ct-x} e^{k\xi} f(\xi)\, d\xi & (0 \leq x \leq ct) \\[2mm] \frac{1}{2}[f(x - ct) + f(x + ct)] & (x \geq ct) \end{cases}$

Exercises 3.7

1. $u(x, t) = \frac{3}{4} \sin x \cos t - \frac{1}{4} \sin 3x \cos 3t$.

2. $u(x, t) = (3\sqrt{2}/8) \sin x \sin \sqrt{2}\, t - (\sqrt{10}/40) \sin 3x \sin \sqrt{10}\, t$.

3. $u(x, t) = \sin t + (3\sqrt{2}/8) \cos x \sin \sqrt{2}\, t + (\sqrt{10}/40) \cos 3x \sin \sqrt{10}\, t$.

4. $u(x, t) = e^{-x}[2 \sin 2\pi x \cos(4\pi^2 + 1)^{1/2} t - 3 \sin 5\pi x \cos(25\pi^2 + 1)^{1/2} t]$.

5. $u(x, t) = \dfrac{3}{4} te^{-t/2} \sin\left(\dfrac{x}{2}\right) - \dfrac{\sqrt{2}}{8} e^{-t/2} \sin \sqrt{2}\, t \sin\left(\dfrac{3x}{2}\right)$.

6. $u_n(x, t) = \sin\left[\frac{1}{2}(2n - 1)\pi \ln x\right] \sin\left[\frac{1}{2}(2n - 1)\pi t\right]$.

7. $u_n(x, t) = e^{-(x+t)} \cos(n^2 + 1)^{1/2} t \sin nx$.

8. $u_n(x, t) = x^{1/2} \sin\left(\dfrac{n\pi \ln x}{\ln 2}\right) \sin\left(\dfrac{n^2\pi^2}{\ln^2 2} + \dfrac{1}{4}\right)^{1/2} t$.

9. $u_n(x, t) = (1 + t^{1/2}) \sin[n\pi \ln(t + 1)/\ln 2] \sin(n\pi \ln x/\ln 2)$.

Chapter 4

Exercises 4.1

1. $(d/dx)(e^{bx}u') + ce^{bx} = 0.$ 2. $(d/dx)(x^2u') + x^2u = 0.$
3. $(d/dx)(e^x u') + (e^x/x)u = 0.$ 4. $(d/dx)(xu') + (1/x)u = 0.$
5. $(d/dx)(xe^{-x}u') + e^{-x}u = 0.$
6. (a) $u(x) = C(x - 1).$
    (b) $u = 0.$

7. $u(x) = C \sin x.$ 8. $u(x) = 0.$
9. $u(x) = 0.$ 10. $u(x) = 0.$
11. $u(x) = C \ln x.$ 12. $u(x) = Cx^{-2}.$
13. $u(x) = Cx.$ 14. $u(x) = 0.$
16. (a) No solution.   (b) $u(x) = 2 \sin x - \cos x.$ (c) $u(x) = -\sin x.$
17. (a) $u(x) = e^x.$ (b) $u(x) = e^{-1} \cosh x.$ (c) $u(x) = e^{-x}.$
    (d) $u(x) = e^{-x}.$
18. (a) $u(x) = e^{2x}/(1 - e^4) + e^{-2x}/(1 - e^{-4}).$ (b) $u(x) = \cosh 2x.$
19. (a) No solution.   (b) $u(x) = \frac{1}{2} \sin 2x - \cos 2x.$
    (c) $u(x) = \frac{1}{4} \sin 2x + \frac{1}{2} \cos 2x.$

20. (a) $u(x) = 2 \ln x.$ (b) $u(x) = 1 + \dfrac{2 \ln x}{1 - 2 \ln 2}.$ (c) $u(x) = \ln x - \ln 2.$

21. (a) $u(x) = \cos(\ln x) + (\tan 1) \sin(\ln x).$ (b) $u(x) = \cos(\ln x).$
    (c) $u(x) = \sin(\ln x).$

Exercises 4.2

1. (a) $G(x, \xi) = \begin{cases} -x & (0 \le x \le \xi) \\ -\xi & (\xi \le x \le 1) \end{cases}$

    (b) $G(x, \xi) = \begin{cases} \xi & (0 \le x \le \xi) \\ x & (\xi \le x \le 1) \end{cases}$

    (c) $G(x, \xi) = \begin{cases} -(x - 1) & (0 \le x \le \xi) \\ -(\xi - 1) & (\xi \le x \le 1) \end{cases}$

2. (a) $G(x, \xi) = \begin{cases} -\sin x \cos \xi & (0 \le x \le \xi) \\ -\sin \xi \cos x & (\xi \le x \le \pi) \end{cases}$

    (b) $G(x, \xi) = \begin{cases} \cos x \sin \xi & (0 \le x \le \xi) \\ \cos \xi \sin x & (\xi \le x \le \pi) \end{cases}$

3. $G(x, \xi) = \begin{cases} -e^{x-\xi} \sin x \cos \xi & (0 \le x \le \xi) \\ -e^{x-\xi} \sin \xi \cos x & (\xi \le x \le \pi/2) \end{cases}$

4. $G(x, \xi) = \begin{cases} (x\xi - 2x)/\xi^3 & (1 \le x \le \xi) \\ (x^2 - 2x)/\xi^3 & (\xi \le x \le 2) \end{cases}$

5. $G(x, \xi) = \begin{cases} x \ln \xi - x(1 + 2 \ln 2)/\xi^3 & (1 \le x \le \xi) \\ x \ln x - x(1 + 2 \ln 2)/\xi^3 & (\xi \le x \le 2) \end{cases}$

6. $G(x, \xi) = \begin{cases} -\ln(1 + x) & (0 \le x \le \xi) \\ -\ln(1 + \xi) & (\xi \le x \le 1) \end{cases}$

12. $u(x) = \displaystyle\int_0^1 G(x, \xi) f(\xi) \, d\xi + \dfrac{B \sin 2x}{\sin 2} - \dfrac{A \sin 2(x - 1)}{\sin 2}$

where

$$G(x, \xi) = \begin{cases} \dfrac{\sin 2x \sin 2(\xi - 1)}{2 \sin 2} & (0 \le x \le \xi) \\[3mm] \dfrac{\sin 2\xi \sin 2(x - 1)}{2 \sin 2} & (\xi \le x \le 1) \end{cases}$$

13. $u(x) = \displaystyle\int_0^1 G(x, \xi) f(\xi) \, d\xi + B \dfrac{\sin kx + k \cos kx}{\sin kx + k \cos k} - A \dfrac{\sin k(x - 1)}{\sin k}$

where

$$G(x, \xi) = \begin{cases} \dfrac{(\sin kx + k \cos kx) \sin k(\xi - 1)}{k(\sin k + k \cos k)} & (0 \le x \le \xi) \\[3mm] \dfrac{(\sin k\xi + k \cos k\xi) \sin k(x - 1)}{k(\sin k + k \cos k)} & (\xi \le x \le 1) \end{cases}$$

with $\sin k + k \cos k \ne 0$.

14. $G(x, \xi) = \begin{cases} \ln \xi & (0 \le x \le \xi) \\ \ln x & (\xi \le x \le 1) \end{cases}$

15. $G(x, \xi) = \begin{cases} x^n(\xi^n - \xi^{-n})/2n & (0 \le x \le \xi) \\ \xi^n(x^n - x^{-n})/2n & (\xi \le x \le 1) \end{cases}$

16. $G(x, \xi) = \begin{cases} -\frac{1}{2} \ln[(1 + x)/(1 - x)] & (0 \le x \le \xi) \\ -\frac{1}{2} \ln[(1 + \xi)/(1 - \xi)] & (\xi \le x \le 1) \end{cases}$

17. A solution of the differential solution that vanishes as $x \to -\infty$ is given by $u_1(x) = e^{sx}$. On the other hand, $u_2(x) = e^{-sx}$ vanishes as $x \to \infty$. Then $W(u_1, u_2; x) = -2s$. Formula (2.12) gives the result.

Exercises 4.3

1. $u_0(x) = 1$, $u_2(x) = x$ so that

$$G^*(x, \xi) = \begin{cases} \xi & (0 \le x \le \xi) \\ x & (\xi \le x \le 1) \end{cases}$$

2. $G^*(x, \xi) = \begin{cases} (1 - x)\xi & (0 \le x \le \xi) \\ (1 - \xi)x & (\xi \le x \le 1) \end{cases}$

3. $G^*(x, \xi) = \begin{cases} -\sin x \cos \xi & (0 \le x \le \xi) \\ -\sin \xi \cos x & (\xi \le x \le \pi/2) \end{cases}$

4. $G^*(x, \xi) = \begin{cases} \ln \xi & (0 \leq x < \xi) \\ \ln x & (\xi \leq x \leq 1) \end{cases}$

5. $G^*(x, \xi) = \begin{cases} -\frac{1}{2} \ln[(1 + \xi)/(1 - \xi)] & (0 \leq x \leq \xi) \\ -\frac{1}{2} \ln[(1 + x)/(1 - x)] & (\xi \leq x \leq 1) \end{cases}$

6. Let u_0 denote a nontrivial solution. If u_1 and u_2 are linearly independent on $[a, b]$, there exist constants c_1 and c_2, not both zero, such that $u_0(x) = c_1 u_1(x) + c_2 u_2(x)$. Then $c_2 u_2(a) = 0$ and $c_1 u_1(b) = 0$, which imply either $u_2(a) = 0$ or $u_1(b) = 0$. If $u_1(b) = 0$, then the Wronskian of u_1 and u_2 vanishes at $x = b$, while if $u_2(a) = 0$, the Wronskian vanishes at $x = a$. Either case contradicts the assumption that u_1 and u_2 are linearly independent.

7. Consider the Wronskian $W = u_0(x)u'(x) - u_0'(x)u(x)$, at $x = a$ and $x = b$.

9. Consider $\int_a^b u_0^2 \, dx = \int_a^b u_0 L u \, dx$ and use Lemma 3.1 of this chapter to get a contradiction.

10. No solution.

11. $\int_a^b u(x)[(Au_0)'' - (Bu_0)' + Cu_0] \, dx = \int_a^b f(x)u_0(x) \, dx.$

Exercises 4.4

1. $\lambda_n = (2n - 1)^2\pi^2/(4L^2)$, $u_n(x) = \cos \sqrt{\lambda_n}\, x$; $n = 1, 2, \ldots$.

2. $\lambda_n = n^2$, $u_n(x) = \cos nx$; $n = 0, 1, 2, \ldots$.

3. $\lambda_0 = -1$, $u_0(x) = e^{-x}$; $\lambda_n = n^2$, $u_n(x) = \sin nx - n \cos nx$; $n = 1, 2, \ldots$.

4. $\lambda_0 = -1$, $u_0(x) = e^x$; $\lambda_n = n^2$, $u_n(x) = \sin nx + n \cos nx$; $n = 1, 2, \ldots$.

5. $\lambda_n = n^4\pi^4/L^4$, $u_n(x) = \sin(n\pi x/L)$; $n = 1, 2, \ldots$.

6. $\lambda_n \cong (2n - 1)^2\pi^2/4$, $u_n(x) = \sin \sqrt{\lambda_n}\, x - \sqrt{\lambda_n} \cos \sqrt{\lambda_n}\, x$.

7. $\lambda_n \cong (2n - 1)^2/4$, $u_n(x) = \sin \sqrt{\lambda_n}\, x$.

8. $\lambda_n \cong n^2\pi^2$, $u_n(x) = \cos \sqrt{\lambda_n}\, x$.

9. $\lambda_n \cong n^2$, $u_n(x) = \sin \sqrt{\lambda_n}\, x - \sqrt{\lambda_n} \cos \sqrt{\lambda_n}\, x$.

10. $\lambda_n \cong n^2$, $u_n(x) = \sin \sqrt{\lambda_n}\, x - \sqrt{\lambda_n} \cos \sqrt{\lambda_n}\, x$.

11. (a) $\lambda_n = n^2\pi^2$, $u_n(x) = \sin(n\pi \ln x)$; $n = 1, 2, \ldots$.
(b) $\lambda_n = (2n - 1)^2\pi^2/4$, $u_n(x) = \sin[(2n - 1)\pi \ln x/2]$; $n = 1, 2, \ldots$.
(c) $\lambda_n = n^2\pi^2$, $u_n(x) = \cos(n\pi \ln x)$; $n = 0, 1, \ldots$.

12. $\lambda_n = (4n^2\pi^2 + 1)/4$, $u_n(x) = x^{-1/2} \sin(n\pi \ln x)$.

13. $\lambda_n = n^2 + 1$, $u_n(x) = x^{-1} \sin(n\pi \ln x)$; $n = 1, 2, \ldots$.

14. $\lambda_n = n^2\pi^2 + 1$, $u_n(x) = x \sin(n\pi \ln x)$; $n = 1, 2, \ldots$.

15. $\lambda_n = n^2\pi^2/L^2$, $u_n(x) = A_n \cos(n\pi x/L) + B_n \sin(n\pi x/L)$. A_n and B_n are arbitrary constants, $n = 0, 1, 2, \ldots$.

16. $\lambda_n = 4n^2\pi^2/L^2$, $u_n(x) = A_n \cos(2n\pi x/L) + B_n \sin(2n\pi x/L)$. A_n and B_n are arbitrary constants, $n = 0, 1, 2, \ldots$.

18. $u_n(x) = J_0(\sqrt{\lambda_n}\, x)$, where $J_0(\sqrt{\lambda_n}) = 0$.

Exercises 4.5

1. $\phi_0(x) = [2/(1 - e^{-2\pi})]^{1/2}e^{-x}$; $\phi_n(x) = \sqrt{2}$ (sin $nx - n$ cos $nx)/[\pi(n^2 + 1)]^{1/2}$;
   $n = 1, 2, \ldots$.

2. $\phi_n(x) = (2/L)^{1/2} \sin(n\pi x/L)$; $n = 1, 2, \ldots$.

3. $\{1/\sqrt{2L}, (1/\sqrt{L}) \cos(n\pi x/L), (1/\sqrt{L}) \sin(n\pi x/L)\}$.

5. Make the substitution $t = \ln x$.

9. Let $\phi_1, \phi_2, \ldots$, be a sequence of eigenfunctions with weight function r on $[a, b]$. Suppose $c_1\phi_1(x) + \cdots + c_n\phi_n(x) = 0$ for some n. Multiplying this by $r(x)\phi_m(x)$ and integrating from a to b, there results $c_m = 0$ for $m = 1, 2, \ldots, n$.

14. Consider $-\lambda \int_a^b v(x)u^2(x)\, dx = \int_a^b u(x)Lu\, dx = [pu(x)u'(x)]_a^b - \int_a^b p(x)u'^2(x)\, dx + \int_a^b qu^2(x)\, dx$. If $u(a) = u(b) = 0$ or $u'(a) = u'(b) = 0$, then the left-hand side is ≤ 0 since $q \leq 0$. Therefore, $\lambda \geq 0$. Under (c), $pu(x)u'(x)]_a^b = -c_2 p(b)u^2(b) - c_1 p(a)u^2(a) \leq 0$, so that also $\lambda \geq 0$.

15. Let u and v be eigenfunctions corresponding to distinct eigenvalues μ and v respectively. Then $(v - \mu) \int_0^L u(x)v(x)\, dx = \int_0^L (uv^{(iv)} - vu^{(iv)})\, dx = [uv''' - u'''v - u'v'' + u''v']_0^L = 0$. Since $v \neq \mu$, u and v are orthogonal.

Exercises 4.6

1. Multiply the series by $r(x)\phi_k(x)$ and integrate from a to b.

2. $a_n = \{\int_a^b r(x)f(x)u_n(x)\, dx/\|u_n\|^2\}$.

3. $x^2 \sim 2\pi \sum_{n=1}^{\infty} \frac{(-1)^{n+1}}{n} \sin nx - \frac{8}{\pi} \sum_{n=1}^{\infty} \frac{\sin(2n - 1)x}{(2n - 1)^3}$ $(0 \leq x < \pi)$.

4. $x \sim -\frac{8L}{\pi^2} \sum_{n=1}^{\infty} \frac{1}{(2n - 1)^2} \cos\left(\frac{2n - 1}{2}\right) \frac{\pi}{L} x$ $(0 \leq x \leq L)$.

5. $x \sim \frac{\pi}{2} - \frac{4}{\pi} \sum_{n=1}^{\infty} \frac{\cos(2n - 1)x}{(2n - 1)^2}$ $(0 \leq x \leq \pi)$.

6. $1 \sim \frac{4}{\pi} \sum_{n=1}^{\infty} \frac{\sin[(2n - 1)\pi \ln x]}{(2n - 1)}$ $(1 < x < e)$.

7. $f(x) \sim a_0 e^{-x} + \sum_{n=1}^{\infty} a_n(\sin nx - n \cos nx)$ $(0 < x < \pi)$.

   where

   $$a_0 = \frac{2}{1 - e^{-2\pi}} \int_0^{\pi} e^{-x}f(x)\, dx$$

   $$a_n = \frac{2}{\pi(n^2 + 1)} \int_0^{\pi} f(x)[\sin nx - n \cos nx]\, dx$$

8. If the series were the eigenfunction expansion of a square integrable function, then by Bessel's inequality the series $\sum(1/\sqrt{n})^2$ must converge. But $\sum(1/n)$ is a divergent series.

9. If f is orthogonal to all the functions ϕ_n, then $c_n = 0$ for all n. By Parseval's equation, $\int_a^b f^2(x)\, dx = 0$. This implies that $f \equiv 0$, since f is continuous.

11. If f is orthogonal to all the functions $\phi_n + \phi_{n+1}$, $n \geq 1$, then $c_n + c_{n+1} = 0$ for $n \geq 1$. Thus $c_{n+1} = (-1)^n c_1$ which violates Bessel's inequality unless $c_n = 0$ for all n. If all the c_n are zero, then by the preceding result f must be identically zero.

12. $f(x) = \sum\limits_{n=1}^{\infty} \dfrac{(-1)^{n+1}}{(n-1)!} \phi_n(x)$.

Exercises 4.7

1. $u(x) = \dfrac{2 \sin 2x}{\lambda - 4} - \dfrac{4 \sin 3x}{\lambda - 9} \qquad (\lambda \neq 4, 9).$

2. $u(x) = \dfrac{2 \cos 2x}{\lambda - 4} - \dfrac{3 \cos 5x}{\lambda - 25} \qquad (\lambda \neq 4, 25).$

3. $u(x) = \dfrac{3 \cos(\pi x/2)}{\lambda - \pi^2/4} + \dfrac{2 \cos(7\pi/2)}{\lambda - (49\pi^2/4)} \qquad (\lambda \neq \pi^2/4, 49\pi^2/4).$

4. $u(x) = \sum\limits_{k=1}^{n} \dfrac{\sin[(2k-1)x/2]}{k[\lambda - (2k-1)^2/4]} \qquad (\lambda \neq (2k-1)^2/4, k = 1, 2, \ldots, n).$

5. $u(x) = \dfrac{a_0 e^{-x}}{(\lambda + 1)} + \sum\limits_{n=1}^{\infty} \dfrac{a_n(\sin nx - n \cos nx)}{\lambda - n^2},$

where a_0 and a_n are the Fourier coefficients of f given in Problem 7, Exercises 4.6.

6. $u(x) = \sum\limits_{n=1}^{\infty} \dfrac{b_n}{\lambda - n^2\pi^2} \sin(n\pi \ln x),$

where $b_n = 2 \int_1^e (1/x) f(x) \sin(n\pi \ln x)\, dx.$

7. $u(x) = \dfrac{3 \sin(\pi \ln x)}{\lambda - \pi^2} - \dfrac{4 \sin(3\pi \ln x)}{\lambda - 9\pi^2}.$

8. $G(x; \xi) = \dfrac{2}{L} \sum\limits_{n=1}^{\infty} \dfrac{\sin(n\pi\xi/L) \sin(n\pi x/L)}{\lambda - (n^2\pi^2/L^2)}, \qquad \lambda \neq \dfrac{n^2\pi^2}{L^2} \qquad (n = 1, 2, \ldots).$

9. $2 \sum\limits_{n=1}^{\infty} \dfrac{\sin(n - 1/2)\pi\xi \, \sin(n - 1/2)\pi x}{\lambda - (n - 1/2)^2\pi^2}$

$$= \begin{cases} -(\sin \sqrt{\lambda}\, x \cos \sqrt{\lambda}\, \xi)/\sqrt{\lambda} & (0 \leq x \leq \xi) \\ -(\sin \sqrt{\lambda}\, \xi \cos \sqrt{\lambda}\, x)/\sqrt{\lambda} & (\xi \leq x \leq 1) \end{cases}$$

11. $G(x; \xi; \lambda) = \begin{cases} \dfrac{\sin(\lambda \ln x) \cos[\lambda(1 - \ln \xi)]}{-\lambda \cos \lambda} & (1 \leq x \leq \xi) \\[3mm] \dfrac{\sin(\lambda \ln \xi) \cos[\lambda(1 - \ln x)]}{-\lambda \cos \lambda} & (\xi \leq x \leq e) \end{cases}$

Chapter 5

Exercises 5.1

1. $f(x) \sim -\dfrac{\pi}{4} + \displaystyle\sum_{n=1}^{\infty} \left[\dfrac{(-1)^n - 1}{\pi n^2} \cos nx + \dfrac{1 + 2(-1)^{n+1}}{n} \sin nx \right].$

2. $f(x) \sim \dfrac{\pi}{8} + \dfrac{1}{\pi} \displaystyle\sum_{n=1}^{\infty} \left[\dfrac{(-1)^n - 1}{2n^2} \cos 2nx + \dfrac{2(-1)^{n+1}}{(2n-1)^2} \sin(2n-1)x \right].$

3. $f(x) \sim \dfrac{4}{\pi^2} \displaystyle\sum_{n=1}^{\infty} \dfrac{\cos(2n-1)\pi x}{(2n-1)^2}.$

4. $e^{ax} \sim \dfrac{\sinh aL}{aL} + 2(\sinh aL) \displaystyle\sum_{n=1}^{\infty} \dfrac{(-1)^n}{a^2L^2 + n^2\pi^2} \left(aL \cos \dfrac{n\pi x}{L} - n\pi \sin \dfrac{n\pi x}{L} \right).$

5. $f(x) \sim \dfrac{1}{\pi} - \dfrac{2}{\pi} \displaystyle\sum_{n=1}^{\infty} \dfrac{\cos 2nx}{4n^2 - 1} + \dfrac{1}{2} \sin x.$

6. $x \cos \dfrac{\pi x}{L} \sim -\dfrac{L}{2\pi} \sin \dfrac{\pi x}{L} + \dfrac{2L}{\pi} \displaystyle\sum_{n=2}^{\infty} (-1)^n \dfrac{n}{n^2 - 1} \sin \dfrac{n\pi x}{L}.$

7. $x + x^2 \sim \dfrac{L^2}{3} + \dfrac{4L^2}{\pi^2} \displaystyle\sum_{n=1}^{\infty} \dfrac{(-1)^n}{n^2} \cos \dfrac{n\pi x}{L} + \dfrac{2L}{\pi} \displaystyle\sum_{n=1}^{\infty} \dfrac{(-1)^{n+1}}{n} \sin \dfrac{n\pi x}{L}.$

8. $\cosh ax \sim \dfrac{\sinh a\pi}{a\pi} + \dfrac{2a}{\pi} \sinh a\pi \displaystyle\sum_{n=1}^{\infty} \dfrac{(-1)^n}{a^2 + n^2} \cos nx.$

9. $\sinh ax \sim \dfrac{2 \sinh a\pi}{\pi} \displaystyle\sum_{n=1}^{\infty} (-1)^{n+1} \dfrac{n}{a^2 + n^2} \sin nx.$

11. $f(x) \sim \dfrac{1}{\pi} - \dfrac{2}{\pi} \displaystyle\sum_{n=1}^{\infty} \dfrac{\cos 2nx}{4n^2 - 1} - \dfrac{1}{2} \sin x.$

12. $f(x) \sim \dfrac{\pi}{2} + \dfrac{4}{\pi} \displaystyle\sum_{n=1}^{\infty} \dfrac{\cos(2n-1)x}{(2n-1)^2}.$

13. Consider

$$a_n = \dfrac{1}{L} \int_{-L}^{0} f(x) \cos \dfrac{n\pi x}{L} \, dx + \dfrac{1}{L} \int_{0}^{L} f(x) \cos \dfrac{n\pi x}{L} \, dx$$

and set $x = t - L$ in the first integral on the right and use $f(t - L) = f(t)$.

14. $f(x) \sim \pi/2 - \sum_{n=1}^{\infty} (\sin 2nx)/n.$

Exercises 5.2

1. $f(x) \sim \dfrac{1}{4} - \dfrac{2}{\pi^2} \displaystyle\sum_{n=1}^{\infty} \dfrac{\cos 2(2n-1)\pi x}{(2n-1)^2}$

$\sim \dfrac{4}{\pi^2} \displaystyle\sum_{n=1}^{\infty} \dfrac{(-1)^{n+1}}{(2n-1)^2} \sin(2n-1)\pi x.$

2. $\pi^2 - x^2 \sim \dfrac{2\pi^2}{3} + 4\displaystyle\sum_{n=1}^{\infty}\dfrac{(-1)^{n+1}}{n^2}\cos nx$

$\sim \displaystyle\sum_{n=1}^{\infty}\left[\dfrac{2\pi}{n} + \dfrac{4}{\pi}\dfrac{1-(-1)^n}{n^3}\right]\sin nx.$

3. $1 - x \sim \dfrac{8}{\pi^2}\displaystyle\sum_{n=1}^{\infty}\dfrac{\cos[(2n-1)\pi x/2]}{(2n-1)^2}$

$\sim \dfrac{2}{\pi}\displaystyle\sum_{n=1}^{\infty}\dfrac{\sin n\pi x}{n}.$

4. $f(x) \sim \dfrac{3}{4} - \dfrac{2}{\pi^2}\displaystyle\sum_{n=1}^{\infty}\dfrac{\cos(2n-1)\pi x}{(2n-1)^2}$

$\sim -\dfrac{4}{\pi^2}\displaystyle\sum_{n=1}^{\infty}\dfrac{\cos[(2n-1)\pi x/2]}{(2n-1)^2}.$

5. $e^x \sim \dfrac{e^\pi - 1}{\pi} + \dfrac{2}{\pi}\displaystyle\sum_{n=1}^{\infty}\dfrac{(-1)^n e^\pi - 1}{1+n^2}\cos nx$

$\sim \dfrac{2}{\pi}\displaystyle\sum_{n=1}^{\infty}\left(\dfrac{n}{n^2+1}\right)[e^\pi(-1)^{n+1} - 1]\sin nx.$

7. $f(x) \sim \dfrac{1}{2}\left(1 + \dfrac{2}{\pi}\right) - \dfrac{1}{\pi}\cos \pi x - \dfrac{2}{\pi}\displaystyle\sum_{n=2}^{\infty}\dfrac{\cos n\pi x}{n^2-1}.$

8. $\sinh x \sim \dfrac{2}{\pi}(\cosh \pi - 1) + \dfrac{4}{\pi}\cosh \pi\displaystyle\sum_{n=1}^{\infty}\dfrac{(-1)^n}{n^2+1}\cos nx - \dfrac{4}{\pi}\displaystyle\sum_{n=1}^{\infty}\dfrac{\cos nx}{n^2+1}.$

9. $f(x) \sim \dfrac{1}{4} - \dfrac{2}{\pi^2}\displaystyle\sum_{n=1}^{\infty}\dfrac{\cos(2n-1)\pi x}{(2n-1)^2}$

$+ \dfrac{4}{\pi^2}\displaystyle\sum_{n=1}^{\infty}\left[\dfrac{\pi}{2}\dfrac{(-1)^{n+1}}{(2n-1)} - \dfrac{1}{(2n-1)^2}\right]\cos\left(\dfrac{2n-1}{2}\right)\pi x.$

10. $\sin x \sim \dfrac{2}{\pi} - \dfrac{4}{\pi}\displaystyle\sum_{n=1}^{\infty}\dfrac{\cos 2nx}{4n^2-1}.$

11. $f(x) \sim \dfrac{1}{2}\sin x - \dfrac{4}{\pi}\displaystyle\sum_{n=1}^{\infty}(-1)^n\dfrac{n}{4n^2-1}\sin nx.$

12. $x(1-x) \sim \dfrac{8}{\pi^3}\displaystyle\sum_{n=1}^{\infty}\dfrac{\sin(2n-1)\pi x}{(2n-1)^3}.$

13. $f(x) \sim \displaystyle\sum_{n=1}^{\infty}\left[b_{2n}\sin n\pi x + b_{2n-1}\sin\left(\dfrac{2n-1}{2}\right)\pi x\right]$

where

$b_{2n} = \dfrac{2}{\pi^3 n^3}[(-1)^n - 1] - \dfrac{1}{n\pi}$

$b_{2n-1} = (-1)^{n+1}\dfrac{8}{(2n-1)^2\pi^2} - \dfrac{16}{\pi^3(2n-1)^3} + \dfrac{2}{\pi(2n-1)}.$

14. $\cosh x \sim \dfrac{2}{\pi} \sum\limits_{n=1}^{\infty} \left(\dfrac{n}{n^2 + 1}\right) [(-1)^{n+1} \cosh \pi + 1] \sin nx.$

15. $\cos \pi x \sim \dfrac{8}{\pi} \sum\limits_{n=1}^{\infty} \dfrac{n}{4n^2 - 1} \sin 2n\pi x.$

Exercises 5.7

1. $F(s) = \left(\dfrac{2}{\pi}\right)^{1/2} \dfrac{1 - \cos s}{s^2}.$

2. $F(s) = \left(\dfrac{2}{\pi}\right)^{1/2} \dfrac{a}{a^2 + s^2}.$

3. $F(s) = \left(\dfrac{\pi}{2}\right)^{1/2} e^{-s}.$

5. (c) $G(s) = \dfrac{1}{\sqrt{2\pi}} \displaystyle\int_{a}^{\infty} e^{-isx} f(x - a)\, dx$

$= \dfrac{1}{\sqrt{2\pi}} \displaystyle\int_{0}^{\infty} e^{-is(a+t)} f(t)\, dt$

$= e^{-ias} F(s).$

6. $\dfrac{1}{\sqrt{2\pi}} \displaystyle\int_{-\infty}^{\infty} e^{-isx} f'(x)\, dx$

$= \dfrac{1}{\sqrt{2\pi}} e^{-isx} f(x) \Big|_{-\infty}^{\infty} + \dfrac{is}{\sqrt{2\pi}} \displaystyle\int_{-\infty}^{\infty} e^{-isx} f(x)\, dx = isF(s).$

7. (a) $F_c(s) = \left(\dfrac{2}{\pi}\right)^{1/2} \dfrac{\cos(s\pi/2)}{1 - s^2}.$

(b) $F_c(s) = \left(\dfrac{2}{\pi}\right)^{1/2} \dfrac{1 - s^2}{(1 + s^2)^2}.$

8. (a) $F_s(s) = \left(\dfrac{2}{\pi}\right)^{1/2} \dfrac{s - \sin(s\pi/2)}{s^2 - 1}.$

(b) $F_s(s) = 2 \left(\dfrac{2}{\pi}\right)^{1/2} \dfrac{s}{(1 + s^2)^2}.$

9. (a) $f(s) = \dfrac{2}{\pi} \dfrac{s^3}{s^4 + 4}.$

(b) $f(s) = \dfrac{2}{\pi} \dfrac{2 - s^2}{s^4 + 4}.$

11. $f(x) = 2xe^{-x} \qquad (x \geq 0).$

Chapter 6

Exercises 6.1

3. $\phi(x, t) = [(L - x)/L]a(t) + (x/L)b(t).$

4. $\phi(x, t) = xa(t) + (x^2/2L)[b(t) - a(t)].$

5. $\phi(x, t) = ((\pi - x)/\pi)t^2 + (x/\pi)e^t$.

6. $v_t - kv_{xx} = xt - (x - 1) \cos t - (1/(1 + t)); v(x, 0) = x, v_x(0, t) = v(1, t) = 0$;
    $\phi(x, t) = (x - 1) \sin t + \ln(1 + t)$.

7. (a) $\phi(x) = -(A/ka^2)e^{-ax}$.

    (b) $\phi(x) = -\dfrac{Ae^{-ax}}{ka^2} + \dfrac{A(e^{-aL} - 1)}{Lka^2} x + \dfrac{A}{ka^2}$.

8. Set $v(x, t) = u(x, t) - h(t)$.   9. Set $v(x, t) = u(x, t) - xh(t)$.

10. $u(x, t) = e^{-hx} \int_0^x e^{h\xi} v(\xi, t) \, d\xi$.

Exercises 6.2

1. Let $w(x, t) = v(x, t) - u(x, t)$. Then $w(0, t) \geq 0$ and $w(L, t) \geq 0$ for $t \geq 0$,
    and $w(x, 0) \geq 0$ for $0 \leq x \leq L$. By the maximum principle, $w(x, t) \geq 0$ for
    $0 \leq x \leq L, t \geq 0$.

3. If u assumed a maximum at a point (x_0, t_0), where $0 < x_0 < L, 0 < t_0 \leq T, T$
    an arbitrary number, then $u_t(x_0, t_0) \geq 0$ and $u_{xx}(x_0, t_0) \leq 0$ so that $u_t(x_0, t_0) -$
    $ku_{xx}(x_0, t_0) \geq 0$, contradicting the fact that $F(x_0, t_0) < 0$.

5. (a) Integration by parts yields

$$\frac{1}{2} \frac{\partial}{\partial t} \int_0^L u^2 \, dx - kuu_x \Big|_0^L + k \int_0^L u_x^2 \, dx = 0$$

Since $u(0, t) = u(L, t) = 0$ and $k > 0$,

$$\frac{1}{2} \frac{\partial}{\partial t} \int_0^L u^2 \, dx = -k \int_0^L u_x^2 \, dx \leq 0$$

6. Since u tends to zero uniformly in t as $|x| \to \infty$, there is a number L sufficiently
    large such that $|u(\pm L, t)| \leq \max|f(x)|$ for $|x| \leq L$. Then, by the maximum
    principle, $|u(x, t)| \leq \max|f(x)|$ for $|x| \leq L, 0 \leq t \leq T$ for sufficiently large
    L and T. Hence, $|u(x, t)| \leq \max|f(x)|$ for all (x, t).

7. If u is a solution of the heat equation $u_t - k(u_{xx} + u_{yy}) = 0$ that is continuous
    in Ω, then u assumes its maximum either in D at $t = 0$ or on C for $0 \leq t \leq T$.
    Let $v(x, y, t) = u(x, y, t) + \varepsilon x^2$. Then $v_t - k(v_{xx} + v_{yy}) < 0$ and hence v
    cannot attain a maximum in the interior of Ω.

8. Suppose u_1 and u_2 are two solutions. Take $u = u_1 - u_2$. Then u vanishes in
    D and on C for $0 \leq t \leq T, T$ being arbitrary. By the maximum principle,
    $u \equiv 0$ for all (x, y, t).

9. By Green's identity,

$$\iint_D uu_t \, dx \, dy - k \iint_D u \, \Delta u \, dx \, dy$$

$$= \frac{1}{2} \frac{\partial}{\partial t} \iint_D u^2 \, dx \, dy - k \iint_C u \frac{\partial u}{\partial n} \, ds + k \iint_D (u_x^2 + u_y^2) \, dx \, dy = 0.$$

Since $u = 0$, it follows that

$$\frac{1}{2}\frac{\partial}{\partial t}\iint_D u^2 \, dx \, dy = -k\iint_D (u_x^2 + u_y^2) \, dx \, dy \le 0$$

Exercises 6.3

1. $u(x, t) = \dfrac{4A}{\pi}\displaystyle\sum_{n=1}^{\infty}\dfrac{e^{-k(2n-1)^2 t}}{(2n-1)}\sin(2n-1)x.$

2. $u(x, t) = \frac{3}{4}e^{-kt}\sin x - \frac{1}{4}e^{-9kt}\sin 3x.$

3. $u(x, t) = \frac{1}{2}(1 + e^{-4kt}\cos 2x).$

4. $u(x, t) = \dfrac{8}{\pi}\displaystyle\sum_{n=1}^{\infty}\dfrac{e^{-k(2n-1)^2 t}}{(2n-1)^3}\sin(2n-1)x.$

5. $u(x, t) = \dfrac{4}{\pi}\displaystyle\sum_{n=1}^{\infty}\dfrac{e^{-k(2n-1)^2 t}}{(2n-1)^2}\sin(2n-1)x.$

6. $u(x, t) = \dfrac{32}{8}\displaystyle\sum_{n=1}^{\infty}(-1)^n\dfrac{e^{-k(2n-1)^2 t/4}}{(2n-1)^3}\sin\left(\dfrac{2n-1}{2}\right)x.$

7. $u(x, t) = \dfrac{8}{\pi^2}\displaystyle\sum_{n=1}^{\infty}\left[\dfrac{(-1)^n}{(2n-1)^2} + \dfrac{4}{\pi(2n-1)^3}\right]$

$\qquad\qquad \times\, e^{-[k(2n-1)^2\pi^2/4 - 1]t}\sin\left(\dfrac{2n-1}{2}\right)\pi x.$

8. $u(x, t) = e^{-(k+1)t}\cos x.$ 9. $u(x, t) = \frac{3}{4}\sin x - \frac{1}{4}e^{-3t}\sin 2x.$

11. $u(x, t) = \dfrac{32}{\pi^3}\displaystyle\sum_{n=1}^{\infty}\dfrac{(-1)^{n+1}}{(2n-1)^3}e^{-[(2n-1)^2\pi^2/4 + 1]t}\cos\left(\dfrac{2n-1}{2}\right)\pi x.$

12. $u(x, t) = \sum_{n=1}^{\infty} b_n e^{-k\mu_n^2 t}\sin\mu_n x,$ where $b_n = (2/L)\int_0^L f(x)\sin\mu_n x \, dx$ with $\mu_n = -h\tan\mu_n L.$

13. $u(x, t) = \sum_{n=1}^{\infty} b_n e^{-k\mu_n^2 t}(h\sin\mu_n x - \mu_n\cos\mu_n x),$ where $b_n = (2/L)\int_0^L f(x)\times$ $(h\sin\mu_n x - \mu_n\cos\mu_n x)\,dx,$ with $\mu_n = h\tan\mu_n L.$

Exercises 6.4

1. $u(x, t) = A - \dfrac{4A}{\pi}\displaystyle\sum_{n=1}^{\infty}\dfrac{e^{-k(2n-1)^2\pi^2 t/L^2}}{(2n-1)}\sin\left(\dfrac{2n-1}{L}\right)\pi x.$

2. $u(x, t) = (x - L)A + \dfrac{8AL}{\pi^2}\displaystyle\sum_{n=1}^{\infty}\dfrac{e^{-k(2n-1)^2\pi^2 t/(2L)^2}}{(2n-1)^2}\cos\left(\dfrac{2n-1}{2}\right)\dfrac{\pi x}{L}.$

3. $u(x, t) = \dfrac{L-x}{L}\sin\omega t - \dfrac{2\omega}{\pi}\displaystyle\sum_{n=1}^{\infty}\dfrac{\sin(n\pi x/L)}{n(k^2\lambda_n^2 + \omega^2)}$

$\qquad\qquad \times\, [k\lambda_n\cos\omega t + \omega\sin\omega t - k\lambda_n e^{-k\lambda_n t}]$

where $\lambda_n = n^2\pi^2/L^2, \; n = 1, 2, \ldots.$

4. $u(x, t) = w(x, t) + x \cos \omega t$ where

$$w(x, t) = \frac{8\omega L}{\pi^2} \sum_{n=1}^{\infty} \frac{(-1)^{n+1}}{(2n-1)^2} \left(\int_0^t e^{-k\lambda_n(t-\tau)} \sin \omega\tau \, d\tau \right)$$

$$\times \sin \sqrt{\lambda_n} \, x + \frac{8L}{\pi^2} \sum_{n=1}^{\infty} \frac{(-1)^n}{(2n-1)^2} e^{-k\lambda_n t} \sin \sqrt{\lambda_n} \, x$$

$$\lambda_n = \frac{(2n-1)^2\pi^2}{4L^2} \qquad (n = 1, 2, \ldots)$$

5. $u(x, t) = w(x, t) + x/\pi$, where

$$w(x, t) = \frac{2h}{\pi} \sum_{n=1}^{\infty} \frac{(-1)^n}{n(n^2 + h)} \left[1 - e^{-(n^2+h)t} \right] \sin nx$$

$$+ \frac{2}{\pi} \sum_{n=1}^{\infty} \frac{(-1)^n}{n} e^{-(n^2+h)t} \sin nx.$$

6. $u(x, t) = v(x, t) + \phi(x) + \sum_{n=1}^{\infty} b_n \sin\left(\frac{2n-1}{2}\right) x,$

where

$$v(x, t) = \frac{16}{\pi} \sum_{n=1}^{\infty} \frac{2e^{-\pi}(-1)^{n+1} + 2n - 1}{(2n-1)^2[(2n-1)^2 + 4]} e^{-k\lambda_n t} \sin\left(\frac{2n-1}{2}\right) x$$

$$\phi(x) = -e^{-x} - xe^{-\pi} + 1$$

$$b_n = \frac{2}{\pi} \int_0^{\pi} f(x) \sin\left(\frac{2n-1}{2}\right) x \, dx$$

$$\lambda_n = \left(\frac{2n-1}{2}\right)^2$$

7. $u(x, t) = (a_0/2) + \sum_{n=1}^{\infty} a_n e^{-kn^2 t} \cos nx + (A/\omega) \sin \omega t$ where $a_n = (2/\pi) \times \int_0^{\pi} f(x) \cos nx \, dx, n = 0, 1, 2, \ldots$.

8. $u(x, t) = \sum_{n=1}^{\infty} \int_0^t e^{-k\lambda_n(t-\tau)} \left[(-1)^{n+1} \frac{2kn\pi}{L^2} h(\tau) + g_n(\tau) \right] d\tau$

where $g_n(\tau) = (2/L) \int_0^L g(x, t) \sin(n\pi x/L) \, dx$ and $\lambda_n = n^2\pi^2/L^2$, $n = 1, 2, \ldots$.

9. $u(x, t) = (u_0(t)/2) + \sum_{n=1}^{\infty} u_n(t) \cos(n\pi x/L)$ where $u_n(t) = \int_0^t e^{-k\lambda_n(t-\tau)} \times$ $[g_n(\tau) - (2k/L)h(\tau)] \, d\tau$ with $\lambda_n = n^2\pi^2/L^2$ and $g_n(t) = (2/L) \int_0^L g(x, t) \times$ $\cos(n\pi x/L) \, dx, n = 0, 1, 2, \ldots$.

Exercises 6.5

1. $u(x, t) = (1/2\sqrt{\pi t}) \int_0^{\infty} [e^{-(x+\xi)^2/(4t)} + e^{-(x-\xi)^2/(4t)}]e^{-\xi} \, d\xi.$

2. $u(x, t) = \frac{1}{2} \text{erf}\left(\frac{x + L}{2\sqrt{kt}}\right) - \frac{1}{2} \text{erf}\left(\frac{x - L}{2\sqrt{kt}}\right).$

3. $u(x, t) = \frac{1}{2}(B - A) \, \text{erf}(x/2\sqrt{kt}) + \frac{1}{2}(A + B).$

5. Let $u(x, t)$ denote the solution of the problem (6.1), (6.2), where f is odd, and define $v(x, t) = -u(-x, t)$. Then v is also a solution of (6.1), (6.2). Since the solution is unique, $u(x, t) = v(x, t)$; that is, $u(x, t) = -u(-x, t)$. If f is even, set $v(x, t) = u(-x, t)$.

6. Set $s = (x - \xi)/[2\sqrt{k(t - \tau)}]$.

9. Let $V(s, t)$ denote the Fourier transform of the solution $v(x, t)$. Then $\partial V/\partial t + (ks^2 + h)V = 0$, $V(s, 0) = F(s)$, where $F(s)$ is the Fourier transform of f. Thus, $V(x, t) = F(s)e^{-(ks^2+h)t}$ so that

$$v(x, t) = \frac{e^{-ht}}{\sqrt{2\pi}} \int_{-\infty}^{\infty} F(s)e^{-ks^2t+isx} \, ds$$

$$= \frac{e^{-ht}}{2\sqrt{k\pi t}} \int_{-\infty}^{\infty} e^{-(x-\xi)^2/(4kt)} f(\xi) \, d\xi$$

11. $u(x, t) = \int_0^t \int_{-\infty}^{\infty} e^{-h(t-\tau)}G(x - \xi, t - \tau)f(\xi, \tau) \, d\xi \, d\tau$ where $G(x - \xi, t - \tau)$ is as it appears in (6.21) of the present chapter.

Exercises 6.6

4. $u(x, t) = e^{a^2kt} \cosh ax - \dfrac{1}{2} e^{a^2kt} \left[e^{-ax} \operatorname{erf}\left(a\sqrt{kt} - \dfrac{x}{2\sqrt{kt}}\right)\right.$

$$\left. + e^{ax} \operatorname{erf}\left(a\sqrt{kt} + \dfrac{x}{2\sqrt{kt}}\right)\right].$$

5. $u(x, t) = A[1 - \operatorname{erf}(x/2\sqrt{kt})]$.

6. $u(x, t) = (2k/\pi) \int_0^{\infty} s \sin sx \int_0^t e^{-ks^2(t-\tau)}h(\tau) \, d\tau \, ds$.

7. $u(x, t) = -\sqrt{\dfrac{k}{\pi}} \int_0^t \dfrac{e^{-x^2/[4k(t-\tau)]}h(\tau)}{\sqrt{t - \tau}} \, d\tau$

$$+ \int_0^t \int_0^{\infty} [G(x + \xi, t - \tau) + G(x - \xi, t - \tau)]f(\xi, \tau) \, d\xi \, d\tau.$$

8. $u(x,t) = \dfrac{e^{-ht}}{2\sqrt{k\pi t}} \int_0^{\infty} [e^{-(x-\xi)^2/(4kt)} + e^{-(x+\xi)^2/(4kt)}]f(\xi) \, d\xi$.

10. $u(x, t) = 2k/\pi \int_0^{\infty} s \sin sx \int_0^t e^{-(t-\tau)(ks^2+b)}h(\tau) \, d\tau \, ds$.

11. $u(x, t) = -\left(\dfrac{k}{\pi}\right)^{1/2} \int_0^t \dfrac{\exp(-x^2/[4k(t - \tau)] - b(t - \tau))}{\sqrt{t - \tau}} h(\tau) \, d\tau$.

12. $u(x, t) = \dfrac{2e^{-t^2/2}}{\pi} \int_0^{\infty} \dfrac{e^{-ks^2t} \cos sx}{1 + s^2} \, ds$.

13. $u(x, t) = -\int_x^{\infty} e^{-h(\xi-x)}v(\xi, t) \, d\xi$, where

$$v(x, t) = \frac{1}{2\sqrt{k\pi t}} \int_0^{\infty} [f'(\xi) - hf(\xi)][e^{-(x-\xi)^2/(4kt)} - e^{-(x+\xi)^2/(4kt)}] \, d\xi$$

14. $u(x, t) = -\int_x^{\infty} e^{-h(\xi-x)}v(\xi, t) \, d\xi$, where v is the solution of Problem 6 of these exercises.

15. $u(x, t) = e^{-bt}v(x, t)$, where $v(x, t)$ is the solution of Problem 13 of these exercises.

16. $u(x, t) = (aA/x)[1 - \text{erf}((x - a)/2\sqrt{kt})]$.

Chapter 7

Exercises 7.1

2. Apply formula (2.11) of this section.

3. Let u_1 and u_2 be two solutions and set $u = u_1 - u_2$. Then $\Delta u + ku = 0$ in D and $u = 0$ on C. By formula (2.4), $\int_D \int [-ku^2 + u_x^2 + u_y^2] \, dx \, dy = 0$. Since $k < 0$ the integrand is nonnegative. The vanishing of the integral means $-ku^2 + u_x^2 + u_y^2 = 0$, which implies $u \equiv 0$.

5. Let u_1 and u_2 be two solutions and set $u = u_1 - u_2$. Then $\Delta u + ku = 0$ in D and $\partial u/\partial n + hu = 0$ on C. By formula (2.4), $-\int_C hu^2 \, ds = \int_D \int (-ku^2 + u_x^2 + u_y^2) \, dx \, dy$. If $k < 0$ and $h > 0$, then the integral on the left is nonpositive and the integral on the right is nonnegative. This means that both integrals must vanish, which implies $u \equiv 0$.

6. By Green's theorem

$$\int_D \int uLu \, dx \, dy = - \int_D \int (x^2 u_x^2 + e^y u_y^2) \, dx \, dy$$

$$+ \int_C u(-e^y u_y \, dx + x^2 u_x \, dy) = 0$$

which gives $\int_D \int (x^2 u_x^2 + e^y u_y^2) \, dx \, dy = 0$, since $u = 0$ on C. Since the integrand is nonnegative $u \equiv 0$.

7. If u_1 and u_2 are two solutions and $u = u_1 - u_2$, then

$$Lu = \frac{\partial}{\partial x} [(1 + x^2)u_x] + \frac{\partial}{\partial y} [(1 + y^2)u_y] + ku = 0$$

and

$$uLu = \frac{\partial}{\partial x} [(1 + x^2)uu_x] + \frac{\partial}{\partial y} [(1 + y^2)uu_y]$$

$$- (1 + x^2)u_x^2 - (1 + y^2)u_y^2 = 0$$

By Green's theorem,

$$\int_D \int uLu \, dx \, dy = - \int_D \int [(1 + x^2)u_x^2 + (1 + y^2)u_y^2] \, dx \, dy = 0,$$

which implies $u \equiv 0$.

8. If u_1 and u_2 are two solutions and $u = u_1 - u_2$, then $\Delta u = 0$ in D, $u = 0$ on C_1, and $\partial u/\partial n + hu = 0$ on C_2. By formula (2.4),

$$\int_{C_1 + C_2} u \frac{\partial u}{\partial n} \, ds = \int_D \int (u \Delta u + u_x^2 + u_y^2) \, dx \, dy$$

Hence,

$$- \int_{C_2} hu^2 \, ds = \int\int_D (u_x^2 + u_y^2) \, dx \, dy$$

which, as in Problem 5, implies $u \equiv 0$.

Exercises 7.2

1. $\Delta u = u_{rr} + (1/r)u_r + (1/r^2)u_{\theta\theta} = 0$.

2. Let $\xi = x/r^2$, $\eta = y/r^2$ and introduce polar coordinates. Then $v(r, \theta) = u(\xi, \eta)$ and $v_{rr} + (1/r)v_r + (1/r^2)v_{\theta\theta} = (1/r^4)(u_{\xi\xi} + u_{\eta\eta}) = 0$.

3. Let $v(\xi, \eta) = u(r, \theta)$. Then

$$\begin{aligned}
v_{\xi\xi} + v_{\eta\eta} &= 0 & (0 < \xi < \infty, 0 < \eta < b) \\
v(\xi, 0) &= f(ae^{-\xi}) & (0 \le \xi < \infty) \\
v(0, \eta) &= 0 & (0 \le \eta \le b) \\
v(\xi, b) &= 0 & (0 \le \xi \le \infty)
\end{aligned}$$

6. Since $w - v \ge 0$ and $v - u \ge 0$ on C, Theorem 3.1 implies that $w - v \ge 0$ and $v - u \ge 0$ in D. Hence, $u \le v \le w$ in D.

7. Let $w = v - u$. Then $\Delta w = \Delta v \ge 0$ in D. Since $w = 0$ on C, the maximum of w is zero. Hence, $w \le 0$ in D; that is, $v \le u$.

8. If u attains a maximum in D, then $\Delta u \le 0$, contradicting the fact that $q > 0$.

9. If u has a positive maximum at a point in D, then at that point $\Delta u \le 0$, contradicting the fact that $hu > 0$.

11. Let $v = u + \varepsilon x^2$ with $\varepsilon > 0$. Then $\Delta v = 2\varepsilon > 0$ so that v cannot attain its maximum in D.

Exercises 7.3

1. $u(x, y) = \sum_{n=1}^{\infty} b_n \dfrac{\sinh[n\pi(b - y)/b]}{\sinh n\pi} \sin \dfrac{n\pi x}{a}$

where

$$b_n = \frac{2}{a} \int_0^a f(x) \sin \frac{n\pi x}{a} \, dx \qquad (n = 1, 2, \dots).$$

2. $u(x, y) = \sum_{n=1}^{\infty} b_n \dfrac{\sinh(n\pi x/b)}{\sinh(n\pi a/b)} \sin \dfrac{n\pi y}{b}$

where $b_n = (2/b) \int_0^b g(y) \sin(n\pi y/b) \, dy$, $\qquad (n = 1, 2, \dots)$.

3. $u(x, y) = \dfrac{\sinh 2(\pi - y)}{\sinh 2\pi} \sin 2x + \dfrac{\sinh 2x}{\sinh 2\pi} \sin 2y$.

4. $u(x, y) = x(\pi - x)/2 - w$, where

$$w(x, y) = \frac{4}{\pi} \sum_{n=1}^{\infty} \frac{1}{(2n-1)^3} \frac{\sinh(2n-1)(\pi - y) + \sinh(2n-1)y}{\sinh(2n-1)\pi} \sin(2n-1)x$$

5. Set $w(x, y) = u(x, y) - \cos x$ and solve the problem $\Delta w = 0$, $w(0, y) = -1$, $w(\pi, y) = 1$, $w_y(x, 0) = 0$, $w(x, 1) = -\cos x$.

6. Set $w(x, y) = u - (x^3 - y^3)/6$ and solve the problem $\Delta w = 0$, $w_x(0, y) = 0$, $w(1, y) = (y^3 - 1)/6$, $w(x, 0) = -x^3/6$, $w_y(x, 1) = \frac{1}{2}$.

7. Define $v(x, y) = -u(y, x)$. Then $\Delta v = 0$, $v(0, y) = 0$, $v(a, y) = f(y)$, $v(x, 0) = 0$, and $v(x, a) = -f(x)$. Thus, v is also a solution of the problem. Since the solution u is uniquely determined, $u(x, y) = v(x, y)$; that is, $u(x, y) = -u(y, x)$. In particular, setting $x = y$, there follows $u(x, x) = -u(x, x) = 0$.

8. $u(x, y) = \frac{3}{4}(\sinh x \sin y - \sinh y \sin x)/\sinh \pi$
$$- \tfrac{1}{4}(\sinh 3x \sin 3y - \sinh 3y \sin 3x)/\sinh 3\pi.$$

9. $u(x, y) = \displaystyle\sum_{n=1}^{\infty} \frac{A_n}{\cosh[(2n - 1)\pi/2]} \left[\cosh\left(\frac{2n - 1}{2}\right) x \cos\left(\frac{2n - 1}{2}\right) y \right.$
$$\left. + \cosh\left(\frac{2n - 1}{2}\right) y \cos\left(\frac{2n - 1}{2}\right) x \right]$$

where
$$A_n = \frac{2}{\pi} \int_0^{\pi} f(x) \cos\left(\frac{2n - 1}{2}\right) x\, dx \qquad (n = 1, 2, \ldots)$$

10. $u(x, y) = \displaystyle\sum_{n=1}^{\infty} b_n \frac{\sinh(h + n^2)^{1/2} y}{\sinh(h + n^2)^{1/2}\pi} \sin nx$

where $b_n = (2/\pi) \int_0^{\pi} f(x) \sin nx\, dx$ $\quad (n = 1, 2, \ldots)$.

11. $u(x, y) = A - \dfrac{b}{\pi} \displaystyle\sum_{n=1}^{\infty} a_n \frac{\cosh[n\pi(x - a)/b]}{n \sinh(n\pi a/b)} \cos \frac{n\pi y}{b}$

where $a_n = (2/b) \int_0^b g(y) \cos(n\pi y/b)\, dy$ $\quad (n = 1, 2, \ldots)$ and A arbitrary.

12. $u(x, y) = \dfrac{b}{\pi} \displaystyle\sum_{n=1}^{\infty} \frac{a_n \cosh(n\pi x/b)}{n \sinh(n\pi a/b)} \cos \frac{n\pi y}{b}$
$$- \frac{a}{\pi} \sum_{n=1}^{\infty} \frac{b_n \cosh[n\pi(y - b)/a]}{n \sinh(n\pi b/a)} \cos \frac{n\pi x}{a}$$

where $\quad a_n = (2/b) \int_0^b g(y) \cos(n\pi y/b)\, dy$ and $b_n = (2/a) \int_0^a f(x) \cos(n\pi x/a)\, dx$
$$(n = 1, 2, \ldots).$$

13. $u(x, y) = A + \dfrac{1}{2} y + \dfrac{4}{\pi^2} \displaystyle\sum_{n=1}^{\infty} \left[\frac{\cosh[(2n - 1)(\pi - y)] + \cosh(2n - 1)y}{(2n - 1)^3 \sinh n\pi} \right]$
$$\times \cos(2n - 1)x.$$

14. $u(x, y) = -\dfrac{\cosh(x - \pi)}{\sinh \pi} \cos y - \dfrac{8}{\pi^2} \displaystyle\sum_{n=1}^{\infty} \frac{\cosh(2n - 1)(y - \pi)}{(2n - 1)^3 \sinh(2n - 1)} \cos(2n - 1)x.$

15. $u(x, y) = a_0 \dfrac{y}{2\pi} + \displaystyle\sum_{n=1}^{\infty} \frac{\sinh ny}{\sinh n\pi} \cos nx$

where $a_n = (2/\pi) \int_0^{\pi} f(x) \cos nx\, dx$ $\quad (n = 1, 2, \ldots)$.

16. $u(x, y) = \sum_{n=1}^{\infty} a_n \dfrac{\cosh[(2n - 1)(y - \pi)/2]}{\cosh[(2n - 1)\pi/2]} \cos\left(\dfrac{2n - 1}{2}\right) x$

$\qquad + 2 \sum_{n=1}^{\infty} \dfrac{b_n}{(2n - 1)} \dfrac{\sin[(2n - 1)(x - \pi)/2]}{\cosh[(2n - 1)\pi/2]} \sin\left(\dfrac{2n - 1}{2}\right) y$

where

$$a_n = \frac{2}{\pi} \int_0^{\pi} f(x) \cos\left(\frac{2n - 1}{2}\right) x \, dx \qquad (n = 1, 2, \ldots)$$

$$b_n = \frac{2}{\pi} \int_0^{\pi} g(y) \sin\left(\frac{2n - 1}{2}\right) y \, dy \qquad (n = 1, 2, \ldots)$$

Exercises 7.4

1. $u(r, \theta) = \frac{3}{4} a^2 r \sin \theta - \frac{1}{4} r^3 \sin 3\theta$.

2. $u(r, \theta) = \frac{1}{2} + \frac{1}{2} r^2 \cos 2\theta + r \sin \theta$.

3. $u(x, y) = \frac{1}{2}(a^2 + x^2 - y^2)$.

4. $u(x, y) = \frac{1}{8}(x^4 - 6x^2 y^2 + y^4) - 2(x^2 - y^2) + 6$.

5. Set $v(r, \theta) = u(r, \theta) + u(r, -\theta)$. Then $\Delta v = 0$ and $v(a, \theta) = f(\theta) + f(-\theta) = f(\theta) - f(\theta) = 0$. Hence, $v \equiv 0$; that is, $u(r, -\theta) = -u(r, \theta)$. In particular, $u(r, 0) = -u(r, 0) = 0$.

6. $u(r, \theta) = (2r^2/a^2) \sin 2\theta$.

7. If f is an odd function of θ, then according to Problem 5, the same is true of the solution u and thus it vanishes at $\theta = 0, \pi$. Set $v(r, \theta) = u(r, \theta + \pi) - u(r, \theta)$. Clearly, $\Delta v = 0$ and $v(a, \theta) = f(\theta + \pi) - f(\theta) = 0$. Hence, $v \equiv 0$, that is, $u(r, \theta + \pi) = u(r, \theta)$. Setting $\theta = -\pi/2$ yields $u(r, \pi/2) = u(r, -\pi/2) = -u(r, \pi/2)$; thus, $u(r, \pi/2) = 0$.

8. $u(r, \theta) = (2/a^3)r^4 \sin 2\theta \cos 2\theta$.

9. $u(r, \theta) = (3/2)r \sin \theta - (r^3/8) \sin 3\theta$.

10. $u(r, \theta) = (\alpha_0 + \beta_0 \ln r)/2 + \sum_{n=1}^{\infty} [(\alpha_n r^n + \beta_n r^{-n}) \cos n\theta + (\gamma_n r^n + \delta_n r^{-n}) \sin n\theta]$,
    where

$$\alpha_0 + \beta_0 \ln a = 0 \qquad\qquad \alpha_n a^n + \beta_n a^{-n} = 0$$
$$\alpha_0 + \beta_0 \ln b = a_0 \qquad\qquad \alpha_n b^n + \beta_n b^{-n} = a_n$$
$$\gamma_n a^n + \delta_n a^{-n} = 0 \qquad\qquad \gamma_n b^n + \delta_n b^{-n} = b_n$$

with $\alpha_n = (1/\pi) \int_0^{2\pi} f(\theta) \cos n\theta \, d\theta$, $\beta_n = (1/\pi) \int_0^{2\pi} f(\theta) \sin n\theta \, d\theta$, $n = 1, 2, \ldots$.

12. Define $f(\theta) = -f(-\theta)$ for $-\pi \le \theta \le 0$ and use the solution formula of Problem 10.

13. $u(r, \theta) = -\sum_{n=1}^{\infty} \dfrac{b_n}{\sinh[n\pi/\ln(b/a)]} \sinh\left[\dfrac{n\pi}{\ln(b/a)}(\theta - \pi)\right] \sin\left[\dfrac{n\pi}{\ln(b/a)} \ln\dfrac{r}{a}\right]$

where

$$b_n = \frac{2}{\ln(b/a)} \int_0^{\ln(b/a)} f(ae^{\xi}) \sin \frac{n\pi\xi}{\ln(b/a)} \, d\xi$$

Exercises 7.5

3. Multiply the inequality $m \le u(a, \theta) \le M$ by the sum of (6.2) and integrate over $[0, 2\pi]$.

4. For $r < a$,

$$u(r, \theta) \le \frac{1}{2\pi} \int_{-\pi}^{\pi} \frac{a^2 - r^2}{a^2 - 2ar + r^2} u(a, \phi) \, d\phi$$

$$\le \frac{1}{2\pi} \frac{a^2 - r^2}{(a - r)^2} \int_{-\pi}^{\pi} u(a, \phi) \, d\phi$$

$$\le \frac{a + r}{a - r} u(0, 0)$$

and

$$u(r, \theta) \ge \frac{1}{2\pi} \frac{a^2 - r^2}{(a + r)^2} \int_{-\pi}^{\pi} u(a, \phi) \, d\phi$$

$$\ge \frac{a - r}{a + r} u(0, 0)$$

5. Let $r \to \infty$ in Harnack's inequality.

8. $u(r, \theta) = \int_0^{\pi/2} [K^*(a, r, \theta, \phi) - K^*(a, r, \theta, \pi - \phi)] f(\phi) \, d\phi$, where $K^*(a, r, \theta, \phi) = K(a, r, \theta - \phi) - K(a, r, \theta + \phi)$.

11. Since $\Delta u = 0$ inside the sphere, it follows from the Green's identity

$$\iint_S \frac{\partial u}{\partial n} \, ds = \iiint_D \Delta u \, d\xi \, d\eta \, d\zeta$$

that

$$\iint_S \frac{\partial u}{\partial n} \, dS = r^2 \int_0^{2\pi} \int_0^{\pi} \frac{\partial u}{\partial r} \sin \phi \, d\phi \, d\theta = 0$$

Define

$$U(x, y, z; r) = \frac{1}{4\pi} \int_0^{2\pi} \int_0^{\pi} u(\xi, \eta, \zeta) \sin \phi \, d\phi \, d\theta$$

Then

$$\frac{\partial U}{\partial r} = \frac{1}{4\pi} \int_0^{2\pi} \int_0^{\pi} \frac{\partial u}{\partial r} (\xi, \eta, \zeta) \sin \phi \, d\phi \, d\theta = 0$$

so that U is independent of r. Therefore, in particular, $U(x, y, z; a) = U(x, y, z; 0) = u(x, y, z)$.

12. Suppose $\Delta u > 0$ at a point (x, y, z). There is a sphere S of radius r about this point throughout which $\Delta u > 0$. Consider

$$u(x, y, z) = \frac{1}{4\pi} \int_0^{2\pi} \int_0^{\pi} u \sin \phi \, d\phi \, d\theta$$

over the sphere S. Then

$$\frac{\partial u}{\partial r} = \frac{1}{4\pi} \int_0^{2\pi} \int_0^{\pi} \frac{\partial u}{\partial r} \sin \phi \, d\phi \, d\theta$$

$$= \frac{1}{4\pi r^2} \iint_S \frac{\partial u}{\partial n} \, dS = \frac{1}{4\pi r^2} \iiint_D \Delta u \, d\xi \, d\eta \, d\zeta > 0$$

contradicting the fact that $\partial u/\partial r = 0$.

Exercises 7.6

1. $u(r, \theta) = (r^2/4)(1 - \cos 2\theta) + C$.

2. $u(r, \theta) = (3/2)r \sin \theta - (r^3/24) \sin 3\theta + C$.

3. $u(r, \theta) = (r^2/2) \sin 2\theta + C$.

4. $u(x, y) = \frac{1}{6}y^3 - \frac{1}{2}x^2y + 6y + C$.

5. $u(x, y) = \frac{1}{3}x^3 - xy^2 + C$.

8. $u(r, \theta) = (\alpha_0/2) + (a/2\pi) \int_{-\pi}^{\pi} f(\phi) \ln[a^2 - 2ar \cos(\theta - \phi) + r^2] \, d\phi$.

10. $u(r, \theta) = (\alpha_0/2) - (a/2\pi) \int_0^{\pi} f(\phi) \ln[(a^2 - 2ar \cos(\theta + \phi) + r^2)$
$$\cdot (a^2 - 2ar \cos(\theta - \phi) + r^2)] \, d\phi.$$

Exercises 7.7

3. $u(x, y) = \dfrac{y}{\pi} \displaystyle\int_0^{\infty} \left[\dfrac{1}{(x + \xi)^2 + y^2} + \dfrac{1}{(x - \xi)^2 + y^2} \right] f(\xi) \, d\xi.$

4. $u(x, y) = \dfrac{x}{\pi} \displaystyle\int_0^{\infty} \left[\dfrac{1}{x^2 + (y - \eta)^2} - \dfrac{1}{x^2 + (y + \eta)^2} \right] f(\eta) \, d\eta.$

6. $u(x, y) = \dfrac{2}{\pi} \displaystyle\int_0^{\infty} \dfrac{\cosh sy}{\cosh sb} \sin sx \int_0^{\infty} f(\xi) \sin s\xi \, d\xi \, ds.$

7. $u(x, y) = -2 \displaystyle\sum_{n=1}^{\infty} \dfrac{b_n}{(2n - 1)} e^{-(2n-1)x/2} \cos\left(\dfrac{2n - 1}{2}\right) y$

where

$$b_n = \frac{2}{\pi} \int_0^{\pi} g(y) \cos\left(\frac{2n - 1}{2}\right) y \, dy$$

8. $u(x, y) = \dfrac{2}{\pi} \displaystyle\int_0^{\infty} \dfrac{\sinh sy}{s \cosh s\pi} \cos sx \int_0^{\infty} f(\xi) \cos s\xi \, d\xi \, ds.$

9. $u(r, \theta) = \dfrac{2}{\pi} \displaystyle\int_0^{\infty} \dfrac{\cosh s\theta}{\cosh sb} \sin\left(s \ln \dfrac{1}{r}\right) \int_0^1 \dfrac{1}{\rho} f(\rho) \sin\left(s \ln \dfrac{1}{\rho}\right) d\rho \, ds.$

10. $u(x, y) = \dfrac{2}{\pi} \displaystyle\int_0^{\infty} \dfrac{\sinh(s^2 + h)^{1/2}y}{\sinh(s^2 + h)\pi} \sin sx \int_0^{\infty} f(\xi) \sin s\xi \, d\xi \, ds.$

11. $u(x, y) = \sum\limits_{n=1}^{\infty} b_n e^{-(n^2 + h)^{1/2} x} \sin ny$

where $b_n = (2/\pi) \int_0^\pi g(y) \sin ny \, dy, \qquad n = 1, 2, \ldots$.

13. $u(x, y) = \dfrac{1}{2\pi} \displaystyle\int_0^{\infty} f(\xi) \ln\{[(x + \xi)^2 + y^2][(x - \xi)^2 + y^2]\} \, d\xi.$

14. $u(x, y) = \dfrac{1}{2\pi} \displaystyle\int_0^{\infty} g(\eta) \ln\left[\dfrac{x^2 + (y - \eta)^2}{x^2 + (y + \eta)^2}\right] d\eta.$

15. $u(x, y) = \dfrac{1}{2\pi} \displaystyle\int_0^{\infty} g(\eta) \ln\{[x^2 + (y - \eta)^2][x^2 + (y + \eta)^2]\} \, d\eta.$

16. Superpose solutions of Problems 13 and 15.

Exercises 7.8

3. In the expression for $G(\xi, \eta; x, y)$; set $\sigma = (x^2 + y^2)^{1/2}$ and note that

$$(x^2 + y^2)\left[\left(\xi - \frac{a^2}{\sigma^2}x\right)^2 + \left(\eta - \frac{a^2}{\sigma^2}y\right)^2\right]$$

$$= (x^2 + y^2)\rho^2 - 2a^2(x\xi + y\eta) + a^4$$

$$= \rho^2\left[x^2 + y^2 - \frac{2a^2}{\rho^2}(x\xi + y\eta) + \frac{a^4}{\rho^4}(\xi^2 + \eta^2)\right]$$

$$= \rho^2\left[\left(x - \frac{a^2}{\rho^2}\xi\right)^2 + \left(y - \frac{a^2}{\rho^2}\eta\right)^2\right]$$

5. By the formula (7.9), write the boundary condition in the form

$$g(a, \theta; \rho, \phi) = -\frac{1}{2\pi}\ln a + \frac{1}{2\pi}\sum_{n=1}^{\infty}\frac{1}{n}\left(\frac{\rho}{a}\right)^n[\cos n\phi \cos n\theta + \sin n\phi \sin n\theta].$$

Assume $g(v, \theta) = \alpha_0/2 + \sum_{n=1}^{\infty} v^n(a_n \cos n\theta + b_n \sin n\theta)$. Equating this to the boundary condition when $v = a$ yields $a_0 = -(1/\pi)\ln a$, $a_n = (1/2\pi n) \times (\rho/a)^n \cos n\phi$ and $b_n = (1/2\pi n)(\rho/a)^n \sin n\phi$, $n \geq 1$. Hence,

$$g(v, \theta) = -\frac{1}{2\pi}\ln a - \frac{1}{4\pi}\ln\left[\frac{a^4 - 2a^2\rho v \cos(\theta - \phi) + \rho^2 v^2}{a^4}\right]$$

$$= \frac{1}{2\pi}\ln a - \frac{1}{4\pi}\ln[a^4 - 2a^2\rho v \cos(\theta - \phi) + \rho^2 v^2]$$

$$= -\frac{1}{2\pi}\ln\left\{\frac{[a^4 - 2a^2\rho v \cos(\theta - \phi) + \rho^2 v^2]^{1/2}}{a}\right\}$$

6. $g(v, \theta; \rho, \phi) = \dfrac{1}{4\pi}\ln[a^4 - 2a^2\rho v \cos(\theta - \phi) + v^2\rho^2]$

$$-\frac{1}{4\pi}\ln\{[a^4 - 2a^2\rho v \cos(\theta - \phi) + v^2\rho^2]$$

$$\times [v^2 - 2v\rho \cos(\theta + \phi) + \rho^2]\}.$$

7. $G(v, \theta; \rho, \phi) = G^*(v, \theta; \rho, \phi) - G^*(v, \theta; \rho, \pi - \phi).$

8. $G^*(v, \theta; \rho, \phi) = G(r^3, 3\theta; \rho^3, 3\phi) - G(r^3, 3\theta; \rho^3, -3\phi).$

11. $G(x, y; \xi, \eta) = \dfrac{1}{4\pi} \ln\{[(x - \xi)^2 + (y - \eta)^2][(x + \xi)^2 + (y + \eta)^2]\}$

$$- \dfrac{1}{4\pi} \ln\{[(x - \xi)^2 + (y + \eta)^2][(x + \xi)^2 + (y - \eta)^2]\}.$$

Index

A

Absolutely integrable function, 5, 7
Auxiliary conditions, 42 (*See also*
    Boundary conditions and Initial
    conditions)

B

Backward wave, 83, 85, 88, 110
Bessel equation, 18, 142
  function, 142
Bessel's inequality, 152, 178
Bilinear expansion, 154, 157, 224
Boundary conditions, 42, 121
  elastic, 74
  first kind, 74
  fixed, 74
  free, 74
  periodic, 138, 165
  second kind, 74, 215–216
  third kind, 74, 215–216
Boundary value problems, 42, 121,
    252–253, 278, 284
Bounded function, 2

C

Canonical forms of second order
    equations, 62

Cauchy-Riemann conditions, 282
Chain rule, 11–13
Characteristic equation
  for first order equations, 50
    hyperbolic equations, 66
    parabolic equations, 66
Characteristic lines, 87–89, 108–112
Characteristic triangle, 87, 90, 95
Classification of second order equations, 61
Completeness of orthogonal system, 153,
    194
Composite functions, 10
Continuous dependence on initial or
    boundary data, 78, 220
Continuous function, 2
  piecewise continuous, 2, 4
Continuity of limit function, 20, 24
Convergence or uniform convergence
  of series, 19
  improper integral, 23
  in the mean, 150
Convolution, 211

D

d'Alembert's formula, 78, 87, 91, 95, 102,
    104, 108
Derivatives
  directional, 28–29
  left-hand and right-hand, 2
  mixed, 9

Derivatives (*cont.*)
  normal, 30–31
  partial, 7, 8
Differentiation
  of improper integrals, 25
  integrals depending on a parameter, 15–18
  series, 21
Dirichlet condition (*See* Boundary
    condition of first kind)
Dirichlet formula, 184
Dirichlet problem, 252
  in annulus region, 271
  disk, 267
  exterior problem, 278
  infinite domain, 285
  rectangle, 260
Domain (or interval) of dependence, 87,
    108, 110
Duhamel's principle, 94, 236, 242

E

Eigenvalue, 116, 139
Eigenfunction, 116, 139
Eigenfunction expansion, 148–149, 225 (*See
    also* Bilinear expansion)
Elliptic equation, 62
  reduction to canonical form, 67–68
Energy integral, 97
Error function, 240, 242
Even function, 98, 171
  extension, 104, 173, 202

F

Forward wave, 83, 85, 88, 109
Fourier coefficients, 118, 149
Fourier cosine integral formula, 202
Fourier cosine series, 173
  convergence, 187
  uniform convergence, 192
Fourier cosine transform, 209
Fourier integral formula, 199
  complex form, 207
  convergence, 199
Fourier inverse transform, 208
Fourier series, 166
  complex form, 169–170
  convergence, 185
  generalized, 149
  uniform convergence, 192
Fourier sine integral formula, 202
Fourier sine series, 118, 174
  convergence, 187
  uniform convergence, 192

Fourier sine transform, 209
Fourier transform, 208, 236–237, 241,
    285–286
Fundamental solution
  heat equation, 239
  Laplace's equation, 294
Fundamental theorem of calculus, 5

G

General solution, 39–41
  first-order equation, 51
  second-order equation, 57
Generalized solution, 79, 119
Green's formula, 133
Green's function for
  a disk, 299, 301
  heat equation, 225, 239
  Laplace's equation, 297–298
  ordinary differential equations, 127–128,
      136
  the half plane, 302
Green's theorem, 32, 253
  first identity, 34, 254
  second identity, 34

H

Hadamard's example, 252
Harmonic conjugate, 282
Harmonic function, 257
  circular harmonics, 268
  rectangular harmonics, 261
Harnack's inequality, 278
Heat equation, 214
Helmholtz equation, 49, 256
Homogeneous differential equation, 45
Homogeneous boundary value problem, 121
Hyperbolic equation, 62
  reduction to canonical form, 62–65

I

Improper integral, 23
Initial-boundary value problems, 42
  wave equation, 97–98, 102
  heat equation, 225, 227, 243
Initial conditions, 42
  first order equations, 53
  heat equation, 215
  wave equation, 74
Initial value problems, 42
  first order equations, 53–54

Initial value problems (*cont.*)
  heat equation, 216, 236–239
  wave equation, 74, 77, 90
Integration of
  Fourier series, 195, 196–197
  improper integral, 24–25
  series, 20

J

Jump discontinuity, 1

K

Kronecker delta, 145

L

Laplace's equation, 250
Legendre's equation and polynomials,
  147–148
Leibnitz rule, 16
Limit, left-hand and right-hand, 1
Line integral, 32–33
Linear combination, 44
Linear independence, 148
Linear operator, 44–45

M

Maximum principle
  heat equation, 218–219
  Laplace's equation, 257, 276
Mean value property of harmonic functions
  two variables, 274
  three variables, 279
Mean value theorems, 5, 6

N

Neumann condition (*See* Boundary
    condition of second kind)
Neumann's function, 306
  in a disk, 307
  in the half plane, 308
Neumann problem, 253
  in a disk, 279
  exterior problem, 284
  half plane, 291

Neumann problem (*cont.*)
  necessary condition for solution, 255
  rectangle, 266
Nonhomogeneous boundary value
    problems, 125–127, 131, 154–156
Nonhomogeneous initial-boundary value
    problems, 108–112, 229–235
Nonhomogeneous initial value problems,
    90–92, 240–241

O

Odd function, 98, 171
  extension, 98, 102, 174, 202
Orthogonality of eigenfunctions, 118, 143,
    144
Orthogonal system, 145, 163
  completeness, 153, 194
Orthonormal system, 145

P

Parabolic differential equation, 62
  reduction to canonical form, 66–67
Partial differential equation, 36, 45
  first order equation, 49
  linear equation, 37, 45
  second order equation, 37, 56, 62
Parseval's equation, 153, 193
  generalized, 194
Period, 4
Periodic function, 4
  extension, 167–168, 173–174
Poisson's equation, 251, 253, 256
Poisson's integral formula, 273, 287
Poisson's kernel, 274
Principle of superposition, 45–46
Propagation of waves, 88–89

R

Radiation equation, 214
Reflection of waves, 109–110, 112
Region of influence, 89–90
Riemann-Lesbegue theorem, 179–181
Robin problem, 253

S

Self-adjoint equation, 122
Separation of variables method, 114, 223,
    227, 230, 234, 260, 267

Simple closed curve, 32
Smooth function, 3
    piecewise smooth, 3
Square integrable function, 153
Sturm-Liouville equation, 122
    problem, 115, 138–139, 154–156

U

Uniqueness of solution
    Dirichlet problem, 254
    heat flow problem, 219, 220
    initial value problem for wave equation,
        95–97, 100, 105–106

Neumann problem, 254
Robin problem, 255

W

Wave equation, 71
    nonhomogeneous, 73, 90
    damped, 95, 107, 114
Weierstrass M-test for
    integrals, 24
    series, 19
Weight function, 143
Well-posed problem, 78, 220, 259
Wronskian, 123, 126